ROYAL COMMISSION ON ENVIRONMENTAL POLLUTION

CHAIRMAN: SIR JOHN HOUGHTON CBE FRS

Twenty-first Report

SETTING ENVIRONMENTAL STANDARDS

Presented to Parliament by Command of Her Majesty
October 1998

Recycled Paper

Cm 4053   £21.40

Information about the current work of the Royal Commission can be obtained from its website at
    http://www.rcep.org.uk
or from the Secretariat at Steel House, 11 Tothill Street, London SW1H 9RE

ROYAL COMMISSION ON ENVIRONMENTAL POLLUTION

TWENTY-FIRST REPORT

To the Queen's Most Excellent Majesty

MAY IT PLEASE YOUR MAJESTY

We, the undersigned Commissioners, having been appointed 'to advise on matters, both national and international, concerning the pollution of the environment; on the adequacy of research in this field; and the future possibilities of danger to the environment';

And to enquire into any such matters referred to us by one of Your Majesty's Secretaries of State or by one of Your Majesty's Ministers, or any other such matters on which we ourselves shall deem it expedient to advise:

HUMBLY SUBMIT TO YOUR MAJESTY THE FOLLOWING REPORT.

Everything changes. We plant
trees for those born later
but what's happened has happened,
and poisons poured into the seas
cannot be drained out again.

What's happened has happened.
Poisons poured into the seas
cannot be drained out again, but
everything changes. We plant
trees for those born later.

Everything Changes
after Brecht, 'Alles wandelt sich'
Cicely Herbert

Some people say that science clears up all the mysteries for us. In
my opinion it only creates more!

Amanda Wingfield
in *The Glass Menagerie* by Tennessee Williams

CONTENTS

Chapter 4

RISK AND UNCERTAINTY 51

Chapter 5

ECONOMIC APPRAISAL 63

Chapter 6

IMPLEMENTING ENVIRONMENTAL POLICIES 77

Chapter 7

ARTICULATING VALUES   **101**

Chapter 8

A ROBUST BASIS FOR ENVIRONMENTAL STANDARDS   **113**

Chapter 9

CONCLUSIONS

Terms defined in the text of the report appear in the index in **_bold italics_**, with the number of the paragraph or box containing the definition also in **_bold italics_**.

The poem featured on page iv is reprinted by permission of the author from *Poems on the Underground.* Eds. G. Benson, J. Chernaik and C. Herbert. Cassell Publishers Ltd. 1988.

INFORMATION BOXES

TABLES

FIGURES

Chapter 1

SIGNIFICANCE OF ENVIRONMENTAL STANDARDS

Environmental regulation, and environmental standards in particular, have assumed much greater importance in the last 30 years. The nature of concerns about the environment has changed. There have also been changes in the policy process. Against that background, can a more consistent and robust basis be found for setting standards for environmental protection?

1.1   We decided to undertake this study because there appeared to be widespread confusion and misunderstanding about the purpose and mechanisms of environmental regulation. Its timeliness was emphasised when the planned disposal at sea of the Brent Spar oil installation (regarded by the operator and the UK government as the 'best practicable environmental option') was abandoned in the face of widespread opposition, including a consumer boycott.

1.2   In the invitation to submit evidence (reproduced as appendix A) we referred to conflicting views on whether the present system of environmental regulation is excessively stringent or not stringent enough. Some evidence we received took the view that present standards are not adequate in relation to chronic exposure to pollutants.[1] Other bodies submitting evidence took the view that some standards are set in inconsistent ways or are set without sufficient consideration of their cost or practicability in relation to the environmental improvement obtained,[2] and that there is a possibility of unnecessary stringency which could be counter-productive.[3] It has been argued elsewhere that many of the concerns raised about environmental hazards have only a flimsy basis.[4]

1.3   The purpose of this study has been to identify a more consistent and robust basis for setting standards for environmental protection, in the broadest sense. The primary basis for such standards has been scientific. We indicated our intention to focus on different types of scientific evidence and the ways in which these are utilised. At an early stage in the study the government announcement that bovine spongiform encephalopathy (BSE) had been linked to health effects in humans highlighted concerns about the relationship between science and policy when faced with great complexity and uncertainty.

1.4   Although related issues have been discussed in all its previous reports, this is the first time the Commission has looked comprehensively at environmental standards, the forms they should take in future, and how they should be set. We found it was essential to do that in a European and global context. We believe our analysis and conclusions have a relevance well beyond this medium-sized developed country in north-west Europe, and are in tune with current thinking in other countries.

1.5   The regulation of impacts on the environment is now a crucial area of public policy and an established part of mainstream politics. It has been estimated that by 2000 $500 billion a year will be spent worldwide on complying with environmental regulations.[5] It is generally agreed that the the external costs imposed by the damage that regulation seeks to limit are several times as large. We believe many of the conclusions of this report have an even wider application to related areas of policy, such as other aspects of health, public safety and worker protection. At some points we have drawn on experience in those areas.

1.6   Some of the issues we have identified are fundamental and challenging. There are various tensions within the present system of environmental regulation. Doubts have been voiced about the objectivity and adequacy of its scientific basis. This report points the direction in which we believe protection of the environment should evolve, and the respective roles that should be played by legally enforced regulation and other approaches. At this stage of the debate we decided that it is more appropriate to set out broad conclusions, than to make specific recommendations for action to be taken by particular bodies. Our main conclusions appear in bold type in the text, and are brought together in chapter 9.

1.7   We begin by summarising briefly the changing nature of environmental concerns (1.8–1.13), characterising the place of standards in environmental policies (1.14–1.21), and reviewing key changes that have taken place in the role of standards and in other aspects of the policy process (1.22–1.31). We then explain the structure of the remainder of the report (1.32–1.43).

Changing nature of environmental concerns

1.8   The commitment of governments to pursue sustainable development[6] has changed the perspective in which environmental policies are viewed. Greater attention is now focused on what is likely to happen in future decades as a consequence of the present generation's activities. While there may be room for dispute over how the principle of sustainable development should be converted into specific policies and actions, there is wide acceptance that it is about 'meeting the needs of the present without compromising the ability of future generations to meet their own needs'.[7] Pursuit of sustainable development thus requires a balance between improving the conditions of human life in an equitable way, now and in the future, and the long-term conservation of the natural environment, which supplies the resources on which development is founded.

1.9   In 1994 a UK strategy for sustainable development was published as a White Paper.[8] The present government is conducting wide-ranging consultations in order to prepare a revised strategy,[9] which is expected to be published at the end of 1998.

1.10 There is much debate about the relative weight that should be placed on the different elements within the overall balance sustainable development is intended to achieve. Environmental protection itself has several distinct facets. In referring in this report to the environment or environmental standards we embrace concerns both about human health and well-being and about the natural world and the built environment (safeguarding cultural and social artefacts). Different conceptions of why the environment should be protected can come into conflict with each other in particular cases, as well as having the potential to conflict with the other elements of sustainable development, pursuit of material well-being and of equity. Protection of the natural world is itself a complex objective: although the World Charter for Nature states that 'every form of life is unique, warranting respect regardless of its worth to Man',[10] and the Convention on Biological Diversity requires national strategies, plans or programmes for the conservation and sustainable use of biological diversity as a whole,[11] many actions designed to safeguard particular species may do so at the expense of other life forms.

1.11 The measures taken over the past century to counter pollution largely resulted from a narrower conception of environmental protection, the desire to protect human health and well-being. Regulation had its origins, at least in the UK, in controlling local pollution of water or air. The effects of pollution were obvious, and so generally was its source. Smoke came out of a factory chimney or dirty water out of a pipe. In time, the more obvious forms of pollution have been much reduced.

1.12 The modifications to the environment that are now of most concern are much broader in scope, and at the same time less apparent to the senses. Some of them, such as climate change or destruction of stratospheric ozone, are global in scale. Many pollutants are carried over very long distances, and may become concentrated or change their physical form. They may also enter into chemical reactions in air, water or soil which result in the production or removal of other substances. Concern about the impact of pollution on human health now often relates to chronic effects, perhaps occurring a long time after exposure. All these types of phenomena are likely to be detectable only through some form of scientific investigation.

1.13 The nature of environmental concerns has changed significantly in terms of the objectives of policy, the time-scales considered, the geographical scales considered, and the kinds of environmental modification that are addressed. These changes have implications for the way environmental standards are used and set. They also have implications for the types of evidence, in particular the types of scientific evidence, required to support decisions on policies and standards.

Place of standards in environmental policies

1.14 Because protection of the environment is a complex objective, and potentially in conflict with other objectives, all environmental policies involve making judgements about the acceptability of current or prospective modifications to the environment resulting from human activities. Much of what we say in this report is of general relevance to environmental policies. We have highlighted standards because they are often the most tangible and precise expression of the judgements that underlie environmental policies. We focus mainly on standards related to pollution, which involves the introduction into the environment of a substance or biological agent or form of energy; but there are other kinds, such as standards related to management of species, interference with habitats or methods of cultivation.

1.15 The term 'standard' has sometimes been used in the environmental field in the narrow sense of a legally enforceable numerical limit.[12] **From the outset of this study (see appendix A) we used the term much more broadly to include standards which are not mandatory but contained in guidelines, codes of practice or sets of criteria for deciding individual cases; standards not set by governments which carry authority for other reasons, especially the scientific eminence or market power of those who set them; and some standards which are not numerical.**

1.16 We understand an *environmental standard* to be any judgement about the acceptability of environmental modifications resulting from human activities which fulfils both the following conditions:

a. it is formally stated after some consideration and intended to apply generally to a defined class of cases;

b. because of its relationship to certain sanctions, rewards or values, it can be expected to exert an influence, direct or indirect, on activities that affect the environment.

1.17 **Environmental standards take diverse forms.** The classes of case they cover may be modifications to the environment, or the repercussions of such modifications, or activities or objects that have the capacity to bring about such modifications. The way environmental standards are categorised in this report is explained, and examples given, in box 1A.[13] This includes cross-references to appendix C, which provides an overview (in terms of their form and geographical scope) of the main environmental standards that apply at present in the UK.

1.18 The first part of box 1A categorises standards by reference to the pathways which substances follow until they meet or enter an entity that is susceptible to damage. Most such standards are expressed as a specified concentration of a substance at a particular point on the pathway. The second part of the box comprises forms of standard which bear more indirectly on modification of the environment. To simplify, box 1A is confined to environmental standards which relate directly or indirectly to the introduction of a substance or a form of energy into the environment. It omits secondary or supplementary standards covering such things as sampling, analysis and testing methods; these also have an essential function, and we touch on them later.

BOX 1A	FORMS OF ENVIRONMENTAL STANDARD

Standards applying directly to a point on a pathway

biological standards defining the limits of physiological changes or other impacts acceptable in an organism (C.4–C.5)

> *example:* European Community (EC) reference level for the concentration of lead in blood

exposure standards defining acceptable exposures or doses at the point of entry to an organism (C.6–C.13)

> *examples:* EC dose limits for external radiation; tolerable daily intake of a substance from all routes determined under the International Programme on Chemical Safety

quality standards defining acceptable concentrations of a substance in air (C.14–C.23), water (C.24–C.30) or soil (C.31–C.36)

> *examples:* World Health Organization guideline values for air quality; EC quality standards for bathing waters; EC guidelines for heavy metals in agricultural soils to which sewage sludge is applied

emission standards defining what releases of pollutants to the environment are acceptable (C.37–C.46)

> *examples:* Protocols under the Convention on Long-Range Transboundary Air Pollution of the United Nations Economic Commission for Europe; EC limit values for emissions from road vehicles

product standards specifying the composition of a product (C.47–C.53)

> *examples:* EC standards for motor fuels; EC limit and guide values for drinking water quality

Other forms of environmental standard

process standards identifying a set or sets of techniques for a specified industrial process in order to provide a criterion for deciding what emissions to the environment should be permitted from any given site (C.54–C.62)

> *examples:* Guidance Notes issued by the Environment Agency for processes subject to integrated pollution control and by the Secretary of State for processes which are regulated by local authorities for emissions to air

life cycle-based standards setting certain criteria that the life cycle of a product should satisfy (C.63–C.65)

> *example:* EC ecolabelling scheme

use standards specifying conditions governing use of a substance or product (or, in some circumstances, banning its use or establishing a programme for phasing it out) (C.66–C.73)

> *examples:* bans and restrictions under the EC Marketing and Use Directive; EC and UK procedures for authorising plant protection, biocidal and veterinary medicinal products

management standards which apply to the capability of a company or other organisation to deal with the environmental effects of its operations (C.74–C.80)

> *example:* International Organization for Standardization standard ISO 14001 for environmental management systems

1.19 This diversity in forms of standard corresponds to the many different forms taken by measures to protect the environment. The complex inter-relationships of such measures and the associated standards are illustrated in figure 1-I for a single substance, lead. Achieving a standard for daily intake of lead, in order to limit the concentration of lead in human blood, involves setting and achieving standards for several aspects of environmental quality and an array of related emission, process, product and use standards.

1.20 Setting a numerical standard has the disadvantage that a single figure cannot adequately reflect the complexities of actual situations. The existence of a standard specifying a concentration of a pollutant might be understood to imply that any concentration below that specified is 'safe' and any concentration above that specified is 'hazardous', whereas in reality there is no sharp dividing line.[14]   Moreover, because circumstances vary from case to case, following a general standard may not achieve what would be the optimal solutions in individual cases.

1.21 Standards have considerable advantages in other respects, as their widespread use confirms. There are many contexts in which the existence of a standard reduces the costs (in the widest sense) of obtaining information and doing business. Those who may be affected in some way by a decision on an environmental matter have a right to know in advance what criteria will be applied. In some contexts an essential function of a standard is to determine the point at which a sanction may be applied against someone damaging the environment. A standard also provides a benchmark for performance. It may provide a basis for assessing the adequacy of policies and regulatory systems. Where a standard relates to a specified future date, it serves as an important guide for the investment plans (including the research, development and design programmes) of companies with polluting processes or products, and of companies providing technologies for reducing pollution.

Key changes in the policy process

1.22 It is clearly important who makes the judgements about acceptability incorporated in environmental standards, and on what bases those judgements are made. **Standards are a crucial element in the environmental policy process**, and in what has been called 'the legal, epistemological and cultural matrix in which environmental politics is conducted'.[15] Over the last 30 years this policy process has undergone some key changes which we now outline. Some of these changes relate directly to the role of standards, others are of a more general character. All of them are relevant in considering what role standards should play in future, which forms of standard should be given most emphasis, and on what basis those standards should be set.

1.23 **The first change is that numerical standards have come to occupy a central position in a much expanded system of environmental regulation**, as appendix C shows. One reason for this has been advances in science and technology. Toxicology and ecotoxicology have become established as disciplines. More sensitive and reliable methods have been devised for measuring concentrations of substances. Understanding of the behaviour of substances in the environment has improved. More and more synthetic substances have been brought into use, and become of interest to those responsible for protecting the environment. Numerical standards seemed to be the most obvious and convenient way of summarising and codifying scientific understanding of human impacts on the environment in order to make it readily usable by policy-makers and regulators.

Figure 1-I
Relationship of forms of standard for one substance (lead)

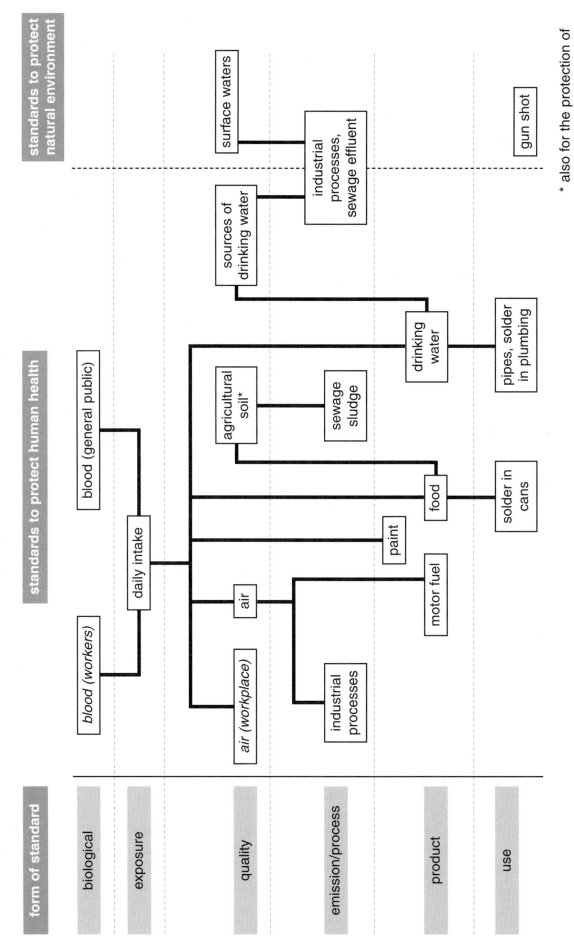

1.24 The second key change for European states is that environmental policies and standards are now determined predominantly on a European scale. Four-fifths of UK environmental legislation now has its origin in European institutions.[16] The examples in box 1A give some indication of the importance of European Community (EC) legislation. The growth of such legislation has been a further factor boosting the importance of numerical standards, particularly for the UK. The predominance of such standards in EC legislation has reflected the previous traditions of regulation in some other Member States, but also the contribution numerical standards can make to securing consistent implementation of policies across several tiers of government.

1.25 The Maastricht Treaty sets out the following basis for the Community's environment policy:

Community policy on the environment shall contribute to pursuit of the following objectives:

– preserving, protecting and improving the quality of the environment;

– protecting human health;

– prudent and rational utilisation of natural resources;

– promoting measures at international level to deal with regional or worldwide environmental problems.

Community policy on the environment shall aim at a high level of protection taking into account the diversity of situations in the various regions of the Community. It shall be based on the precautionary principle and on the principles that preventive action should be taken, that environmental damage should as a priority be rectified at source and that the polluter should pay ...[17]

1.26 There has also been a great growth in the number and importance of international conventions relating to the environment, at both global and regional scale. This trend is described in appendix C (C.82–C.85, C.89–C.91), which also describes the evolution of EC environment policy (C.92–C.96). There has been intense discussion about the relationship between environmental protection and the liberalisation of international trade which is being underpinned by the General Agreement on Tariffs and Trade and the World Trade Organization. Later in this report we return to this controversy and discuss the geographical scope which environmental standards should have.

1.27 Another key change has been the growth in use of formal techniques to aid decision making. In the UK this has been a theme of the 1990s. The 1990 Environment White Paper[18] announced the Department of the Environment's intention to give guidance in this field; components of the guidance were published between 1990 and 1995. Some of it dealt with incorporating cost considerations into decisions on environmental (and other) issues,[19] another part dealt with incorporating environmental considerations into decisions in other fields.[20] A guide was published on risk management;[21] references to risk assessment ran through other components of the guidance, as did references to cost-benefit analysis. In 1991 the Treasury published guidance to government Departments on economic appraisal, to 'help officials and managers in central government to appraise and evaluate expenditure proposals effectively'.[22]

1.28 Some elements of this guidance have been reviewed recently or are now under review. Following a report by consultants which concluded that, although Departments were taking more account of environmental impacts, a more systematic approach was needed, a more straightforward explanation of when and how to carry out an environmental appraisal has been published,[23] and will be followed by technical guidance. Overall, the original set of guidance documents appears to have had relatively little impact. Parts of the guidance have been found difficult to apply to actual cases. Another criticism has been that little attention was paid to protection of the natural environment.[24] The Treasury guidance on economic appraisal was revised in 1997.[25] There have been a number of examples of cost-benefit studies addressing environmental policy issues, but few practical examples of their use for taking decisions on environmental policies; there has been a tendency for policy-makers to rely on cost-effectiveness analysis or on a partial analysis which places money values on a relatively narrow range of costs and benefits.[26]

1.29 The increasing emphasis on use of formal techniques was prompted in part by the emergence of much broader perspectives for analysing and regulating the environmental impact of human activities. The concept of 'best practicable environmental option' provided the foundation for integrated control of releases of pollutants from a given industrial plant to air, water and land. Her Majesty's Inspectorate of Pollution devised a formal technique to help it fulfil the statutory obligation to have regard to the best practicable environmental option (3.12). There was also increasing concern that environmental policies should take full account of different sources of the same pollutant and interactions between different pollutants. Environmental impact is now being analysed in still wider terms through the use of concepts such as life cycle analysis (3.21–3.31).

1.30 Another factor that has stimulated use of formal techniques has been the growing emphasis on the integration of environmental policies with policies in other fields. Adoption of sustainable development as the aim has reflected, and reinforced, the strong trend towards 'ensuring that decisions throughout society are taken with proper regard to their environmental impact'.[27]

1.31 **The final change we have identified as important is the greater influence of environmental non-governmental organisations (NGOs).** At one time the only parties with a recognised claim to be involved in many environmental issues were government, its scientific advisers, the regulator (if separate from government Departments) and the industry producing pollution (which provided engineers to assess the feasibility of control measures). Environmental NGOs now often have a recognised voice in decisions. Some are mass membership organisations with large staffs and budgets, and can on some issues enlist wide public support. Some are international. The growth in their influence has been, if anything, more striking at that level. Both industrial and environmental NGOs have global organisations and observer status under some international conventions. Individual NGOs may wield significant influence over the positions particular governments adopt in international negotiations. They may even be involved in drafting conventions; the first draft of the Convention on International Trade in Endangered Species of Wild Fauna and Flora, for example, was prepared by the International Union for Conservation of Nature and Natural Resources, which has both NGO and government members.

Structure of this report

1.32 The environmental policy process was described by Eric Ashby in the following way:

> In the first stage – let us call it the ignition stage – public opinion has to be raised to a temperature that stimulates action. In the second stage the hazard has to be examined objectively, to find out how genuine and how dangerous it is, and just what is at risk. In the third stage this objective information has to be combined with the pressures of advocacy and with subjective judgements to produce a formula for a political decision.[28]

1.33 Reviewing experience up to 1977, Ashby was struck by how often some special factor had been necessary, for example an unexpected catastrophe such as an explosion or the wreck of a tanker, before action was taken to deal with an environmental problem. There is now much greater awareness of environmental issues and a broader commitment by governments to protecting the environment. As a result the 'temperature that stimulates action' is now lower, and there is much less of an obstacle to obtaining serious consideration for an environmental problem. Environmental groups have the ear of governments, and public debate is much wider and better informed.

1.34 Even if the nature of 'the ignition stage' has changed since Ashby's day, what he saw as the second stage in the policy process remains of crucial importance. This is a dispassionate and rigorous investigation of a presumed hazard. However, the need for, and the conclusions from, such investigations are now less readily accepted. Environmental regulation has become more and more dependent on the advice of scientists. Governments justify their action or inaction by appealing to the authority of science. Yet the changed character of environmental concerns has highlighted the extent to which there are uncertainties in scientific assessments, and the scope for different perceptions of the issues involved. In some cases the interpretations and reassurances originally offered by governments have been shown to be mistaken when the findings from later studies are received or unexpected consequences emerge. This has eroded trust in environmental regulation, which has also been undermined by the scope for evidence to be interpreted in different ways.

1.35 We have given close attention to the analytical stage of the policy process and the outputs that should be expected from it. We have concluded that it must have several complementary components, and that these must be closely inter-related. The assumptions made and the use of data must be consistent between the components. We devote the next five chapters to discussing these individual components, which are:

scientific assessment **(chapter 2)**

analysis of technological options **(chapter 3)**

assessment of risk and uncertainty **(chapter 4)**

economic appraisal **(chapter 5)**

analysis of implementation issues, including the geographical scope of standards **(chapter 6)**.

1.36 Each chapter indicates how the relevant kind of analysis has provided an input to standard setting hitherto, the nature of its potential contribution, and how that contribution can be improved in the future. The key terms, techniques and assumptions of each kind of analysis are critically examined. To ensure that the analysis is rigorous and impartial, we emphasise that not only the findings from each component, but the assumptions and data used should be transparent and available for scrutiny by a wider audience.

1.37 Devoting a separate chapter to each kind of analysis, while inevitable as a practical device, carries the danger of implying that the tasks described are discrete, and can be easily separated. In reality this is not the case, as the analyses themselves will inevitably overlap in time and in subject matter, and each kind of analysis may provide an essential input to others. For example, an analysis of the risks consequent on a proposal requires input from the scientific assessment and the analysis of technological options.

1.38 The order of the chapters is not intended to represent a chronological order in which the analyses should be carried out. We start with the scientific assessment because, except where there is already a good scientific understanding of a hazard, that must normally be the first stage. This apart, the stages should be regarded as taking place simultaneously, with iterations as necessary. The emphasis put on each component, and the time and resources devoted to it, will vary according to the nature of the issue under consideration, and the reliability and comprehensiveness of the information already available. Care must of course be taken to ensure that the quality of a decision is not affected by placing an unequal emphasis on any one discipline.

1.39 In chapters 7 and 8 we discuss the third stage in the environmental policy process, which Ashby saw as producing a 'formula for political decision' on the basis of 'subjective judgements'. We prefer to regard it as involving the exercise of practical judgement about the acceptability of modifications to the environment which takes into account the conclusions of all the kinds of analysis mentioned above and is also informed by public values.

1.40 **Chapter 7** considers the relevance of people's underlying values to decisions about environmental policies and standards, and reviews experience to date with various methods that have been used in an attempt to articulate such values.

1.41 **Chapter 8** describes how the separate components discussed in chapters 2–6 should be fitted together to enable decisions to be taken about environmental policies and standards, and what steps should be taken to ensure that such decisions are fully informed by people's values. With the help of examples, we show how the procedures we advocate differ from those used hitherto to set standards, and draw conclusions about the general requirements for bodies performing such a task. Finally, we offer some reflections on some of the wider issues that this study has raised.

1.42 As we have said, our aim in this report is to indicate the broad direction in which we believe protection of the environment should evolve, not to make specific recommendations. There are a number of matters on which we have reached broad conclusions and our main conclusions are brought together in **Chapter 9**.

1.43 In appendix B we record our thanks and appreciation to the many organisations and individuals who have helped us in this study, and provide information about how it was conducted.

Chapter 2

SCIENTIFIC UNDERSTANDING

Scientific understanding is, and must remain, the essential basis for environmental standards. Procedures have been developed for assessing the effects of substances on human health and the natural environment, and a wide range of data is used. The data that would be most relevant, however, are often lacking, and the available data are often subject to much uncertainty. In seeking to base decisions about environmental issues on scientific evidence, there needs to be awareness of the nature of such uncertainties, and their implications.

2.1 We have emphasised the need for rigorous and dispassionate investigation of any presumed environmental hazard. Our consideration of such investigations starts with the scientific evidence because, except where there is already a good scientific understanding of a hazard, the first stage must normally be a scientific assessment.

2.2 When we began this study of environmental standards we indicated our intention to focus on different types of scientific evidence and the ways in which these are utilised. The conflicting interpretations of such evidence sometimes advanced by different experts and the refutation in other cases of explanations originally advanced by governments or regulators have shown how important scientific uncertainties can be. We wished to find out how endemic such difficulties are, and whether there is substance in the doubts that have been expressed about the objectivity and adequacy of the scientific basis for environmental regulation.

2.3 The focus in this report is mainly on standards related to pollution. To illuminate the general issues involved, we take as an example of the scientific investigations made in setting standards, assessments of new and existing chemical substances under European Community (EC) legislation (appendix C, C.69–C.70). These seek to answer three basic questions (the emphasis given to each question may vary in individual cases, and in other assessment procedures):

how intrinsically hazardous is the substance in question in terms of effects on human beings?

how intrinsically hazardous is the substance in terms of effects on the natural environment?

how does the substance move through the environment, and what levels of exposure to it are likely to occur?

2.4 The EC procedure for assessing new and existing chemical substances is first described (2.5–2.13). We then look in turn at the sources from which evidence is obtained so that this and other forms of scientific assessment can seek to answer the three questions above. After identifying certain basic features of assessing the toxicity of substances (2.14–2.22), we look at the assessment of human health effects (2.23–2.37) and effects on the natural environment (2.38–2.50). In both contexts we discuss how dose-effect relationships are determined. We review briefly understanding of environmental pathways and exposures (2.51–2.56) and consider whether, and to what extent, the environment should be considered to have a capacity to assimilate pollution (2.57–2.64). This chapter concludes by considering how scientific evidence can contribute most usefully to decisions on environmental policies (2.65–2.74), how the conclusions of scientific assessments should be presented (2.75–2.82) and the need to extend scientific understanding through research (2.83–2.87).

Case study: new and existing chemical substances

2.5   An advantage of using the assessment procedure for chemical substances as the example is that it has been prescribed in some detail.[1] It is essentially the same for new and existing substances, and is shown in figure 2-I. The initial stage is *hazard identification*, examining evidence about the adverse effects a substance has the inherent capacity to cause, so that a human health toxicity assessment and an ecotoxicity assessment can be produced. The next stage is assessment of pathways and exposures. Central to the assessment for both humans and the natural environment is determination of the relationship between actual or predicted exposure to the substance and the level of exposure at which adverse effects might occur. In EC legislation this stage is called *risk characterisation*. It may or may not involve quantifying the incidence and severity of the effects that might occur in a human population or the natural environmental.

2.6   Estimating the concentrations at which a substance is or may be present in each environmental compartment (water, sediment, air, soil, biota) involves considering all the potential sources of the substance, including manufacture or importation, transport, storage, processing, use, and disposal or recovery. Estimating the doses of the substance to which human populations are or may be exposed involves considering in addition all the routes by which people might be exposed as workers, as consumers, and through environmental pathways. Exposure depends on the nature and number of pathways that exist and the rates at which the substance moves along them. For a substance used widely in many products and processes, or released from many scattered sources, the pathways that need to be considered are correspondingly diverse. In other cases, for example a chemical that is produced and then entirely consumed during production of another chemical, the possible routes for exposure are far fewer. The concentration a substance reaches in an environmental compartment is a function of the amount released into the environment (and of the duration of releases and the intervals between them), how it disperses (which depends on the properties of the substance and the characteristics of the receiving environment), and the rate at which it is removed from the environment by transformation or degradation processes.

2.7   The basic procedure of human health risk characterisation is to compare the estimated human dose (EHD) of a given substance with either the no observed adverse effect level (NOAEL) for that substance or the lowest observed adverse effect level (LOAEL). (Definitions of these and other toxicological terms are in box 2A.[2]) Separate comparisons are made for each population potentially exposed and for each potential health effect. For example, one effect of concern might be eye irritation caused by brief exposure to a substance airborne in the workplace; another could be damage to an internal organ caused by long-term exposure of the general public to the same substance in drinking water.

2.8   For the purposes of such comparisons the NOAEL or LOAEL derived from test data is usually adjusted to obtain a number regarded as a closer approximation to the true NOAEL or LOAEL for the relevant human population (2.35).[3] Alternatively an unadjusted NOAEL or LOAEL is used to make the comparison with the EHD, and a judgement is then made as to whether the margin between the two numbers is sufficiently wide as not to raise concerns for potential health consequences in real life situations, bearing in mind the uncertainties in estimation and the size and nature of the relevant human population. Substances which the weight of evidence suggests are genotoxic carcinogens (2.36) in humans are treated differently in the assessment, and assumed to have an adverse effect at any dose level.

2.9   In environmental risk characterisation the aim is to make a comparison, for each environmental compartment, between the predicted environmental concentration (PEC) and the predicted no effect concentration (PNEC). The PEC is calculated using realistic or worst-case scenarios.[4] If relevant data are not available, estimated figures, or figures derived by analogy with similar substances, are used. Particular consideration is given to the type of release (point source, diffuse source, continuous, semi-continuous or intermittent), as this affects the duration and frequency with which an ecosystem may be exposed to the substance. The PNEC is derived from the available toxicity data by applying assessment factors (2.47). Risk characterisation also considers the environmental properties of the substances into which the original substance may be transformed or degraded.

Figure 2-I
Assessing hazards: new and existing substances

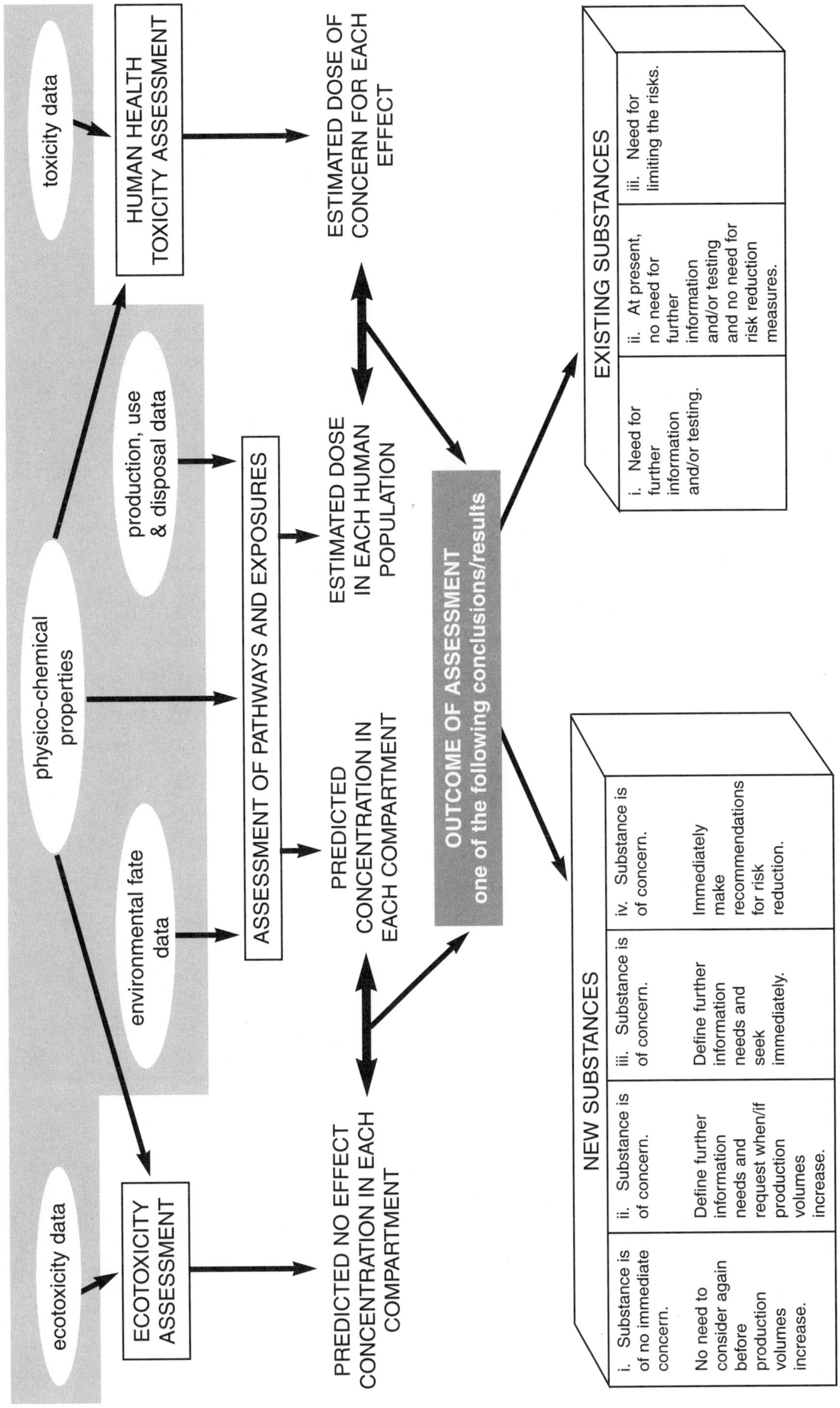

BOX 2A	TOXICITY DEFINITIONS

dose – the total amount of a substance administered to, taken, or absorbed by an organism; concentration multiplied by time

exposure – the process by which a substance becomes available for absorption by the target population, organism, organ, tissue, or cell, by any route; the concentration, amount or intensity of a particular physical or chemical agent or environmental agent that reaches the target population, organism, organ, tissue, or cell, usually expressed in numerical terms of substance concentration, duration and frequency (for chemical agents and micro-organisms) or intensity (for physical agents such as radiation)

effect – the effect of exposure to a substance on an organism is defined as **adverse** when it represents a change in morphology, physiology, growth, development, or life-span which results in impairment of functional capacity or impairment of capacity to compensate for additional stress, or increase in susceptibility to the harmful effects of other environmental influences

dose-effect relationship/dose-response relationship – the association between dose and the magnitude or incidence of an effect (response) in an individual or in a population or in experimental animals. A **dose-effect/dose-response curve** is the graph of the relation between dose and the magnitude of the biological effect (response) produced

acute toxicity – adverse effects occurring within a short time (usually up to 14 days) after administration of a single dose (or exposure to a given concentration) of a test substance, or after multiple doses (exposures), usually within 24 hours

chronic toxicity – adverse effects following chronic exposure. Tests for chronic toxicity use exposures over an extended period of time, or over a significant fraction of the lifetime of the test species, group of individuals, or population

LC(D)$_{50}$ – median lethal concentration (dose) – the statistically derived concentration of a substance in an environmental medium (dose of a chemical or physical agent) expected to kill 50% of organisms in a given population under a defined set of conditions

EC(D)$_{50}$ – median effective concentration (dose) – the concentration (dose) of a substance that causes 50% of the maximum response in a given population under a defined set of conditions

NO(A)EL – no observed (adverse) effect level – the greatest concentration or amount of a substance, found by experiment or observation, that causes no detectable (adverse) alteration of morphology, functional capacity, growth, development, or life-span of the target organisms distinguishable from those observed in normal (control) organisms of the same species and strain under the same defined conditions of exposure

LO(A)EL – lowest observed (adverse) effect level – the lowest concentration or amount of a substance, found by experiment or observation, that causes any (adverse) alteration of morphology, functional capacity, growth, development, or life-span of the target organisms distinguishable from those observed in normal (control) organisms of the same species and strain under the same defined conditions of exposure

2.10 The primary source of evidence for assessing new and existing chemical substances is the manufacturer or importer of a substance, who is required to submit toxicity data when notifying a new substance to the regulator, and was required to supply all the available data on existing substances to the regulator by specified dates.[5]

2.11 For new substances the aim is to prevent those which are potentially hazardous posing an actual risk. The manufacturer or importer may include in the notification a preliminary risk assessment using the methodology described above, and in most cases does so. The role of the regulator is to check any such assessment, and to carry one out if one has not been submitted. The possible outcomes are shown in figure 2-I. The purpose of the original EC legislation was to ensure enough information was available about a new substance to enable it to be appropriately labelled and packaged and handled safely (the subject matter of use standards, in the terminology defined in box 1A). Another form of risk reduction measure would be a product standard. The category of substances for which risk reduction measures are warranted will normally include any substance which may be a genotoxic carcinogen (2.36) and to which humans may be exposed.

2.12 For existing substances the aim is to identify any need for better management of the risks posed by a substance. If additional risk reduction measures are found to be required, these might take the form of use standards, product standards, or emission or process standards. In serious cases they might take the form of banning use of a substance, either for certain purposes or altogether (the most extreme form of use standard).

2.13 Assessments of new and existing chemical substances are typical examples of the scientific assessments carried out to provide the basis for decisions on environmental standards. We now examine in more detail the methods used to obtain the numbers used in these and other scientific assessments, although in the case of other assessment procedures the primary source of evidence may not be industry.

Assessing toxicity

2.14 Any substance is potentially toxic in that it can cause injury or death if exposure is sufficiently high. Even water and oxygen, which are essential to human life, are toxic at high enough doses. There are millions of naturally occurring and synthetic substances. Most of the substances to which biological systems are exposed in the environment occur naturally. In investigating the effects of substances on biological systems certain methods and approaches are equally applicable, whether the objective is to protect human health or the natural environment.

2.15 Laboratory tests to investigate toxicity are either *in vitro* or *in vivo*. *In vitro* tests are carried out on cells or micro-organisms, ranging from bacteria and yeasts through mammalian cells to mammalian tissues, and have been used to explore the mechanisms by which substances exert toxic effects. A few standard *in vitro* tests have been developed and are used for assessing chemical toxicity, most notably the Ames test to show whether a substance causes mutations in cells.

2.16 *In vivo* testing provides the opportunity to observe the effects of a substance on the entire interacting collection of cells, tissues and organs which makes up a living organism; where the effects of a substance are not known, this form of testing can show whether there are in fact effects on numerous potential targets, resulting from numerous potential interactions. The effects observed may be behavioural or functional or occur in organs, tissues or body fluids. In the absence of data about effects on humans, testing with mammals provides data from which predictions can be made about the toxicity of the same substances to humans.

2.17 Toxicokinetic experiments are carried out in order to investigate the behaviour of a substance within an organism. They commonly examine absorption (uptake of potentially toxic substances by the organism), metabolism (transformation of the substance within the organism), distribution (movement of the substance and any metabolites within the organism), and elimination of the substance and any metabolites from the organism. Toxicity assessment has to take into account the effects of metabolites as well as the effects of the original substance.

2.18 Toxicity tests are usually classified according to:

the length of dosing, from acute studies lasting a few days to studies spanning the lifetime of a test species (18–30 months in rodents);

the route by which the dose is administered: intravenous, oral, dermal, ocular or inhalation;

the end-point being studied, which may be death, appearance of a tumour, reproduction or development, sensitisation, or a neurotoxic or behavioural effect.

2.19 Acute tests yield a number for the median lethal concentration (LC_{50}, the concentration that brings about the death of 50% of the individuals in a test population) or the median lethal dose (LD_{50}, the single dose that brings about 50% mortality). On their own, these measures provide only a very rough idea of the relative toxicity of substances. Two chemicals may appear to be equally toxic because they have the same LC_{50} but one may kill individuals in a test population at concentrations where the other has no effect. For these reasons, LC_{50} and LD_{50} data are rarely, if ever, the sole basis for regulation.

2.20 The results of tests for sub-lethal effects of a substance are expressed as the median effective concentration (EC_{50}) or the median effective dose (ED_{50}), the concentration or dose which, in a given time under given conditions, causes 50% of the maximum response in a particular parameter or process relative to unexposed controls. The response might be a 50% reduction in growth rate or a 50% change in a physiological process (for example, photosynthesis or respiratory rate).

2.21 Methods for toxicity and ecotoxicity testing have become increasingly standardised across the world. The Organisation for Economic Co-operation and Development (OECD) has produced guidelines for tests in order to avert an escalation of testing to meet different data requirements by individual governments for the same substance.[6] The International Organization for Standardization (ISO) has also been active in this direction. Tests are also required to be carried out in accordance with good laboratory practice as specified by OECD.

2.22 As the result of the development of quantitative structure activity relationships (QSARs), knowledge of a substance's chemical structure and physico-chemical properties can be used to supplement the available data on its effects. Estimates of biological activity and thus of effects are made by comparing key properties or structural elements of a substance with those of a group of related and better known chemicals for which the relevant toxicity information is available. The validity of this method is dependent on establishing a reliable relationship between the physico-chemical characteristics of a substance and its toxic effects.

Human health effects

2.23 The outcome of a human health toxicity assessment is a toxicity profile covering the types of adverse effect which a substance produces in humans, their incidence and the relationship to dose. Toxicity assessments utilise whatever relevant data are available, whether from laboratory tests of the kinds already described, chemical structure relationships, mathematical models or studies with humans. The data submitted by the manufacturer or importer when notifying a new substance under EC legislation come from animal tests carried out in accordance with the test methods specified by the legislation (which are based on methods recommended by competent international bodies, in particular OECD) and under good laboratory practice.

2.24 In regulatory toxicity testing it is usual to provide information from tests with several species in order to indicate species differences in response. An extreme example of such a difference is the wide variation in susceptibility shown by different animal species to dioxins, for which the LD_{50} ranges from 1 μg/kg body weight/day for guinea pigs to 5,000 μg/kg body weight/day for hamsters.[7] One reason for differences in susceptibility may be that the kinetics of uptake, metabolism and excretion for a substance differ between species, resulting in differences in the amounts of toxic substances which reach vulnerable sites in the body; there may be other physiological or anatomical reasons for differences.

2.25 Much effort has been devoted to designing statistical models and methods to describe and quantify the relationships between substances and effects. Models and methods have been proposed for a wide range of types of pollutants and effects.[8] Applying different mathematical models to the same data can give very different results. **Use of any model of pollutant-effect relationships should be dependent on careful consideration of the way it represents understanding of the development of the specific toxic effect being considered.** As with other kinds of model (2.56), validation is a crucial consideration and sensitivity analyses are essential.

2.26 The main types of empirical evidence which relate directly to humans, in order of their usefulness for toxicity assessment, are epidemiological studies, controlled experiments with human volunteers, and case reports.

2.27 In the workplace people may be exposed to higher concentrations of a substance over a shorter period than the general public. This makes it likely that any effects among workers will become apparent earlier than in comparable individuals in the general population. If the substance or substances causing an effect among workers are not known or immediately apparent, they first have to be identified. It may be easier in the workplace than elsewhere to relate different severities of effect to exposure to different concentrations of a substance or to different durations of exposure. Account needs to be taken of the fact that some groups in the general population may be more vulnerable than workers to a given substance or effect.

2.28 While the best data for toxicity assessment in human populations would be from experimental studies, in practice, observational epidemiological studies are the most relevant that are available. These studies may be of occupational groups or a wider population and seek associations between human exposure and adverse health effects. In evaluating such studies, there are potential sources of bias that must be taken into account (see box 2B[9]). Extrapolation of results from occupational studies to the general population is also problematical. It is difficult in epidemiological studies to isolate exposure to one substance. If an association is found between an exposure and an effect, this must be assessed to determine whether or not the association is a causal one; standard criteria for that purpose are described in box 2C.[10]

2.29 There is little information available from controlled experiments with human volunteers because of the practical and ethical considerations involved in deliberate exposure of individuals to chemical substances. This type of study is most useful for trials of new consumer products or for assessing exposure levels associated with acute effects, as in patch tests for skin irritation and sensitisation and other sensory irritation studies. Case reports describe a particular effect in an individual or group of individuals who were exposed to a substance; they are often of an anecdotal nature and are of limited use for toxicity assessment.

BOX 2B   **BIAS IN EPIDEMIOLOGICAL STUDIES**

Biases are unlikely to alter the fundamental conclusions of epidemiological studies which show strong effects. For studies that show a relatively weak association, as is typical for exposures to environmental hazards, problems caused by biases must be assessed carefully.

The principal biases in epidemiological studies are:

selection bias, occurring when participants in a study are selected in a way that makes them unrepresentative of the underlying population from which they should be drawn. In other words, those selected for a study differ systematically from those not selected. This is particularly an issue when the degree of selection bias varies with the exposure;

misclassification of both exposure and health effects occurs both randomly and systematically; systematic misclassification will lead to biased results. There are different types of misclassification bias; one example is 'recall bias', which may occur when there is differential recall of past events between people who are ill and healthy controls. Random misclassification will, in general, make it more likely that an association will be missed, or its effect under-estimated;

confounding is a common source of error in epidemiological studies, occurring when an apparent association between an exposure and an effect is caused by another factor in the population which is related both to the exposure under study and the effect. One way of controlling for confounding is to repeat a study under different conditions.

BOX 2C   **ESTABLISHING CAUSE AND EFFECT**

If a clear and statistically significant association is observed between some form of health effect and some feature of the environment, the Bradford Hill criteria are used to help establish whether the relationship is one of cause and effect. The criteria examine the following features:

strength of the observed association
consistency of the observed association
specificity of the observed association
temporal relationship of the observed association
presence of a dose-effect relationship (a biological gradient)
biological plausibility – this depends on the state of biological knowledge
coherence with the generally known facts of the history and biology of a disease
(occasionally) experimental or semi-experimental evidence
(in some circumstances) analogous observations.

Bradford Hill stated that

Clearly none of these nine [features] can bring indisputable evidence for or against a cause-and-effect hypothesis and equally none can be required as a *sine qua non*. What they can do, with greater or less strength, is to help us to answer the fundamental question – *is there any other way of explaining the set of facts before us, is there any other answer more likely than cause and effect?*

2.30 Before considering how toxicity data are used to establish dose-effect relationships, some of the principal uncertainties and limitations of these data can be summarised. Scientific understanding of the mechanisms by which substances exert effects is imperfect. There is also uncertainty due to random variation: this includes natural variation between the responses of individuals to the same exposure and variation in the levels and patterns of exposure that individuals experience due to the uneven way the substance is spread through the environment and the different ways in which individuals come into contact with it. This variation introduces considerable uncertainty into the estimation of EHD values (2.7) for assessment purposes. Further uncertainty and variation are introduced by any imprecision in the measurements or observations that are necessary to quantify the effects of substances.[11]

2.31 In addition to these sources of uncertainty, extrapolations often have to be made either from data on occupational exposure or from data on animals in laboratories. Such data have important limitations as the basis for setting environmental standards to protect the health of the general population:

> *a.* animal data are usually based on relatively short-term exposures involving high concentrations of a substance, whereas there is invariably more interest in, and need for information about, exposure to lower concentrations over longer periods (up to a human lifetime). To some extent occupational data suffer from the same limitations;

> *b.* many protocols for *in vivo* laboratory studies specify use of organisms with low genetic variability because their aim is easily reproducible tests with high precision. The human population is not homogeneous and some individuals are more vulnerable than others, for example, the elderly or those with pre-existing medical conditions;

> *c.* a primary consideration is how the species used in tests compare to humans. There are obvious differences in susceptibility between species and in the mechanisms by which toxic effects occur in different species;

> *d.* people are rarely exposed to just one potentially toxic substance at a time. Exposure to mixtures is far more common; the toxicity of a substance could be increased by additive, or even synergistic, effects from other substances, or could be mitigated by the antagonistic effect of another substance. There are very limited data about the effects of mixtures of substances. If this factor is taken into account at all in assessments, the effects of the substances in a mixture are generally assumed to be additive.

Determining dose-effect relationships for human health effects

2.32 The aim in assessing toxicity is to determine the relationship between dose received and the effect or effects of concern produced in humans, preferably in the form of a dose-response curve (see box 2A). Figure 2-II shows a dose-response curve in humans for kidney damage caused by cadmium: the concentration of cadmium in urine is an indication of dose and the presence of ß_2-microglobulin in urine is an early indication of an effect produced by cadmium, damage to renal tubules.[12] This can be regarded as a fairly typical dose-response curve in that, first, it has an 'S' shape and, second, no effect appears to occur at low concentrations of cadmium.

2.33 Only rarely are there sufficient data for a dose-response curve to be drawn. Such curves are most often based on data from studies of specific sub-lethal effects (as in this example) or on information from long-term studies, not on the relatively crude conclusions that can be drawn from LD_{50} or LC_{50} studies (2.19).

2.34 In practice, determination of the dose-effect relationship is often confined to determining the *threshold concentration* or *threshold dose,* the minimum concentration or dose required to produce a detectable response in a test population. Thresholds can never be determined with absolute certainty. For humans the threshold is normally taken to be the LOAEL or NOAEL, derived from tests with laboratory animals and then adjusted by applying an 'assessment factor' or 'safety factor'.

2.35 An example of such adjustments are those made by the World Health Organization (WHO) in its derivation of drinking water quality guideline values. The LOAEL or NOAEL derived from test data is divided by a number up to 10 to allow for each of the following causes of uncertainty in extrapolation:

> inter-species variation (from laboratory animal to human);

> intra-species variation (between individuals of the same species).

Figure 2-II
Example of dose-response curve: renal damage and cadmium exposure

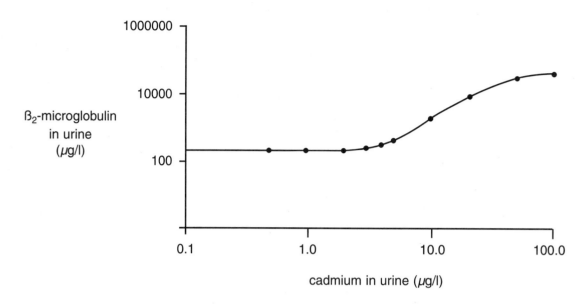

Other considerations increasing the uncertainty may also attract application of a safety factor. These include:

the adequacy of the overall database;

the nature and severity of the critical effect.

Thus, an overall safety factor of between 1 and 10,000 may be applied to the available data in order to extrapolate from the LOAEL or NOAEL derived from test data to an exposure standard in the form of a tolerable daily intake (TDI) (see appendix C, C.11), which those carrying out the assessment are confident would not result in adverse health consequences in the exposed human population. The TDI then forms the basis for deriving other forms of environmental standards, such as product standards.[13]

2.36 For some types of effect a threshold dose cannot be determined with confidence and it is questionable whether a threshold exists. An important type of effect in this category is *genotoxic carcinogenicity* (damage to genetic material). Any exposure of a cell to a substance which is a genotoxic carcinogen could potentially produce a mutation which might lead to cancer (if in somatic cells) or (if in germ cells) to effects that could be inherited. Equally, there may well be a threshold dose below which such effects do not occur because physiological processes rapidly detoxify the organism or repair the damage before it becomes established in the genetic material.

2.37 As it is not possible to demonstrate that there is a threshold dose for genotoxic carcinogens, or for some other substances, scientific assessments assume that any exposure of an organ or organism to those substances increases the probability of adverse effects. It has been argued that a *de minimis* approach should be adopted in assessing genotoxic carcinogens, with the aim of deriving a pragmatic threshold which would adequately protect public health.[14] Box 2D[15] describes the approach that has been followed in practice in recommending an air quality standard for a genotoxic carcinogen, benzene.

BOX 2D **STANDARD FOR A GENOTOXIC CARCINOGEN: BENZENE**

Sources of information Evidence of the harmfulness of benzene comes from both occupational exposure and laboratory studies. Tests on laboratory animals show that exposure to benzene increases the risk of certain types of leukaemia. *In vitro* testing indicates that benzene is a genotoxic carcinogen and may cause malignant disease even at very low levels of exposure.

Epidemiological studies relate largely to occupational exposure. Short-term exposure to extremely high benzene concentrations, likely only as a result of an accident, may cause fatal narcotic or anaesthetic effects. For long-term exposures, the effect of most concern is non-lymphocytic leukaemia, initially described in workers exposed to very high concentrations, but subsequently confirmed in studies of workers exposed to much lower exposures.

Key studies The human studies were more useful than the animal studies. Occupational exposures were probably under-estimated, so the risk of effects of exposure at a given concentration are likely to have been over-estimated. Nevertheless, several occupational studies gave reasonable estimates, especially two cohort studies giving evidence of an association between exposure to benzene and the likelihood of developing leukaemia.

Conclusion of assessment The Expert Panel on Air Quality Standards (EPAQS) considered that a concentration of benzene in air can be identified at which the risks are exceedingly small and unlikely to be detectable by any practical method.

From the available data, EPAQS concluded that the risk of leukaemia in workers is not detectable when average exposure over a working lifetime is around 500 ppb. To take account of the difference between a working lifetime (of approximately 77,000 hours) and chronological life (about 660,000 hours), the figure of 500 ppb was divided by 10. A further safety factor of 10 was applied in order to extrapolate from the fit, young to middle-aged male working population to the general population which might reasonably contain individuals unusually sensitive to the effects of benzene.

An air quality standard of 5 ppb, as a running annual average, was therefore recommended. In making this recommendation, EPAQS considered that the uncertainties in the data were such that accurate extrapolation of risk from high occupational to low ambient exposure was impossible. Because, in principle, exposure to benzene should be kept as low as practicable, EPAQS adopted a pragmatic approach by recommending in addition a target standard of 1 ppb, as a running annual average.

Effects on the natural environment

2.38 Ecotoxicology is concerned with the adverse impacts of substances on ecosystems. An *ecosystem* is an interdependent body of living organisms, usually of diverse species, together with the physical environment in which they live. Within such a system, several communities of interacting organisms may occupy more or less distinguishable physical environments; within these communities populations of species exist. Whereas in assessing effects on humans attention is generally focused on the health of the individual, in ecotoxicology it is populations and communities that are of concern.

2.39 Ecotoxicity tests may be carried out at levels ranging from biochemical to whole organism or whole ecosystem (usually replicated for this purpose in a laboratory, in simplified form). Biochemical tests on cells and tissues are usually simple and of short duration, and may be used for initial screening of substances for toxicity. Tests on ecosystems are of long duration, labour-intensive, often imprecise, and produce results which are usually relevant only to the particular ecosystem studied.

2.40 OECD has produced guidelines for ecotoxicity tests for substances in the aquatic environment. The general approach adopted for regulatory toxicity testing when carrying out assessments for the aquatic environment is to cover three trophic levels in water: algae (as primary photosynthetic producers), *Daphnia* (as primary consumer) and fish (as secondary consumer). It is assumed that a PNEC derived from results obtained at these three levels will protect all aquatic species exposed to the relevant substance via water. Amphibians are rarely used in tests (no existing form of regulation requires that) and no standard test methods for them have been developed. Nor are there officially recognised test methods for sediment-dwelling organisms, even though many substances with high potential for bioaccumulation tend to migrate towards sediments.[16]

2.41 Test methods for the terrestrial environment are less well-developed than for the aquatic environment. The species most commonly used in tests are earthworms (for which an OECD guideline is available); tests using nematodes, slugs, collembola and millipedes have also been developed. Tests of pesticides often use birds (for which OECD test guidelines are available) and bees. In general, ecotoxicity tests have not been developed for small mammals, except for bats in tests of wood preservatives and the occasional use of wild mammals in the USA.

2.42 Testing for toxicity to mammals thus relies on the standard laboratory tests used for assessing toxicity to humans. Laboratory mammals are not representative of animals in the natural environment. They are usually chosen for their ease of handling in the laboratory, easy reproduction and limited genetic variation. They do not show any seasonality in breeding and their physiological responses to environmental variables are atypical; for example, thermoregulation in laboratory rodents tends to be by endocrine stimulation to burn food, which would not occur in the wild.[17] The combined effect of species used and method design has been to improve the precision of testing but reduce its accuracy in reflecting toxicity to heterogeneous wild populations.

2.43 A useful source of information for ecotoxicological assessments is surveys of wildlife and vegetation. These also establish baselines for the state of the natural environment and reveal trends. Concern about endocrine-disrupting chemicals arose from field observations, and this led to further investigations both in laboratories and in the field.

2.44 As the basis for setting standards to protect the natural environment, ecotoxicological data are subject to kinds of uncertainty already discussed in the context of human health (2.30). The most useful data would be on effects at ecosystem or population level, but such data are seldom available. Instead, extrapolations have to be made, mainly from laboratory test data for single species or individuals. Key limitations of the data are:

a. laboratory data are invariably based on short-term exposures to high concentrations of a substance, whereas the effects of exposure to lower concentrations over longer periods are invariably more relevant;

b. extrapolation from an individual to a population is a complex task;

c. there are many different wildlife species to be protected, and they vary considerably in their characteristics. Test species are selected on limited criteria and it is questionable whether the sets of test species prescribed for certain regulatory purposes are adequate. Some species turn out to be especially sensitive to one chemical. For example, high mortality among wild geese revealed that they are about a hundred times more sensitive to carbophenothion (an organophosphate pesticide used as a seed dressing) than any of the species on which it had been tested;

d. as with humans (2.31*d.*), wildlife is much more likely to be exposed to mixtures of substances than to the single substances normally used in testing. Physical factors can also be important in determining the impact of substances: the effects of airborne pollutants such as sulphur dioxide and ozone on vegetation depend to a significant extent on temperature and water availability.

Determining dose-effect relationships for the natural environment

2.45 Ecotoxicological data may be used in different ways in order to determine dose-effect relationships. Two such methods, called for convenience the UK and Dutch approaches, are discussed briefly here. The UK approach was developed in order to set quality standards for water but is also applicable in principle to the terrestrial environment. The Dutch approach was originally developed for application to soil invertebrates but is now being extended to other groups of organisms and the transfer of substances through the food chain.

2.46 In the UK approach all the available data are examined in order to identify the species which is most sensitive to a particular substance. It is assumed that, although ecosystem sensitivity is a complex attribute, the sensitivity of the most sensitive species can provide an approximation to it; and that protecting the most sensitive species therefore also protects the functioning of the ecosystems of which that species is part. The objective is to estimate a PNEC (2.9) for a substance, below which there will be no significant adverse effects on aquatic organisms, and which will protect all populations in the most sensitive habitats against effects from either long-term or episodic exposure.

2.47 To derive this PNEC, assessment factors (analogous to the safety factors described in 2.35) are applied to the data on the most sensitive species to address the uncertainties created for extrapolation by:

> the difference between a single species and an ecosystem;
>
> inter-species variation;
>
> the difference between acute and chronic effects (if there are no data for chronic effects);
>
> (in most cases) the difference between the laboratory situation and the situation in the field.

The assessment factor used may vary according to the data available, the purpose of the assessment, and the body carrying it out. For example, under the EC procedure the lowest LC_{50} from a standard set of acute toxicity data for aquatic organisms (2.40) is normally divided by 1,000 to derive the PNEC, whereas the practice of the US Environmental Protection Agency has been to divide the same figure by 100 to derive the PNEC.[18] The EC procedure recognises that in some circumstances an assessment factor of less than 1,000 may be appropriate, for example if data are available on additional taxonomic groups or from chronic toxicity tests.[19]

2.48 In the Dutch approach the available ecotoxicological data are transformed into a probability distribution, and from this distribution curve is derived the concentration of a substance which is estimated to be hazardous (in terms of the end-point of the test for which data are available) for a specified proportion of species, usually 5% (HC_5). Thus the aim is to protect a high proportion of species, rather than all species as in the UK approach.

2.49 The test data on which both approaches are dependent are open to uncertainties and limitations that affect all ecotoxicological assessments (2.44). Some specific problems with the two approaches are:[20]

> (UK approach) it cannot be known with certainty that the most sensitive species for which data are available is in reality the most sensitive species;
>
> (Dutch approach) the small proportion of species excluded from protection may include rare species in need of conservation or organisms crucial for the functioning of the ecosystem;
>
> (Dutch approach) in statistical terms, the distribution of sensitivity across all the organisms in the environment may not be a normal distribution, and in any event the available data may not be representative of the real distribution;

(Dutch approach) the approach is purely statistical, with no biological input beyond the results of simple laboratory tests. The functioning of ecosystems is not considered, only the populations within them.

There is some evidence that the Dutch approach over-estimates the toxicity of substances in the field; in the case of copper for example, the HC_5 derived to protect soil organisms is below the concentration at which soils are considered copper-deficient for the grazing of livestock.

2.50 Despite the great difficulties involved, determining dose-effect relationships for the effects of substances on the natural environment is an essential exercise if appropriate environmental policies are to be adopted. When environmental policies or standards are adopted, it should always be made clear in an explicit statement whether they are designed to protect the natural environment, human health, or both, and the degree and nature of protection they are intended to afford.

Environmental pathways and exposures

2.51 The third essential element of scientific assessments identified at the beginning of this chapter and in figure 2-I is assessment of pathways and exposures. Assessment of new and existing chemical substances covers all the pathways by which exposure to a substance can occur (including, for example, occupational exposure), but the present discussion is confined to environmental pathways. For a substance to have an adverse effect on an organism (human or non-human) or on a component of the environment, a pathway must exist between the source of the substance and the entity which is susceptible to harm. Where the effect occurs only if a threshold dose or concentration is reached, the pathways and the behaviour of the substance have to be characterised in enough detail for estimates to be made of exposure to the substance.

2.52 This third element of assessment has been described already in general terms (2.6). There is extensive knowledge of the basic processes by which substances move through the environment and react with other substances. The way a substance behaves is governed by its physical, chemical and biological properties.

2.53 Assessments of pathways and exposures are usually produced by using models. For new substances or initial screening of existing substances, relatively simple models employing data for a few physico-chemical parameters can be used to assess the potential distribution of a substance between environmental compartments. Models based on the concept of *fugacity* (the tendency of chemicals to escape) are an example.[21] More complex exposure models can help quantify expected concentrations under different conditions and can be applied either to a single medium such as air or to multiple media.[22]

2.54 For some existing substances (for example List I and II substances under the EC Dangerous Substances in Water Directive), monitoring data may be available to show their actual distribution in the environment. For other substances, monitoring or experiments may be carried out more or less extensively to obtain data.

2.55 Given the complexity of the environment and the number of substances that have to be assessed, the use of models to predict pathways is inevitable. However, models will never be able to capture all the complexities of the environment; at best, they are only an approximation to reality. Unexpected effects may occur if a substance is transformed into another substance by reactions in the environment, is carried unexpectedly long distances, behaves differently in one location to another, or causes exposure through several different pathways simultaneously. Box 2E gives examples of adverse effects which were not foreseen because of incomplete understanding of the pathways and fates of substances.

BOX 2E	SOURCES OF ERROR IN ASSESSING PATHWAYS AND EXPOSURES

The form in which a substance is released is not necessarily that in which it remains. Substances released to the environment are subject to a wide range of possible transformation processes, including biodegradation, hydrolysis and photodegradation, as a result of which they may be transformed to more or less harmful products or more or less permanently immobilised by adsorption onto soils and sediments. One example of transformation leading to a more toxic substance is provided by mercury. Bacterial transformation of insoluble, inorganic, biologically unavailable mercury salts in Minamata Bay, Japan, led to the formation of soluble, bioaccumulative and toxic methyl mercury, capable of entering the aquatic ecosystem. Methyl mercury accumulated in fish which were then eaten by the human population. Toxic effects ensued, including the birth of handicapped children to mothers who themselves appeared unaffected.

The location in which a substance is released is not necessarily that in which it has its most important effect. Environmental transport mechanisms move substances from their point of release to other locations or to other environmental media. Processes such as volatilisation, advection and adsorption determine the distribution of a chemical in the environment in space and time, and have been responsible for the discovery of pollutants in unexpected places. The presence of persistent organic pollutants, such as polychlorinated biphenyls (PCBs), in otherwise unpolluted parts of the globe, for example the polar regions, and their subsequent bioaccumulation in the fat tissues of organisms, has been attributed to repeated volatilisation, condensation and deposition cycles which transport them away from their point of release.

Behaviour in one location does not guarantee the same behaviour in another. The effects in Cumbria from the Chernobyl nuclear accident illustrate the need to take into account local conditions. The assumption that in Cumbria radioactive caesium would quickly become immobilised in soils and would not pose a long-term threat to the sheep feeding on local grass was based on the response of the clay mineral soils of southern England to radioactive exposure. The peaty, acidic soils of Cumbria did not immobilise caesium as expected. It remained available for root uptake into grass and found its way into the bodies of sheep; exposure of lambs to radioactivity through grass consumption, which was predicted to last a few weeks only, has continued for much longer.

There may be simultaneous exposure to the same substance from different media and sources. Exposure of humans and animals can occur through inhalation of airborne pollutants, ingestion of pollutants in food and drinking water, and skin absorption. As another example, limit values have been set to protect agricultural soils from the adverse effects of certain metals through the addition of sewage sludge. Other sources, including airborne deposition from industrial and transport sources, deposition in other wastes or the presence of natural metal deposits, which are not as well-characterised or controlled as sewage sludge, may be more significant in terms of overall concentrations and accumulation of metals in soil.

2.56 **All exposure models (indeed, all mathematical models used within scientific assessments) should be regarded with caution until they are properly validated.** Empirical models built by statistical analysis of a set of data must be validated by being tested on an independent data set. Methods for this are well-established.[23] The need for validation against actual data is even stronger for models which are based on postulated environmental processes rather than empirical data.[24] Confidence in the scientific principles on which they are built sometimes gives those who construct such models an excessive faith in their predictions.

Assimilative capacity of the environment

2.57 So far, this discussion of the scientific basis for environmental standards has focused on the release of substances into the environment. Examination of the assessment procedures for new and existing chemicals helps to explain and illuminate many of the issues that arise in decisions on environmental standards but environmental policies also raise wider issues. One such issue is the ability of the environment to absorb substances without undergoing significant measurable change, what has been called its *assimilative capacity*. Natural biogeochemical cycles have a certain resilience. Although innumerable synthetic substances have become widely diffused, the natural environment is able to accommodate some exposure to potentially hazardous substances. Just as organisms can display resistance to the toxic effects of substances at some levels of exposure, for example through cell or tissue repair mechanisms or the metabolism or excretion of substances, so natural processes in the environment can break down potentially hazardous substances into simple compounds such as water or carbon dioxide, or into by-products that are harmless compared to the original substance. Another dimension of assimilation is the ability of various compartments of the environment to retain particular substances in *sinks* (for example, deep sediments) where they are removed from circulation and either destroyed or stored, the general assumption being that they do not then pose any hazard to human health or the natural environment.

2.58 In past discussions of the significance of the presence of potentially hazardous substances in the environment, a distinction was drawn between 'pollution' – regarded as resulting from the release to the environment by human action of a substance, or energy, that is liable to cause hazards to human health, harm to living resources and ecological systems, damage to structures, or amenity or interference with legitimate uses of the environment'[25] – and 'contamination' – defined as detectable concentrations of substances where either the substances involved 'are believed (or positively asserted) to be harmless or [they are] not present in sufficient quantities or concentrations to cause damage'.[26] It will be apparent from previous sections of this chapter that such a distinction is very much more problematic than was at one time assumed.

2.59 Assessing whether particular quantities or concentrations of particular substances, or combinations of substances, will cause harm, in other words estimating the assimilative capacity of the environment, depends on scientific understanding. It has been seen already (box 2E) that there are gaps in that understanding, and that the release of substances can have unexpected effects. Mathematical models can be used to estimate the distribution of substances between media and the capacity of a particular medium to assimilate known substances, but such estimates are inherently uncertain. Unpredictable disruption of environmental processes can occur in many ways; changes in physical environmental conditions can lead to a reduced ability to degrade substances. Substances can on occasion cross from one environmental compartment to another in unexpected ways, invalidating the original assessments of their effects. It has been shown that environmental risk characterisations for particular substances or releases are generally based on the results of a series of relatively simple ecotoxicity tests covering only a few readily observable end-points such as death or induction of disease in fish. Estimation of the assimilative capacity may appear precise but only at the expense of excluding the possibility of other end-points, indirect effects or interactions between chemicals or between chemicals and other factors.

2.60 The environment is exposed to many different stresses and determining the assimilative capacity of the environment for simultaneous exposure to more than one substance is difficult. The introduction of too many substances or too much of any one substance over a short period of time can overload the assimilative capacity of the system. The time-scale over which assimilation occurs in different parts of the environment is an important factor; an example is provided by consideration of the effects of major oil spills on the marine environment. Major oil spills occurring near coastal ecosystems invariably cause immediate damage to marine flora and fauna. Within a relatively short period micro-organisms will begin to degrade the oil hydrocarbons into smaller short-chain molecules and eventually simple compounds like water and carbon dioxide. Following one such incident off the coast of Brittany in 1980, hydrocarbons were being degraded within 24 hours of the disaster; a threefold increase in the biomass of hydrocarbon-utilising bacteria was observed.[27] The negative impact of oil spills on sea bird, mammal and fish populations would not, however, be reversible on such a short time-scale. In estimating the assimilative capacity, the conclusion reached depends on which part of the environment attention is focused.

2.61 Soil is a largely static medium and, although substances may move through soils, occasionally adsorbed onto soil particles, to groundwater, rivers and the sea, harmful levels can build up in soils. Although soils have considerable adsorptive and buffering capacities for a wide range of pollutants, exceedance of these capacities can result in considerable damage; for example, exceedance of the buffering capacity for acidic species results in the release of aluminium from acidified soils. One approach which has been developed to guide decisions on air pollution policies and standards as they affect soil or fresh water is the determination of the critical load of one or more pollutants which an environmental compartment or a species, species type, particular ecosystem or habitat can receive without harm.[28] So far this approach has been applied only to certain very common and straightforward pollutants.

2.62 One major area where problems have arisen is the fate of persistent substances. For example, chlorofluorocarbons (CFCs) are very persistent and not significantly reactive in the general environment, and were, therefore, regarded as harmless: assessments failed to take account of their fate in the stratosphere where they are broken down by solar radiation into highly reactive substances which destroy ozone. An older example is persistent organochlorine compounds, such as DDT, for which the sink turned out to be the fatty tissues of animals and birds. This illustrates the particular hazards of substances which are not only persistent but bioaccumulative, that is, they are brought together in higher concentrations through the operation of biological systems.

2.63 Another way in which mistaken assessments of the assimilative capacity of the environment can arise is through failure to consider all the uses and functions of a particular part of the environment. As an example, the river systems feeding the Norfolk Broads have long been used to dilute and disperse discharges of effluent from sewage treatment works. If the only function of the Broads had been to provide boating facilities and disperse sewage effluent, there would have been little conflict but the Broads also supported a unique and highly valued mix of flora and fauna. The inputs of nutrients, principally phosphates, into the Broads from sewage effluent favoured the growth and development of certain species and habitat types, which over time came to dominate the ecosystem; the more nutrient-sensitive populations of flora and fauna were partly or completely destroyed.[29]

2.64 These examples show that the use made of the assimilative capacity of the environment in the past has sometimes had damaging consequences. Scientific calculations of the impact of releasing specified amounts of specified substances may in due course be made more precise and more robust. However, decisions about what use to make of the environment always involve judgements and depend on questions of values. This is highlighted by use of the word 'significant' in the definition of assimilative capacity quoted above (2.57). The value judgements are also very clearly signalled in policy statements which described the environment as 'a resource we can use but must not misuse'[30] or 'an asset which may be used, but not abused'.[31] The extent to which such values can be disputed has been shown by the Brent Spar case. The strong public opposition to disposal of the Brent Spar oil installation in the deep ocean appears to have been prompted to a large extent, not by the global impacts that would have followed from disposal (these have been assessed as very small) nor the local impacts (which would have been appreciable only within a few square kilometres at most),[32] but by opposition on principle to use of the deep ocean for waste disposal.

Output from scientific assessment

2.65 It has long been a central theme of UK environmental policies that decisions should be based on what has frequently been called 'sound science'. The 1990 Environment White Paper, said 'We must base our policies on fact not fantasy, and use the best evidence and analysis available'. It stressed 'the need, in environmental decisions as elsewhere, to look at all the facts and likely consequences of action on the basis of the best scientific evidence'.[33] Statutory guidance given by Ministers to the Environment Agencies affirmed that they should 'operate to high professional standards, based on sound science, information and analysis of the environment and of the processes which affect it'.[34] Until recently little attention was devoted to examining what constitutes sound science, either generally or in the context of deciding environmental policies and setting environmental standards. There has been much confusion on these points.

2.66 We believe it is essential that environmental policies should have a sound scientific basis, and that there is an adequate scientific basis for most such policies at present. There is, however, a widely held view, even an expectation, that scientists can provide the answer to whatever issues are under consideration. Science is not a matter of certainties but of hypotheses and experiments. It advances by examining alternative explanations for phenomena, and by abandoning superseded views. It has provided very powerful tools for gaining understanding of complex environmental processes and systems. At the same time there are many cases, some of which we have mentioned, in which damage has been caused to health or the natural environment because of gaps in understanding. Such incompleteness is inherent in the nature of science, especially environmental science, which deals with 'the world outside the laboratory'.[35] **In a scientific assessment of an environmental issue there are bound to be limitations and uncertainties associated with the data at each stage. Standard setting and other decision-making procedures should recognise that.**

2.67 The types of scientific assessment considered in this chapter represent, in effect, applied science, what has sometimes been called 'regulatory science'. Groups of recognised experts follow prescribed routines. We have found that, even within these established procedures, there are major sources of uncertainty in the conclusions reached both about effects on human health (2.30–2.31) and about effects on the natural environment (2.44), not to mention the considerable and inevitable uncertainties about the pathways of substances (2.55 and box 2E). The conventional approach in countering such uncertainties is to apply safety margins to the scientific data when setting environmental standards. The extent of those safety margins in any given case is essentially a matter of judgement.

2.68 **In setting an environmental standard, the starting-point must be scientific understanding of the cause of the problem or potential problem under consideration.** However, environmental policies cannot be decided simply on the basis of scientific evidence. For the majority of environmental standards, as well as for broader policies, there needs to be a prior stage, of defining what the problem is, framing questions and formulating policy aims. This will determine the relative emphasis to be placed on different types of scientific assessment in a given case, or even which types of scientific assessment should be carried out. There will also be other crucial components in the decision procedure besides the scientific assessment. We discuss those components in subsequent chapters.

2.69 Decisions over whether to release pollutants into the environment raise questions of values which cannot be answered simply by referring to the scientific evidence. Estimation of the assimilative capacity of the environment is a scientific procedure. Judgements on whether, and to what extent, the assimilative capacity of the environment should be used in particular circumstances, or the degree of precaution that should be exercised in taking policy decisions, are part of a wider political process. **A clear dividing line should be drawn between analysis of scientific evidence and consideration of ethical and social issues which are outside the scope of a scientific assessment.**

2.70 Given that it is an essential input to the decision procedure, and given also that it will usually be affected by considerable uncertainty, what form can a scientific assessment most usefully take, so that the nature and extent of the uncertainty can be taken into account appropriately when decisions are made? The issue was considered in a description of UK practices in setting environmental standards published by the Department of the Environment (DOE) in 1977, which said 'The first requirement in setting standards or objectives is a realistic appraisal of all relevant scientific data, particularly evidence of damage in relation to dosage'; and also that 'The tendency in setting standards in the United Kingdom is less to seek an absolute scientific base than to use scientific principles and all relevant and reliable evidence'.[36]

2.71 The issue was revisited in a lecture given by the Chief Scientist of DOE in 1996.[37] He echoed some of the language of the 1977 account but with major differences. He spoke of critical assessment rather than 'realistic appraisal', he referred not only to evidence of damage but to evidence for concerns about future damage, and he emphasised that the assessment must reflect the state of uncertainty about the evidence and cover all possible interpretations of it. He also emphasised the need to deal with possible sources of bias in the assessment.

2.72 The following quality control criteria were offered for scientific assessments of environmental issues:

> A sound science assessment reviews all the scientific evidence, not just the most recent research.

> The assessment should display what is held to be beyond dispute, what is the range of speculative interpretations of the data, and weightings as to their likelihood.

> The assessment must be undertaken with peer review if any element is likely to be speculative. (Peer review reduces bias in assessments arising from an individual expert's judgement or experience (expert bias); comments by one or two experts or colleagues in the same field provide a quality check.)

> The assessment must be undertaken by a multi-disciplinary panel with a secretariat if speculative issues relate to discipline sensitive assumptions. (This reduces bias arising from the inherently different approaches of different disciplines.)

> The review's emerging findings should be open for public comment at an interim stage. (This may help quality control in two ways: wider consultation may help to uncover new data which have been collected but not published (researchers, and journals, are generally reluctant to publish negative findings); wider consultation may uncover new interpretations of existing data.)

2.73 **The requirement for sound science as the basis for environmental policy is not a requirement for absolute knowledge or certainty and should not be interpreted as such.** Rather than give the impression that scientific evidence can or does resolve all uncertainties, its limitations should be made explicit. A conclusion that there is insufficient information available to carry out an assessment which policy-makers have requested may represent sound science.

2.74 **When considering the process of scientific assessment and its output, two separate issues need to be addressed. First, is the science well done, and are uncertainties and limitations in the data properly recognised? The answer to this question determines whether the assessment represents good science. Second, does the science provide a firm basis for policy decisions? The answer to this question determines how useful the assessment will be to the policy-maker, whether decisions will have to be taken in the face of uncertainty, and whether further studies (perhaps including experimental work) should be carried out.**

Presentation of scientific assessments

2.75 **Scientific assessments should indicate clearly where the boundaries of knowledge lie. To be helpful to policy-makers they should indicate clearly both what is known or considered to be indisputable and what is considered to be speculative.**

2.76 **Transparency should be the watchword in presenting assessments. It is essential that there should be a succinct narrative summary of the assessment covering the underlying scientific basis, uncertainties in the evidence and the rationale for any methods used to cope**

with variability and uncertainties (for example, any safety factors used) and the assumptions implicit in their use. The quality of the assessment and its results and the confidence placed in them will be higher as a result of more open and transparent presentation.

2.77 In 1997 the government's Chief Scientific Adviser produced a set of principles (the May principles) for government Departments and agencies to guide them on the use and presentation of scientific advice in policy making.[38] These principles cover, amongst other issues, the use of a wide range of expert sources both within and outside government and within and outside the UK, and early peer review of data. They emphasise that 'Scientific advance thrives on openness and competition of ideas.' **We welcome the monitoring by the Office of Science and Technology (OST) of the extent to which Departments are modifying their procedures for using scientific advice in policy making in response to the principles produced by the Chief Scientific Adviser.**

2.78 In view of the uncertainties in scientific assessments of environmental issues transparency is especially important. Science has its own procedures for quality control, including peer review. Table 2.1 illustrates an approach that has been proposed for assessing the 'pedigree' of scientific data, from both cognitive and social aspects.[39] Pedigree becomes a relevant consideration only if data have passed the basic test of relevance. Other things being equal, experimental data score highly in terms of pedigree, but in the environmental field they are unlikely to be available to illuminate the issues that are of most concern. Other kinds of information may be more useful than experimental data that are, at best, of only marginal relevance.

Table 2.1
The 'research-pedigree' matrix proposed by Funtowicz and Ravetz

	cognitive phases		social aspects	
rank	theoretical structures	data-input	peer-acceptance	colleague consensus
4	established theory	experimental data	total	all but cranks
3	theoretically-based model	historic/field data	high	all but rebels
2	computational model	calculated data	medium	competing schools
1	statistical processing	educated guesses	low	embryonic field
0	definitions	uneducated guesses	none	no opinion

2.79 Another consideration that becomes important in a situation of high uncertainty is the overall impartiality of the procedures used for assessment. Judgements can be swayed, perhaps imperceptibly, by one or another kind of vested interest. One much remarked upon, and criticised, feature of regulatory science in the past has been the extent to which experts in an industry, the contract laboratories carrying out the standard tests for it and the regulatory body itself have functioned in some instances as a largely closed community.[40]

2.80 A scientific assessment should present the range of possible interpretations of the available evidence, or the range of scientific possibilities and options concerning a particular course of action, accompanied by acknowledgement of the assumptions and uncertainties implicit in the assessment. The output of a scientific assessment should not normally be presented as a single option or statement; an assessment yielding a single answer (especially a single number) may give a spurious impression of accuracy.

2.81 The precise way in which the output of an assessment is presented depends on the type of assessment being carried out and the type of environmental concern that is being addressed. For example, the assessment may be based on the dose-effect relationship derived for a substance, and its results expressed as statements of effects on individuals, specific populations or species arising at certain exposures with, preferably quantified, expressions of the uncertainties and assumptions implicit in that dose-effect relationship. The margins of error or uncertainties in the data and models used to derive the dose-effect curve will form a major element of the output.

2.82 Another example of how uncertainties in an assessment can be presented has been provided by the Scientific Assessment Working Group of the Intergovernmental Panel on Climate Change (IPCC) (box 2F[41]).

Implications for scientific research

2.83 Two issues for scientific research arise out of this discussion of scientific assessments and environmental standard setting. The first is that **it is necessary to build review processes and the potential for revision into standard-setting procedures**, and to ensure that research and monitoring are undertaken to provide inputs to those reviews. **Scientific knowledge can move rapidly and standards must be readily adjustable and regularly reviewed, so that new insights can be incorporated.** Updates required on a predetermined timetable would enhance the transparency of this procedure. In the USA such updates take place by statute and are open to public scrutiny. Different US government Departments and agencies co-operate in this procedure. In addition, a mechanism is in place for members of the public to propose substances for scientific scrutiny and submit supporting evidence.[42] In the UK, the Health and Safety Executive regularly reviews the basis of its occupational exposure standards, publishing annual revisions, and may add new substances to the existing list.

2.84 Incomplete knowledge and the exercise of precaution (for example, through the use of large safety or assessment factors) can result in standards being set which those to whom such standards apply (usually industry), and who are faced with the resulting cost implications, regard as unnecessarily stringent. There may, therefore, be considerable financial incentives to undertake further scientific investigation in order to reduce the margin of uncertainty and revise the level of a standard on the basis of evidence rather than precaution.[43]

2.85 The May principles on science and policy highlight the importance of a more pro-active approach to resolving scientific uncertainties through targeted research, stating that:[44]

> Departments should systematically review priorities to see whether funding needs to be directed to programmes of further research to illuminate outstanding areas of uncertainty identified [during assessment].

2.86 The second issue for scientific research, also highlighted by the May principles, is the ability of government to respond to new environmental issues. Within their own programmes of research, government Departments seek to maintain 'adequate support for broadly-based longer term research to help them identify and/or respond to new and unexpected findings'. Despite Departments' best efforts to anticipate as early as possible those issues for which scientific advice or research will be needed, some issues will inevitably arise with little or no prior warning. Departments should ensure that they have the capacity to recognise the implications and to react

---

BOX 2F   PRESENTING THE SCIENTIFIC ASSESSMENT OF CLIMATE CHANGE

The assessments of the Intergovernmental Panel on Climate Change (IPCC) have aimed to achieve maximum ownership both by the international scientific community and by governments. Both ownerships are necessary if scientists and governments are to have the confidence to move forward with an effective response to issues as complex and as controversial as those of climate change.

Ownership by the international scientific community is achieved by involving as many scientists (including the leading scientists with the highest scientific reputation) as possible from as many countries as possible either as contributors, lead authors or reviewers of the assessment. In Working Group 1 (Science) for the 1995 report, well over 500 scientists from 40 countries were so involved; for all three working groups, the total number approached 2,000. In order to involve governments, the assessments have gone through a second review stage by governments (the first has been a scientific peer review) and the 'Summaries for Policymakers' have been approved line by line at intergovernmental meetings at which about 100 governments have been represented.

It is important that reports produced by scientists should convey clear messages to policy-makers. The debate at these intergovernmental approval meetings has led to substantial improvement in the presentation of the science – in particular its relevance, its consistency and its clarity. At the same time, representatives of the scientific authors have been present to ensure that scientific accuracy is preserved.

The assessments have taken care in their presentation to distinguish between what is known with reasonable certainty and where the main uncertainties lie. For example, the executive summary of the Summary for Policymakers of the 1990 Report of the Scientific Assessment Working Group presented the findings of the Working Group in three broad bands:

> those the Group was **certain of**, for example, that there is a natural greenhouse effect;
>
> those that the Group had **calculated with confidence**, for example, the relative effectiveness of different greenhouse gases;
>
> those that the Group had **predicted, based on model results**, for example, the rates of global mean temperature increase during the next century on the basis of different emission scenarios.

The Working Group acknowledged the **many uncertainties** in its predictions, particularly with regards to the timing, magnitude and regional patterns of climate change, due to its incomplete understanding of factors including greenhouse gas sources and sinks, and the effects of clouds, oceans and polar ice sheets.

The Summary for Policymakers continued with statements of the Group's **judgement** based on the above findings and bearing in mind the acknowledged uncertainties, for example, the statement that global mean surface air temperature has increased by 0.3°C to 0.6°C over the last 100 years.

It concluded with a list of actions necessary in order **to improve predictive capability**, for example, to understand better the various climate-related processes, especially those associated with clouds, oceans and the carbon cycle.

quickly and efficiently to such crises.[45] **To prevent development of new understanding being restricted by established regulatory procedures, vested interests or small closed communities of experts, publicly funded programmes of environmental research should include provision for independent investigation and inquiry.**

2.87 **We welcome monitoring by OST of Departmental and agency procedures for early identification of issues for which scientific research or advice will be needed.**

Chapter 3

TECHNOLOGICAL OPTIONS

Many environmental standards have been based on a view about what was practicable in the context of a particular industrial process or in the design or composition of a particular product. Impact on the environment is now being analysed in a broader way, covering whole companies or product chains. Effective protection of the environment will depend increasingly on taking environmental considerations fully into account when technologies are selected, developed and applied. Standards must be set in ways that stimulate companies to adopt clean technology.

3.1   In discussing scientific assessment of the effects of human activities the previous chapter took as a case study assessments of new and existing chemical substances. The introduction of new substances is one example of rapid and far-reaching changes in technology which have sometimes given rise to concern and controversy because of fears about their consequences for the environment and society. It is essential that, as happens with new substances, the environmental implications of technological developments should be assessed before they are applied on a wide scale, and that appropriate forms of regulation should be in place.

3.2   At the same time, technology has been utilised on a massive scale to make many forms of human activity less polluting. Further steps in the same direction have been dismissed by some people as palliatives, on the ground that they might distract attention from the underlying causes of problems, and thus prevent or delay more fundamental changes in life-styles and the economy required for environmental sustainability in the long term. We believe that achieving sustainable development will require both full utilisation of technology and measures on other fronts. It would be dangerous if arguments against 'technical fixes' prevented full advantage being taken of technology's potential contribution to the efficient and appropriate use of resources, including the transfers of technology to less-developed nations which is required under international conventions to protect the environment.

3.3   Analysis of technological options is an essential component in the analyses needed to underpin decisions about environmental policies and standards. Depending on the circumstances, the emphasis may be either on the environmental acceptability of a technological development or on the extent to which new technology can reduce the environmental effects of an activity, or increasingly on an integrated consideration of both aspects. Gaining maximum advantage from technology's potential will involve radical changes in the approaches taken by engineers and by companies.

3.4   In this chapter we first discuss the general nature of technology's contribution to decisions about environmental standards, and what the scope of assessments should be (3.5–3.11). We review the progressively broader perspectives that have been used in analysing the options available (3.12–3.31). We discuss approaches to engineering design that emphasise the objective of minimising environmental impact, and how regulation can best encourage their use (3.32–3.45). We then discuss how the output from assessments of the technological options can be related most constructively to decisions about environmental policies and standards (3.46–3.57).

35

Chapter 3

Importance of technology for environmental standards

3.5   While the capability of available technology may be an important consideration in relation to any form of environmental standard, it enters in different ways into decisions about different forms of standard. In the terminology introduced in box 1A, the regulatory decisions resulting from the assessments of new and existing substances described in the last chapter provide examples of use and product standards. New substances notified to the regulator are the outcome of research and development by manufacturers, which, in the case of products for widespread use, will have covered the conditions under which the product should be used. Technology is also of direct importance in setting product standards; decisions may be constrained by the extent to which it is feasible to remove small traces of a substance from a product or reduce the amount of a substance in a product without impairing its effectiveness.

3.6   Emission standards are often set at the level which it is known an available technology can achieve. Thus the limit values in European Community (EC) stage II legislation on emissions from cars, which came into effect in 1996–97, presupposed that manufacturers would comply by fitting catalytic converters and engine management systems to all new petrol cars.

3.7   Another relevant technological consideration is the precision of available methods for measuring the concentrations at which substances are present. There is no point in setting a standard unless there is a method available to confirm compliance with it. On occasion, the limit of detection of the available analytical techniques has been adopted as an environmental standard. This, rather than toxicology, was the basis for the 0.1 μg/l limit value for individual pesticides set in the 1980 EC Drinking Water Directive. Availability of appropriate analytical techniques was also a major consideration in setting the limit value for emissions of dioxins to air from incineration plants at 1 ng TEQ/Nm^3; a more stringent standard of 0.1 ng TEQ/Nm has the status only of a guide value.[1]

3.8   Technology standards would prescribe use of a particular technology to limit emissions, and have not been used in the UK. The form of standard used in the UK in which technology is most directly and explicitly taken into account is the process standards set by the Environment Agency. The guidance notes which contain these standards are discussed later in this chapter. The situation has some similarity to the use of emission standards, in that plants have legal limits placed on their emissions[2] in the light of benchmark levels contained in the guidance notes. The key difference is that these benchmark levels are based on a comprehensive view of the relevant industrial process, covering in particular the release of substances to air, water and land.

3.9   We noted at the beginning of this report (1.29) the development of much broader perspectives for analysing and regulating the environmental impact of human activities. Decisions about environmental policies and standards can be crucially affected by the scope of the review undertaken of technological options. First, the review as a whole must be sufficiently wide-ranging to cover all the options which have a credible claim to represent the best solution in environmental terms.

3.10 Second, the review must be sufficiently comprehensive in its examination of the environmental implications of each option. Of two alternative processes, it is usually the case that one produces less of some types of emission than the other, but more of other types of emission. Selection of a technological option on the basis of too limited an examination can have the effect that environmental damage is not reduced, but displaced to another form or medium or process or location, or even increased. Management of persistent substances is always likely to result in some form of displacement, unless a strategy can be devised and implemented which incorporates an acceptable final destination for each such substance.

3.11 Situations in which failure to adopt a broad perspective can have a damaging effect on the environment can be categorised as follows:

> *a. different substances emitted to the same medium from the same source or class of sources.* An example is the comparison between petrol and diesel engines for cars. A diesel car emits less carbon monoxide, but more nitrogen oxides and a greater mass of particulate matter, than a petrol car with a three-way catalytic converter fitted;

> *b. substances emitted to different media from the same process.* If an overall view was not taken, a persistent substance could be filtered out of discharges to air but released instead in liquid effluent *or* in solid wastes, which might be more damaging to the environment;

> *c. emission of the same substance to the same medium from different sources.* If a number of sources are close together, more stringent limits may have to be applied to emissions to prevent unacceptable deterioration of the environment;

> *d. different waste streams considered in isolation.* Because of their overhead costs and requirements for expertise, some types of waste disposal facility required may not be viable unless a comprehensive view is taken;

> *e. considering environmental impact in one country, or from the activities of one company, without considering other countries or companies.* The result may be that environmentally damaging activities are simply transferred to another country or company;

> *f. considering one point in the life cycle of a product without considering the whole cycle.* What appears to be an environmental improvement in the context of one process may turn out to be merely transferring environmental impact to some other point in the material or energy supply chain.

The desirability in principle of taking a comprehensive view of the environmental implications of each option is sometimes constrained by practicability, both in terms of the analyses that can be carried out and in terms of what actions can be taken on the findings. We now look at some of the approaches that have been used.

Approaches to analysing technological options

Best available techniques not entailing excessive cost

3.12 Integrated pollution control (IPC) was intended to allow regulators to deal with the kind of interaction identified in 3.11*b*. It is based on process standards, so that the operator can be required to adopt the least damaging combination of emissions to different media. The statutory basis for integrated pollution control applied to major industrial processes in the UK is the Environmental Protection Act 1990 (the 1990 Act), which brings together in convoluted provisions two basic concepts: *best practicable environmental option* (BPEO, considered in the next section) and *best available techniques not entailing excessive cost* (BATNEEC). The operator of any prescribed industrial process in England, Wales or Scotland is required to prevent the release into any environmental medium of substances prescribed for that medium or, where that is not practicable using BATNEEC, to use such techniques to reduce releases of substances to a minimum and render them harmless. Where a prescribed industrial process is likely to involve the release of substances into more than one environmental medium, the conditions the regulator attaches to the authorisation for the process must have the objective of ensuring that BATNEEC 'will be used for minimising the pollution … to the environment taken as a whole … having regard to the best practicable environmental option available as respects the substances which may be released'.[4]

3.13 BATNEEC first appeared in legislation in the context of emissions to air from industrial plants in the EC Framework Directive of 1984.[5] The draft of this Directive would have required use of 'state of the art' technology, and was amended following pressure from the UK. In this Directive the 'T' stands for 'technology'. In the 1990 Act the UK government used 'techniques' to ensure BATNEEC could be given as wide an interpretation as the earlier term 'best practicable means' (BPM). Box 3A explains the meanings given to the terms 'best', 'available' and 'techniques' in the context of the 1990 Act.[6]

BOX 3A   **MEANING OF 'BEST AVAILABLE TECHNIQUES'**

The term 'best available techniques', which enters into the concept of BATNEEC, is given the following interpretation in the UK.

Best is interpreted to mean the most effective in preventing or minimising polluting releases or rendering them harmless. There can be more than one set of 'best' techniques. (Mention of effectiveness raises questions, discussed later in this chapter, about how the best practicable environmental option is to be determined in a given case.)

A technique is **available** if the operator of the relevant process would be able to procure it from at least one supplier. The Environment Agency identifies available techniques on the basis of a worldwide review. If a technique is not already in use in the UK, it must be capable of being translated into a UK industrial context. A technique which has so far been used only at pilot scale will be regarded as available provided sufficient is known about it to allow it to be implemented in the relevant industrial context with the necessary business confidence.

Techniques cover the components of which a plant is made up and the manner in which they are connected together to make the whole; how the process is operated; the design, construction, lay-out and maintenance of the buildings in which the process is carried out; working methods; and the numbers, qualification, training and supervision of staff.

The meaning given to 'not entailing excessive cost' is explained in 3.16–3.18.

3.14 The Integrated Pollution Control Guidance Notes which contain the process standards give a detailed description (by plant area, by medium and by substance) of the techniques which the Environment Agency regards as representing BATNEEC. The key stages in preparing a guidance note are that either Agency staff or consultants review the best available techniques for the relevant process; the Agency circulates a list of the key issues likely to be addressed in the note 'to those with a direct interest in the industry sector affected'; and there are then two rounds of consultation on drafts of the note, the first confined to government Departments and 'representatives of the industries and other bodies affected'. If major questions about standards emerge, the Agency may promote fuller discussion before deciding what the guidance note should say.[7] The Process Guidance Notes for processes which have their emissions to air regulated by local authorities are drafted by the Department of the Environment, Transport and the Regions' Local Authority Unit and discussed by working parties of local authority and industry representatives, and occasionally representatives of abatement and monitoring equipment manufacturers. The resulting drafts are sent for written comment to a wider range of organisations, including local government bodies and environmental groups.[8]

3.15 An important advantage claimed for BATNEEC as a regulatory principle is that it is dynamic rather than static: what is 'best' will change over time as techniques improve. Irrespective of the limit values contained in the authorisation, the operator is under a general obligation to use BATNEEC. Guidance notes are intended to be reviewed, and updated if necessary, at intervals of not more than four years, which is also the maximum period allowed between substantial reviews of authorisations. Between revisions, a guidance note may not 'be cited in an attempt to delay the introduction of improved, available techniques'.[10]

3.16 The 1990 Act does not require use of the best available techniques if their cost would be excessive. One factor in determining whether the cost of a particular set of techniques is excessive is the damage to the environment that a process is causing or would otherwise cause. The other factor taken into account is the ability of a representative operator in the industry to bear extra abatement costs. The Agency assesses this by considering the resources a typical operator has available for capital expenditure and the extent to which market conditions allow costs to be passed on to customers or passed back to suppliers or absorbed through lower profitability. The guidance notes therefore contain a section on financial implications, which covers the state of the industry and abatement costs.[11]

3.17 The techniques the Agency regards as BATNEEC are not necessarily in use at existing plants; the guidance notes give separate sets of benchmark levels for emissions from such plants. The regulator has to decide over what time-scale any given plant should be required to upgrade to BATNEEC (or as near as possible to that) or close down. In addition to the costs of upgrading, the Secretary of State has recommended that such decisions should take into account the technical characteristics of a plant, the extent to which it is used and the length of its remaining life, and the nature and volume of polluting emissions.[12] Thus a small and lightly used plant which would be technically difficult to upgrade might be allowed to continue operating in its present form for a relatively long time, unless it has a long future life which makes upgrading commercially viable. Here again, it is the financial capability of a representative operator that is considered, not the capability of the actual operator.

3.18 The effect of requiring use of BATNEEC may be to bring about the restructuring of an industrial sector. Smaller firms with an inadequate technical base or a low market share may not be able to accommodate or finance the new techniques. Their exit will leave the market to a few larger operators which have been able to invest in the equipment and skills needed to comply with the new standard. When cadmium plating in the UK came under effective regulation, those companies which could comply doubled their business, whereas firms which were less capable of adapting had to close down.[13] In such cases regulators need to be alert to any adverse effects on the environment from concentrating the same amount of activity on a smaller number of sites.

Best practicable environmental option

3.19 The purpose of the duty to have regard to the BPEO (3.12) is to impose an obligation to take into account local conditions if they point to the need for more stringent limits on emissions than would be required by the obligation to use BATNEEC taken on its own. The duty to have regard to the BPEO can be fulfilled only in relation to a particular site because circumstances at different sites may vary considerably. It is for the operator of a process to identify what he regards as BATNEEC, having regard to the BPEO, and to justify his conclusions to the regulator. This provision is intended to ensure that the interactions at 3.11c. are taken into account in regulation, and that the interactions at 3.11b. are taken into account more effectively. If operation of a process would cause harm even with the use of BATNEEC, authorisation can be refused.

3.20 The statutory requirement to have regard to the BPEO has two serious limitations. First, it applies only to authorisation of those processes subject to integrated pollution control and not across all the functions of the Environment Agencies, nor to forms of pollution which they do not regulate. Second, even in that context, BPEO is given a narrower meaning than the Commission advocated in its Twelfth Report. In particular, differences in the energy requirements between different options are not taken into account: achieving the lowest possible emissions from a process may not in reality represent the BPEO if that requires large amounts of energy and will result in a large increase in emissions from a generating plant. And, although solid waste arising is taken into account, the regulator is not entitled to take into account how it is dealt with if it is disposed of at another site. This narrowness in the statutory requirement could result in situation *d.* or *f.* in 3.11.

Taking account of the life cycle

3.21 The British system of integrated pollution control will be superseded by the EC Directive on Integrated Pollution Prevention and Control (IPPC).[14] It is not yet clear to what extent this will modify regulation of processes which are already subject to integrated pollution control.[15] The most significant change is that regulation will embrace, as well as an overall view of emissions from a process, its decommissioning and key off-site aspects of the life cycle in the form of the energy requirements for the process and disposal of its wastes, thus potentially addressing the interactions at 3.11 *d–f.*

3.22 The Directive's use of 'best available techniques' (BAT) as the criterion, without the words 'not entailing excessive cost', is not as important as may appear because its definition of 'available' includes consideration of costs and refers to 'implementation ... under economically ... viable conditions'.[16] Moreover, the UK government has said that, for new plants, it expects that 'BAT and BATNEEC will be synonymous ... in many cases'.[17]

3.23 The Directive requires the European Commission to organise an exchange of information between Member States and industry on best available techniques, associated monitoring and ongoing developments; and publish the results every three years in BAT Reference Documents (BREFs). This task is being undertaken by the Institute for Prospective Technological Studies at Seville, part of the European Commission's Joint Research Centre. The first half of the BREF for an industry sector will be a general description covering the range of emissions and consumption of raw materials. The second part will describe techniques that are candidates for BAT and other techniques that are still emerging, and discuss what is likely to happen in the future. The technical working groups that are preparing BREFs include, as well as representatives of the industry sector, companies that supply technologies to it. Wider consultation includes placing draft BREFs on the World Wide Web.[18] The regulators in Member States must take BREFs into account when they determine what represents BAT at site level in order to grant a permit for an installation, but must do so in the context of local conditions (see box 3C).

3.24 *Life cycle assessment* (LCA) is a formal technique which brings into consideration all the environmental impacts associated with the delivery of a service or a product. It involves identifying and quantifying the emissions and resource use at all stages of the life cycle.[19] Looking at the entire material and energy supply chains required to make a product or provide a service (shown diagrammatically in figure 3-I[20]) may lead to different conclusions about environmental impact. The greatest pollution may occur, not from the (manufacturing) process which is subject to, for instance, integrated pollution control, but either upstream (for example, from the extraction and purification of raw materials) or downstream (for example, from use of the product or from its disposal after use). A definition of the principal components of life cycle assessment is given in box 3B.[21]

3.25 The value of a life cycle perspective is not confined to overall comparisons between different technologies. It can be used to identify 'hot spots' in the supply chain where the environmental impacts are particularly significant. The life cycle approach also identifies cases where a reduction in emissions or resource use at one point in the supply chain would lead to an increase in impacts elsewhere. Glass manufacture provides an example of a life cycle assessment affecting decisions on environmental regulation (see box 3C).[22] A life cycle assessment can also highlight the most promising points at which to take action to reduce the overall environmental impact. For example, preventing fertilisers or pesticides entering inland waters may be preferable to removing them from water supplies at water company treatment works; or a significant reduction in environmental impact may depend on changing manufacturing processes in order to facilitate post-consumer recycling of materials.

Figure 3-I
Life cycle assessment

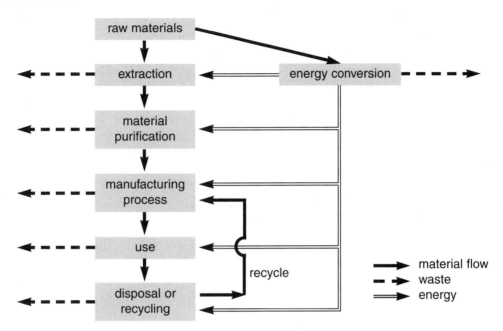

BOX 3B	LIFE CYCLE ASSESSMENT

Building on methodological developments by the Society of Environmental Toxicology and Chemistry (SETAC), International Organization for Standardization standard ISO 14040 defines life cycle assessment (LCA) as follows:

> LCA is a technique for assessing the environmental aspects and potential impacts associated with a product, by
>
> > compiling an inventory of relevant inputs and outputs of a product system;
> >
> > evaluating the potential environmental impacts associated with those inputs and outputs;
> >
> > interpreting the results of the inventory and impact assessment phases in relation to the objectives of the study.

LCA studies the environmental aspects and potential impacts throughout a product's life (i.e. cradle to grave), from raw material acquisition through production, use and disposal. The general categories of environmental impacts needing consideration include resource use, human health, and ecological consequences.

3.26 Some of the processes in the supply chain will be at known plants or production of sites. Others will be 'background operations' which supply or receive materials or energy, but which cannot be identified specifically and which therefore cannot be located geographically. This problem arises, for example, in applying life cycle assessment to recovery of materials or energy from a waste. Use of the recovered energy or material displaces background production of energy or production of fresh material – and the associated resource usage and emissions are credited to the waste management system as avoided burdens – but the activities displaced cannot usually be identified. As a result, life cycle assessment inevitably has to consider a mixture of impacts whose location is identifiable and impacts which cannot be fixed geographically. It therefore has to assess the potential environmental effects of emissions, rather than assessing site-specific impacts as in other approaches such as environmental impact assessment.

BOX 3C   IMPLICATIONS OF LIFE CYCLE ASSESSMENT:
                                                         GLASS MANUFACTURING

Glass manufacture is an industry that has not been subject to integrated pollution control in the UK but will be covered by the Integrated Pollution Prevention and Control (IPCC) Directive. The emissions to air that are of primary concern are particulates, nitrogen oxides and sulphur oxides. Because local conditions are taken into account, the permitted emission levels for an identical process will differ in *different Member States.*

The life cycle elements in the IPPC Directive (3.21) will affect the regulatory approach to *different forms of emissions.* In France and Italy, the competent bodies have concluded that fitting end-of-pipe acid gas and particulate abatement equipment would, on balance, increase environmental impacts when the entire life cycle is considered. In France, the emission limits from gas-fired glass furnaces have therefore been made less stringent for particulates, although they have been made more stringent for nitrogen oxides. A proposed ministerial decree in Italy would also raise permitted particulate emissions but would lower permitted levels of oxides of sulphur and nitrogen, to below the levels permitted in France.

	old limits (mg/Nm³)		new limits (mg/Nm³)	
	France	**Italy**	**France**	**Italy**
particulates	50	100	150	130
oxides of sulphur	750	1,800	750	500
oxides of nitrogen	2,000	2,500	1,100	1,000

Life cycle assessment also takes account of the fate of the product. Targets have been set for reclaiming and recycling packaging waste which, in the case of glass, will have an adverse effect at the manufacturing stage. Recycling will increase the amounts of trace elements in glass and hence the emissions from glass furnaces, and thus make it more difficult for the glass manufacturing industry to meet the requirements of IPPC.

3.27 Emissions and resource use are conventionally assessed by their potential contributions to a set of environmental themes. Themes which are most commonly used, at least in Europe, include depletion of non-renewable resources (including energy), global warming potential and ozone depletion potential, as well as aquatic and terrestrial ecotoxicity, and human toxicity.[23] Emission of one substance can contribute to more than one environmental theme. For example, emissions of hydrocarbon vapours contribute to both global warming and photochemical oxidant creation.

3.28 LCA is not without problems: the methodology is complex, may have to neglect unquantifiable factors, and is data- and resource-intensive. Also, the position of system boundaries is open to judgement; and can determine the outcome of a comparison between alternative products or technologies. For example, re-use, recycling or disposal of a product after use can have a major effect on the life cycle assessment, so that it may only be possible to compare products within the context of a specific waste management regime. Similarly, whether recycling materials or recovering energy from waste is preferred on environmental grounds can depend on the background system providing the energy to the production and recycling processes.[24]

3.29 The general approach developed for life cycle assessment has also been applied for other purposes. ICI has used it as the basis of its 'Environmental Burden System' which measures the environmental performance of a multi-national company on the argument that, as in LCA, it is necessary to aggregate the effects of emissions from a large number of different locations.[25] As yet, the Environmental Burden System has been applied only to the company's own operations but in principle it can be applied for complete life cycles. An example of such an approach is Unilever's

'Overall Business Impact Assessment', which also relates environmental impact to added economic value in order to identify products, businesses and impact categories which should be targeted for environmental improvement.[26] This is described in box 3D.[27] These approaches are still at a preliminary stage and voluntary. While they could form a basis for setting standards for environmental performance in future, they are not yet to be recommended for widespread adoption.

BOX 3D   **UNILEVER'S OVERALL BUSINESS IMPACT ASSESSMENT APPROACH**

The Overall Business Impact Assessment (OBIA) approach was developed by Unilever as a strategic tool to identify areas of disproportionate potential impact for a limited number of environmental themes and to identify priorities for further refinement and possible remedial actions. This approach can also be used to analyse the relationships between environmental impact and economic value along a supply chain.

A common approach to interpreting potential environmental impacts, for example using the set of environmental themes in 3.27, is to normalise each quantified impact by expressing it as a fraction of the estimated potential effects of all human activities in a country or a region or worldwide. Such an approach permits an assessment of the relative contributions of activities to a particular environmental theme, but cannot be used for comparative assessments of impacts across different themes. Furthermore, the approach provides no assessment of the value of an activity.

OBIA uses a life cycle approach to assess potential impacts but includes an additional normalisation step based on economic value. The technique involves a broad brush global assessment of business activities based on a series of product life cycle assessments (LCAs) and a number of estimates and simplifications. The LCAs are aggregated on an annual sales basis. The aggregates for each environmental theme are then divided by the added economic value associated with the business or product generating the potential impact. The resulting metric is then normalised by dividing by the corresponding measure of all human activity: total human impact in the theme divided by gross global product (as a measure of total economic activity worldwide). If the resulting ratio is significantly larger than unity, then the business or product has a potential environmental impact disproportionate to its economic value when compared with the average of all human activity.

3.30 While environmental regulation has broadened from considering emissions to a single environmental medium to considering emissions to all media from a process, analysis of environmental performance has been extended even further to cover the whole material and energy supply chains associated with a product or service.

3.31 Taking account of life cycle considerations is the preferable way of managing the overall environmental impact of particular processes or particular industrial sectors because it directs attention to the points at which intervention to protect the environment will be most effective and efficient.

Emphasising environmental impact in engineering design

3.32 Adding pollution abatement devices to an industrial process inevitably involves economic cost or reduced efficiency. As emission standards are progressively tightened, this 'clean-up' approach, in which pollutants are captured before emission, usually by reaction with some appropriate reagent, becomes more and more cumbersome and expensive.[28] Furthermore, clean-up technology usually involves transforming pollutants to a different form, so that the problem may be alleviated but is rarely eliminated. IPC and IPPC allow the regulator to question choice of process, as opposed merely to accepting end-of-pipe technology for abatement as sufficient. This has focused attention on a preventive approach in which the basic technology of the process is changed so that pollutants are not produced in the first place.

3.33 An example is provided by power generation from coal. In conventional combustion plant, the established form of clean-up technology to abate acid gas emissions is flue gas desulphurisation (FGD) which reacts the acidic components with lime. For this, FGD requires limestone, obtained by mining, and produces calcium sulphate in quantities which may be too large for economic use and therefore have to be disposed of. A newer form of coal-based power generation is gasification with an integrated combined-cycle gas turbine, which both gives higher conversion efficiency and can reduce the production of acid gases. Under the EC IPPC Directive, which takes energy requirements into account, a regulator could query the use of FGD as necessarily BAT, as operation of FGD equipment significantly reduces thermal efficiency.

Cleaner production and clean technology

3.34 An emphasis on prevention encourages the adoption of new engineering approaches. The most direct response is to find ways of obtaining the same product while placing a smaller total burden on the environment over the whole life cycle from extraction of raw materials to disposal of the product. This approach has been characterised by the United Nations Environment Programme as *cleaner production,* defined as:[30]

> a conceptual and procedural approach to production that demands all phases of the life-cycle of a product or process should be addressed with the objective of prevention or minimisation of short- and long-term risks to human health and to the environment.

3.35 The first systematic attempt in the UK to involve a number of companies, including small and medium-sized enterprises, in minimising wastes was a project in the catchments of the Aire and Calder rivers in Yorkshire.[31] This was proposed by the Centre for Exploitation of Science and Technology (CEST) following a study which found that firms on these rivers were contemplating expensive end-of-pipe solutions to meet regulatory pressure for improved effluent discharges. CEST suggested that waste minimisation measures should be considered. Of the opportunities identified, 20% involved good housekeeping, 60% operational changes and 20% changes in products or processes.[32] In a second project, the Dee Catchment Waste Minimisation Project,[33] the stated objective was 'to demonstrate the benefits of adopting a systematic approach to waste minimisation, particularly those arising from procedural changes and cleaner technology'. The project identified savings of £4.55 million a year that companies could achieve through waste minimisation (a further £1.2 million of potential savings were still being assessed): the greater part of these would result from modifications in technology, and nearly half the savings could be achieved with a pay-back period of less than one year. These projects demonstrate that cleaner production can provide a 'win-win' situation: the company profits both from reduced consumption of material going into a process and from a reduction in the wastes requiring treatment and disposal, and the environment benefits from the reduced demands put upon it. The introduction of the landfill duty has made such savings even more attractive for companies.

3.36 Going beyond cleaner production, the broader approach of clean technology concentrates on delivery of a service or benefit rather than provision of a product. *Clean technology* has been defined as[34]

> a means of providing a human benefit which, overall, uses less resources and causes less environmental damage than alternative means with which it is economically competitive.

Like cleaner production, clean technology considers the entire life cycles of material and energy supply through use to post-use recovery or disposal. It also considers further possibilities such as product substitution or recycling or re-use of materials and artefacts. However, no technology can be completely clean. Although often talked about, zero emissions is not an achievable objective. It is self-defeating to set even aspirational standards which are scientifically impossible. The concept of zero emissions contravenes the laws of thermodynamics and has been used only because the whole life cycles of material and energy supply were not considered. Use in California of the term 'zero emission vehicle' obscures the reality: as explained in box 3E[35] the emissions would be displaced to a different location where they might, under the right circumstances, be reduced, but would not be eliminated.

BOX 3E	IMPOSSIBILITY OF ZERO EMISSIONS

Based on the objective of reducing emissions from vehicles in urban areas, a Low Emission Vehicle regulation was introduced in California in 1990 which covered the development of so-called Zero Emission Vehicles (ZEVs). The regulation specified proportions of ZEVs which major manufacturers must sell, rising from 2% in 1998–2000 to 10% in 2003 and beyond. Initially, this attempt to introduce a technology-forcing standard was supported by General Motors with a commitment to a major programme to develop an electric vehicle. Following changes in personnel, that programme was cut back (although other manufacturers have continued with the development of electric and hybrid vehicles). The 1998 deadline has been replaced by a memorandum of understanding, but the statutory requirement that, from 2003, 10% of the vehicles on sale must be ZEVs remains in place.

Even if a vehicle were to have no emissions on the road, elementary life cycle thinking shows that it cannot truly have zero emissions. If it is an electric vehicle, the electricity must be generated somewhere. If, on the other hand, it is powered by a clean fuel such as hydrogen, either by combustion or by using fuel cells, the substance used to transport and store the hydrogen must be produced somewhere. Thus a ZEV actually transfers emissions from vehicles on the road to fixed generating plants or industrial plants. The overall effect can be a reduction in emissions if the fixed plants are regulated and operated to high standards so that they emit proportionately less of the critical pollutants than a vehicle. In other words, there is a displacement effect (3.11*f*), but it is brought about deliberately. In Southern California, the main source of electricity is natural gas-fired plants with relatively low emissions. The increased electricity demand for recharging electric vehicles is estimated to lead to significant increases in power plant emissions, particularly of nitrogen oxides and reactive organic gases, which contribute to the photochemical smog that is a major environmental concern. These increased emissions are not as large as the emissions from refuelling and driving the gasoline vehicles which would be displaced by electric vehicles. There would also be significant net reductions in emissions of carbon monoxide and particulate matter. To complement the ZEV programme, standards have been proposed for an Equivalent Zero Emission Vehicle (EZEV), direct emissions from which would match the emissions resulting indirectly from use of a ZEV.

Thus ZEVs would lead to improvements in air quality, but the life cycle emissions cannot be zero. As overall efficiency of use of hydrocarbons is not similarly improved, the ZEV concept can reduce emissions of local pollutants but not resource use or global impacts.

3.37 A classic example of a simple but effective introduction of clean technology is provided by the recovery and re-use of industrial solvents.[36] Organic solvents are pollutants if they escape, and this has led to pressure for replacement by water-based solvents. However, instead of replacing organic solvents, they may be contained to prevent releases. This approach has led to a change in industrial practices in using solvents, notably for metal surface preparation and degreasing. Rather than being sold, solvents are in effect leased: they are returned after use and reprocessed. The innovation is not so much in the technology, which is no more than simple distillation of used solvents, as in the practice of leasing use of the solvent rather than selling it. The residue left after reprocessing of the solvent may be used as a fuel, subject to the need to take stringent precautions to control emissions. In a similar way, leasing of photocopiers on the basis that machines are returned to the manufacturer at the end of their lives has stimulated re-use and recycling of components and materials.[37]

3.38 Moves toward enforcing 'take-back' of commercial and consumer products, promoted by some current developments in EC legislation, in effect seek to extend to other industries and products the principle of defining the responsibility for post-use waste. Although the immediate motive is to ensure that products subject to take-back do not enter the waste stream, the intended longer-term effect is to avoid the much larger quantities of waste generated in making the virgin product. Taking this approach further leads to products specifically designed to use materials and components whose life cycles are associated with reduced environmental impact and which can be re-used or recycled more readily. This conceptual approach is called 'design for the environment'.

3.39 Some materials may be recovered after their initial use for economic use in another application, so that they pass through a cascade of successive uses, normally with progressively lower performance specifications. Aluminium is a material for which cascaded use is already established. This is an example of the concept of 'industrial ecology', in which waste from one process or industry provides a feedstock for another process or industry. A radical approach to promoting industrial ecology is the 'ecopark', based on co-locating different industries so that one can utilise the waste products of another.

Encouraging cleaner technology through regulation

3.40 There are limitations on the extent to which regulation can be used to bring about the adoption of cleaner technology. One approach is to set emission standards to apply from a future date at a level for which no current technological solution exists. Such a *technology-forcing standard* requires the development of a new technology.[38] This is distinct from *commercialisation-forcing standards* which are set to encourage or require the deployment of existing or test-bed technology.

3.41 To take examples from the motor industry, the 1978 Japanese standard for nitrogen oxides (box 3F) was based on already accessible technology.[39] The 1990 California Zero Emissions Vehicle standard (described in box 3E) is genuinely technology forcing. It is not likely, however, to succeed; in the absence of major technical breakthroughs, electric vehicles may become a new niche market but are unlikely to replace the required proportion of the market for gasoline vehicles. It appears that the Californian regulator took at face value both the commitment of General Motors to produce an electric vehicle from 1995 and their market and technology assessments. This failure was rooted in the poor relationship between industry and regulator.[40] The future of technology-forcing standards depends on realistic appraisals of the prospects for achieving them in practice within a foreseeable time-span.

BOX 3F   **COMMERCIALISATION-FORCING STANDARDS**

Standards for vehicle emissions of nitrogen oxides were first applied in the 1960s in Japan and California. They were based initially on levels already being achieved in some production vehicles and the effect was to enforce good engine/exhaust design on manufacturers. Later emission standards raised disagreements between governments and industry over how far standards could be expected to push technological development.

Japanese car manufacturers testified to the Japanese Environment Agency that a 70% reduction in emissions of nitrogen oxides could be achieved by 1975. When the Agency sought tighter controls, the major manufacturers protested that a 92% reduction in vehicle emissions of nitrogen oxides by 1976 was technically impossible. Information from smaller, more enterprising companies suggested, however, that the technical expertise was already available which could meet the standard. The standard was set at a 92% reduction by 1978. Tax incentives encouraged many manufacturers to meet the standard before 1978.

3.42 The most effective regulatory levers to bring about adoption of cleaner technology may not be emission standards or process standards but other kinds of measure. Measures to deal with waste management, such as requirements to recycle or charges levied for disposal of wastes, may prompt industries to reconsider the entire life cycles of products and the technologies on which these are at present based.

3.43 The most comprehensive specification of what represents cleaner technology would be a life cycle-based standard. However, there are no legally enforceable life cycle-based standards. If such standards were applied to products from other countries, they would contravene the General Agreement on Tariffs and Trade rules (6.14). Life cycle-based standards have, therefore, usually taken the form of an ecolabel, or some other accompanying declaration, intended to provide buyers with information so that they can discriminate between products on the basis of their environmental impacts. Specification of the criteria for ecolabels has proved problematical (6.79).

3.44 The scheme for assessment of existing substances is an important aspect of the regulation of technology. Product standards or use standards can be deployed to force industries to phase out substances and the processes used to produce them, and so eliminate any environmental problems they may have caused. The reaction of industry is likely to be to find substitutes which represent cleaner technologies. Progress in assessing existing substances has been very slow (appendix C, C.68). The UK government is carrying out a review in order to formulate transparent policies and strategies for dealing with chemicals in the environment, set out a vision for their sustainable use over the next 15–20 years, and identify the tools and key players necessary for achieving that vision.[41] The European Commission has announced that it is taking stock of existing legislation covering industrial chemicals which cause health and environmental damage.[42] Momentum is growing, with at least five European governments questioning the present system of risk assessment as the basis for regulating existing chemicals (2.5). Some Member States are pressing for a more pro-active approach of the kind recommended by the Swedish Chemicals Policy Committee.[43] This Committee has formulated radical targets, summarised in box 3G, for reducing the use of substances that represent an environmental hazard.[44] **The very slow progress made with assessment of existing chemical substances has demonstrated the need for an entirely fresh approach. The current reviews provide a timely opportunity.**

3.45 It has for many years been necessary to demonstrate the need for food additives before they can be used commercially. The EC Biocides Directive now includes for the first time in environmental policy, the principle of comparative assessment. This means that an active substance may be prevented from being marketed if there is another available substance for the same product type which presents significantly less risk to human health or the environment. **We consider that the criterion of comparison with the risk presented by other available substances should be introduced into all regulatory procedures for the marketing and use of chemicals, including those covering reactants and intermediates.**

Output from assessment of technological options

3.46 Hitherto, assessments of technological options carried out as a contribution to a decision on an environmental standard have typically looked only at the activity to which that standard relates. Thus assessments carried out in order to set process standards based on the concept of BATNEEC have looked at the relevant industrial process in isolation. For the future, assessments of technological options ought to have a much broader perspective and examine the whole supply chain to see whether it could be managed in a less environmentally damaging way. **To ensure that the full ranges of options and repercussions are considered, assessments of technological options carried out as inputs to decisions on environmental policies or standards should be on a life cycle basis.**

BOX 3G   **SUSTAINABLE USE OF CHEMICALS:**
THE REPORT OF THE SWEDISH CHEMICALS POLICY COMMITTEE

The Chemicals Policy Committee was established in May 1996 in order to review Swedish chemicals policies for the previous ten years and propose a new chemicals policy for the future nationally, within the European Union and internationally. As well as drawing on existing environmental goals formulated by the Swedish Parliament, the Committee's discussions were based on the Esbjerg Declaration agreed at the Fourth Ministerial Conference on the North Sea (1995), a key part of which was that discharges of toxic, persistent and bioaccumulative substances should be reduced with a view to eliminating them by 2020.

The Committee proposed key targets which go further than the goals of the Esbjerg Declaration:

> by 2002, all companies should provide information on the chemical content of their products to allow for informed consumer choice;

> by 2007, all products on the market should be free from: substances that are persistent and liable to bioaccumulate; lead, mercury and cadmium; and substances that give rise to serious or irreversible effects on health or the environment;

> by 2012, manufacturing processes should be free from the deliberate use of persistent and bioaccumulative substances, lead, mercury and cadmium, and the emissions should be free from substances that cause serious or chronic health effects;

> by 2012, other metals should be used only in applications where they are mainly kept intact during use or are collected after use for re-use, recycling or disposal.

The Committee concluded that industry has the main responsibility for controlling chemicals and companies must demonstrate that their products are safe to use. It proposed the following model for sustainable use of chemicals which could be used as guidance for the day-to-day work of companies:

> 1. Use as simple and clean products as possible.

> 2. Use additives with low mobility.

> 3. Do not use substances that are persistent and liable to bioaccumulate in your products, nor substances with carcinogenic, mutagenic or reproductive (including endocrine disruption) effects.

> 4. Do not deliberately use such substances as mentioned under 3. in your manufacturing or production process.

> 5. Do not release any of the substances mentioned under 3. from your manufacturing or production process.

> 6. For all substances used or occurring during the life cycle of your product, assess their properties and show that they are safe to use in the short and long term.

> 7. Substitute hazardous substances by less hazardous ones as far as possible, based on available knowledge.

3.47 It is sometimes claimed that life cycle assessments may be of little help in making realistic assessments of the impacts of pollution because these are often dependent on the time and location of occurrence. Life cycle assessments can, however, help policy-makers and regulators avoid decisions which would make the overall situation worse, or at least yield no net benefit. **Policy guidance is needed on where the boundaries of life cycle assessments should be drawn.**

3.48 The results of life cycle assessments may lead to improvement of the decision immediately under consideration. Glass manufacture provides an example of that (box 3C). Alternatively, or in addition, the results may identify actions that could be taken more effectively at other points to reduce environmental damage. **Particular options should not be excluded from life cycle assessments on the ground that action required to implement them falls outside the responsibilities of the immediate regulator.**

3.49 **To the extent that regulation of industrial activities continues to use permits and forms of standard on lines similar to those used at present, their use should in future be informed by a life cycle perspective. If necessary, there should be changes in legislation so that the full potential for that can be realised.**

3.50 It is vital that environmental improvement is not held back by technical conservatism and an unwillingness to innovate. **As well as adopting a life cycle perspective, the aim of assessments of technological options should be seen as widening the range of options considered, including those that involve technology forcing or commercialisation forcing.**

3.51 Expert knowledge concerning the technologies currently available or under development lies within the industries being regulated or among their suppliers. In setting standards based either explicitly or implicitly on technology, regulators have to work closely with industry. At the Institute for Prospective Technological Studies in Seville a similar approach is being applied to the review of standards in selected sectors of industry.[45] With good leadership, working groups with a respected industrial membership evaluating new proposals or reviewing existing standards can give advance warning to operators and increase acceptance of tighter standards. Such groups have the potential to highlight the needs for and prospects of new technology. **There should be scope for suppliers or users of improved technologies to stimulate tightening of standards.** The time-scale for meeting a new standard should take account of the capital cycle of existing plants, but the regulator needs to be aware that some companies may make capital investments to avoid changing or updating technology. Setting a standard to apply from a future date will reduce the chance of this occurring.

3.52 There is a danger that assessments of technological options made by industry may be narrow or self-interested. Too often in the past, decisions about setting environmental standards have been driven by assessments of practicability which were produced by those with a vested interest in avoiding change and were unduly pessimistic about technological possibilities. By implication **the Environment Agencies must harness highly qualified staff.** Technical ignorance may lead to over-conservative or over-optimistic (head in the clouds) regulation.

3.53 **Broadly based assessments of options on a life cycle basis must not be allowed to become an excuse for avoiding or delaying significant improvements available at particular stages in the cycle.**

3.54 On whatever basis technological options are compared, there remains a fundamental conceptual and methodological problem, exemplified in 3.11*a*. How can different kinds of environmental impact, which are not directly commensurable with each other, be included in an overall assessment? This may arise in determining which option should be regarded as 'best' in terms of BATNEEC or BPEO just as much as in deciding which of the themes considered in life cycle assessments should be accorded most significance. Determining what represents BPEO for a given process, for example, involves assessing the relative environmental impact each of the substances given off by the process would have if released to each medium.

3.55 In the case of integrated pollution control the predecessor of the Environment Agency, Her Majesty's Inspectorate of Pollution (HMIP), devoted much effort to trying to resolve this difficulty. Only a small number of substances are subject to over-riding limits on emissions. For other substances HMIP devised a methodology to establish 'site-specific BPEO', although operators were free to propose use of another methodology if they could demonstrate that it was equally valid. If a quality standard had been set, discharges from the process to the relevant medium could be evaluated in terms of the effect they would have on achievement of that standard. For substances and media for which no quality standard had been set, HMIP found it necessary to set *ad hoc* quality standards in the form of 'environmental assessment levels' for individual substances. These continue to be used by the Environment Agency.[46] Determining the BPEO raises other difficult issues such as the relative importance that should be attached to short-lived versus persistent pollutants.

3.56 IPPC will direct more attention to another difficult issue in assessment, the significance of making releases at different locations. In some cases differences in circumstances at alternative locations mean that identical releases made there will have different effects. In other cases the main result of changing the location may be that one group of people rather than others are exposed to pollution. For example, one country might decide not to permit a particular stage in the life cycle of a product on the ground that it is too environmentally damaging (for example, the manufacturing process for tyres, because of the toxicity of the chemicals used); if it continues to make use of the product by importing it, the effect will be merely to export the pollution to a different country. This cannot be regarded as an acceptable solution in environmental terms.

3.57 Judgements have to be made about which aspects of environmental impact are more important, and about the acceptability of effects in different locations. Such judgements involve questions of values. We consider in subsequent chapters how such judgements can best be made.

Chapter 4

RISK AND UNCERTAINTY

Environmental issues are now frequently addressed through risk assessments. It has been suggested environmental standards might be set by relating the probability of harm from environmental causes to the probabilities of harm from other causes. There are various problems about such an approach. It is now generally accepted that environmental policies should be based on the precautionary principle, properly interpreted. Appraisals of risk are an essential input to decisions about environmental standards, but need to have several dimensions and also cover the extent of uncertainty.

4.1   The word 'risk' is given a wide range of meanings.[1] In ordinary usage it is often synonymous with 'danger'.[2] In economic appraisal 'risk' is 'the possibility of more than one outcome occurring',[3] and the other possible outcomes considered may be more desirable, not less desirable, than the base case. In the financial literature 'risk', as distinct from 'uncertainty', is sometimes used to indicate that it is possible to make a precise estimate of the probabilities of outcomes.[4] In environmental protection and related fields the concept of risk derives from engineering and emphasises both the prospect of an undesirable outcome and that the aim is to attach a probability to such an outcome.

4.2   The definition of *risk* in engineering is 'a combination of the probability, or frequency, of occurrence of a defined hazard and the magnitude of the consequences of the occurrence'.[5] *Hazard* is defined as 'a property or situation that in particular circumstances could lead to harm.'[6] If train crashes are taken as an example of a hazard, an average of x such crashes occur each year in Britain, and the average number of people killed in each crash is y, the risk posed by train crashes to the population of Britain in any one year can be represented as a probability of death of xy divided by 56 million.[7] These are the senses in which we use 'risk' and 'hazard'.

4.3   Systematic analyses of risks have long been familiar in the chemical, oil and nuclear industries, and more generally in the context of safeguarding against industrial accidents and protecting worker health. Risk assessment has become well-established as an approach to assessing the environmental impact of proposed projects or policies in other fields.[8] It has more recently been promoted as an aid to decision making on environmental policies and standards. In 1994 the UK Sustainable Development Strategy stated as its first principle for action that 'Decisions should be based on the best possible scientific information and analysis of risks.'[9] In 1995 the Department of the Environment (DOE) published guidance 'for policy makers and managers who need to ensure they can set guidelines for a risk assessment and can critically appraise what is presented to them'.[10] However, risk assessment is mentioned only in passing in the context of the statutory guidance given to the Environment Agency.[11] Its use by the Agency is so far confined to the secondary tasks of prioritising companies for inspection (through the proposed system of Operator and Pollution Risk Appraisal) and assessing for planning purposes the major industrial pressures on the environment (through its National Centre for Risk Analysis and Options Appraisal).[12]

4.4   The assessment of new and existing chemical substances, which was taken as a case study of standard setting in chapter 2 (figure 2-I), includes a stage described as risk characterisation, which involves identifying the incidence and severity of adverse effects. If there is sufficient information, this stage is followed by *risk estimation*, quantifying the probability of those effects.[13] For most environmental hazards, risk estimation not only includes, or draws on the findings of, the kind of scientific assessments described in chapter 2, but also requires an analysis of the technology employed in the human activities that have created the hazard (chapter 3). Risk characterisation or estimation provides the basis for risk management.

4.5   We regard assessment of risk and uncertainty as a component of the analysis needed to underpin decisions about environmental policies. In this chapter we discuss what such an assessment can contribute to decisions. We first summarise efforts that have been made to relate the acceptability of environmental risks to the acceptability of risks in other contexts (4.6–4.17). We discuss the difficulties involved in estimating statistical probabilities (4.18–4.23) and the meaning that should be placed on them (4.24–4.29). We examine whether the divergence between the general public's attitudes towards hazards and statistical estimates of risks is the result of the information people have available or their perceptions (4.30–4.40). We consider the relevance of the 'precautionary principle' (4.41–4.48). Finally, we consider how the conclusions of risk analyses should be presented in order to provide the most effective input to environmental policy decisions, including decisions about environmental standards (4.49–4.59).

Statistical criteria for tolerability

4.6   A further stage in risk assessment might be called *risk appraisal,* that is, using estimates of risk as an explicit criterion for deciding between options for environmental policies or standards. Among the questions which concerned us at the outset of this study (appendix A) were the relationship which should be sought between risks from pollution and levels of risks in other contexts, and how priorities should be determined within pollution control. We received some evidence supporting the view that pollution should be regulated by comparison with risks in other contexts.[14]

4.7   The argument for using estimates of risk as a criterion for judging the acceptability of environmental modifications would be as follows: if an environmental hazard poses a risk, but that risk does not exceed the risks people accept in other contexts, it can be regarded as acceptable; but if it does exceed risks accepted in other contexts, measures should be taken to reduce it. In this view, analysis of relative risks can both establish which environmental problems merit attention and provide a tool for determining the content of policies.

4.8   In the USA issues of risk assessment and management in the fields of public health, safety and environmental quality have preoccupied regulators and Congress for many years. A review in 1991 found that 'Numerical risk estimates are used not only to balance risk benefits and to set standards but also, increasingly, to compare risks and distinguish between those that merit regulation and those that do not.'[15]

4.9   More general use of risk assessment in the UK was promoted by a Study Group set up by the Royal Society in 1978, which reported in 1983.[16] According to the preface, the time taken reflected the difficulty 'experienced in reconciling the differing approaches of psychologists, statisticians, physicists, biochemists, biologists, epidemiologists, doctors, engineers and economists'. Such differences were, if anything, even more apparent in the 1992 report of a further Royal Society Study Group which, with the help in addition of a sociologist and inputs from political scientists, sought to update and extend the original report.[17]

4.10 The simplest form of numerical standard defines a boundary between acceptability and unacceptability. More complex approaches are possible. In 1975, the Commission proposed using three categories for air quality, although the idea was not taken up by the government.[18] This approach would have involved determining a highest tolerable concentration of a substance which, if exceeded, would signal the need for action to reduce the concentration, and a lower level, below which concern would not normally be reasonable and it would not generally be justifiable to press for a reduction. In the intermediate band local authorities would set target levels (also envisaged as bands) in the light of local circumstances.

4.11 Statistical estimates of risk were adopted as a criterion for tolerability in guidelines published by the Health and Safety Executive (HSE) in 1988, which also defined tolerability in terms of three categories. These guidelines covered levels of individual and social risk to workers and the public from nuclear power stations and implemented a recommendation made in 1987 by the Inspector who conducted the public inquiry into the proposal to construct Sizewell B nuclear power station.

4.12 HSE's guidelines drew on the report of the original Royal Society Study Group. They also drew on recommendations made in 1977 by the International Commission on Radiological Protection (appendix C, C.7), which, on the basis of analogies with risks regularly accepted in everyday life, set the acceptable average risk of death of a member of the public from ionising radiation in any one year in the range 1 in 1,000,000 to 1 in 100,000. It recommended absolute limits on the exposure of individual workers and members of the public to ionising radiation; and said that within those limits exposure should be kept as low as reasonably achievable (ALARA) using a cost-benefit approach.[19]

4.13 The three categories of risk defined by HSE are:

> *a.* where 'a given risk is so great or the outcome so unacceptable that it must be refused altogether';
>
> *b.* where 'the risk is, or has been made, so small that no further precaution is necessary';
>
> *c.* any risk which falls between *a.* and *b.*, which should be 'reduced to the lowest level practicable, bearing in mind the benefits flowing from its acceptance and taking into account the costs of any further reduction'. In other words this is the band in which HSE applies the general principle that levels of risk should be 'as low as reasonably practicable' (ALARP).

4.14 In the guidelines HSE adopted the following levels of risk, in terms of the probability of an individual dying in any one year:

> **1 in 1,000** as the 'just about tolerable risk' for 'any substantial category [of workers] for any large part of a working life';
>
> **1 in 10,000** as the 'maximum tolerable risk' for members of the public from any single non-nuclear plant;
>
> **1 in 100,000** as the 'maximum tolerable risk' for members of the public from any new nuclear power station;
>
> **1 in 1,000,000** as the level of 'acceptable risk' at which no further improvements in safety need be made.

HSE set these guidelines after considering risks in other contexts. A risk of 1 in 1,000,000 is broadly the same as that of being electrocuted at home and about one-hundredth that of dying in a traffic accident.[20] In a revised edition of the guidelines, published in 1992, HSE noted that, although they had been produced in the context of regulation of nuclear power stations by the Nuclear Installations Inspectorate, the approach described was being applied increasingly to regulation of other major industrial risks in the UK.[21]

4.15 Following a government commitment made in 1992, an interdepartmental working party, administered by HSE, was established to review the use of risk assessment across government. It found that it was being used in a variety of policy contexts, with considerable agreement between Departments on what a risk assessment involves and how in broad terms it should be applied. But its use within government had not been systematically developed, and it was sometimes quantitative and sometimes qualitative.[22] Because risks do not follow the boundaries of Departmental responsibilities, several recommendations were made for increasing the consistency of approaches to risk assessment, for example that Departments should adopt consistent frameworks for deciding which risks are unacceptable, tolerable or broadly acceptable.

4.16 Another interdepartmental group considered the scope for further development of the general procedure and methodology of setting safety standards (including the health and safety aspects of environmental standards).[23] It concluded that a fully 'rule-based' approach to safety regulation would be unrealistic, but advocated the development of common frameworks for all safety regulations in order to produce more systematic and consistent regulation, and contribute to a wider public acceptance of 'a balanced approach' to safety regulation. It endorsed the 'Tolerability of Risk' approach and recommended some changes to methodologies as well as measures to improve understanding of public attitudes to risk.

4.17 British Nuclear Fuels plc suggested in evidence that environmental standards should be set 'at levels which correspond to some upper boundary of acceptable risk' such as the upper boundary to HSE's tolerability region (1 in 10,000 probability of an individual dying in any one year). An aspect of environmental policy for which a specific criterion in terms of risk was proposed by the government is the disposal of solid radioactive waste. The criterion related to the design process for the disposal method, and took the form of a target that the risk of developing either a fatal cancer or serious hereditary defect should not exceed 1 in 1,000,000 in any one year.[24] Following the Secretary of State's rejection of the proposal by UK Nirex to construct a rock characterisation facility in Cumbria as part of the studies required to establish a deep underground repository, the status and relevance of this criterion are unclear.[25]

Estimation of statistical probabilities

4.18 Estimating the probability of a specified effect from human activities is straightforward in principle, but may be very difficult in practice. The initial difficulty is to generate realistic scenarios which take into account all the consequences that may be significant. That entails identifying all the possible environmental pathways. If a new situation is encountered, it may not be clear which scientific theory or model should be applied to it.[26] Examples of errors that have been made in the analysis of environmental pathways were given in box 2E. To take another example, the Commission has previously emphasised that releases of substances from industrial plants to the environment as a result of malfunctions must be taken into account alongside authorised routine releases.[27] Estimates of risk can be seriously in error if a relevant possibility is overlooked (for example, because of optimism about the reliability of expert systems to deal with complex, untried problems).[28] Experts are sometimes over-confident in their predictions and subject to biases of judgement.[29]

4.19 After the possible pathways have been identified, probabilities have to be estimated or imputed for each step in each pathway. Some probabilities have to be determined on the basis of the types of scientific evidence discussed in chapter 2, others relate to the reliability of technology. As was shown in chapter 2, scientific understanding leaves considerable uncertainties about the processes involved, and many of these are likely to remain. Crucially, there are few substances for which dose-response curves have been reliably established, especially at low doses. Some uncertainties are due to random variations and chance outcomes in the physical world. As the activities and effects being assessed become more and more complex, errors become more likely. There also come to be more and more possibilities that human behaviour will not be as assumed, for example, that plant operators will make mistakes or that people applying herbicide or using sheep dip will not do so under the stringently controlled conditions recommended.

4.20 In practical terms quantitative risk assessment is most useful in comparing or aggregating the different ways in which risks may be generated by a single hazard, as a basis for devising and implementing control measures if appropriate. These different ways of generating risk might be different routes by which humans may be exposed to a substance, as in figure 2-I, or different substances released by different routes from a given industrial plant.[30] In both contexts some of the most important parameters remain constant (the assumed toxicity of the substance in the first case, the characteristics of the environmental pathways in the second) and potentially important sources of error are therefore removed.

4.21 When uncertainty is recognisable and quantifiable, it can itself be represented statistically, and in that way incorporated into estimates of risk. Objective or frequency-based probability measures can describe uncertainties associated with randomness, and subjective probability measures (based on expert opinion) those associated with lack of knowledge. It would, however, be very misleading to confuse the latter with probabilities estimated on the basis of empirical data. Sometimes uncertainty is not recognised and then amounts to ignorance – the problem of not knowing what you do not know. This can result in the systematic under-estimation of uncertainty with potentially serious implications for the decision process.[31] In other cases, uncertainty is recognised but cannot be quantified. This is especially true of the assessment of risks far into the future, such as those from radioactive waste repositories, where the uncertainty, especially regarding human intrusion into a repository with a life-span of perhaps 10,000 years, is such that 'it is not possible to make scientifically supportable predictions of the probability' of such an intrusion.[32]

4.22 Although estimates of risk are often presented as the objective outcome of a scientific assessment,[33] they frequently go well beyond what could be justified in terms of rigorous use of the scientific evidence. At some points in the assessment, scientific evidence is likely to be inconclusive, at other points, entirely lacking. In the absence of data, working assumptions are usually needed to cope with variability of populations and exposures, weaknesses in toxicity assessments, uncertainty about responses, and lack of knowledge about other data, including the effects of mixtures of chemicals. Inevitably the assumptions used are those of the practitioners making the assessment. These assumptions may be widely shared amongst the expert community but they cannot realistically be said to yield objective assessments. Other people, making different but equally valid assumptions, may produce substantially different estimates of risk.

4.23 One way of handling uncertainty or lack of information which is often adopted in risk assessments is to assume at each stage the worst case realistically possible. This is open to the objection that the cumulative effect of a series of worst-case assumptions may be a seriously unrealistic assessment of the overall risk. A more appropriate approach in complex cases is to undertake sensitivity analysis to identify the uncertainties which create important differences in the assessed outcomes. Formal methods can also be used to address whether potential reductions in uncertainty (such as further experimental results might provide) would make a difference in the decision.

Limitations of statistical probabilities

4.24 Even if it is possible to estimate accurately the statistical probability of a specified event, that probability may not by itself be an appropriate basis for reaching a judgement about the tolerability of the human activities giving rise to that probability. First, various effects may be of concern, and it is not possible to reduce different kinds of effect to a common statistical measure.

4.25 The measure normally used in risk analysis is the probability that one person will die in any one year. Such probabilities can be calculated readily for hazards which are met frequently and cause death immediately or almost immediately, for example transport or industrial accidents. They are more difficult to calculate and interpret if death typically results a number of years after exposure. Choosing probability of death as the measure of severity excludes from consideration other effects on human health, such as non-fatal illness. It also excludes from consideration illness or suffering prior to an eventual death. From a practical point of view these can be significant limitations on the usefulness of risk assessment.

4.26 Many other forms of environmental damage ought to be considered in a comprehensive risk assessment. The probability of a human death offers no guidance about the severity of effects on the natural environment. The concept of ecological health can be given a wide range of meanings. Concern should focus on populations and communities and their ability to reproduce themselves, rather than on deaths of individuals (2.38). Or on entire ecosystems, recognising that these are subject to continual dynamic change through natural processes. A comprehensive assessment of ecological risk would not only have to be systematic and, so far as possible, quantified but also distinguish between use of the environment on a sustainable basis and destruction of critical natural capital. **No satisfactory way has been devised of measuring risk to the natural environment, even in principle, let alone defining what scale of risk should be regarded as tolerable.**

4.27 The second factor which may invalidate simplistic comparisons between the statistical probabilities of different events is that risks arise out of different social contexts and therefore have different social meanings. It is now generally recognised that risks which people undergo voluntarily, or in the course of their employment, cannot legitimately be compared with risks to which they are subjected involuntarily, and perhaps without their knowledge. The reasons why people may be prepared to accept much higher risks from one human activity than another stem from the relationship between the nature of an activity and their own values. They may be prepared to accept a relatively high risk from an activity, for example horse riding, which is a valued part of their own lives, and within their own control and direct experience. Environmental risks are not something an individual can control. There is not the option, as there was with beef on the bone, of giving people full information and leaving them to decide whether they wish to take the risk or not.

4.28 People's willingness to accept risks over which they have no control will be strongly affected by whether they see benefits flowing from the activities that give rise to the risk. HSE characterises a risk of death of 1 in 1,000,000 as one which 'does not worry us or cause us to alter our ordinary behaviour in any way', '*provided there is a benefit to be gained,* and proper precautions are taken' *(emphasis added).*[34] There may be direct or indirect benefits to the people being subjected to the risk. Or they may be more or less well-disposed towards benefits that flow, or would flow, to other people. In the extreme case they may regard the activities in question as not producing any significant benefits for anyone.

4.29 The third important limitation of statistical probabilities is that risks themselves may be unevenly distributed. They may be much higher for certain groups of people than for others (for example, for children or for pregnant women or for those with a genetic susceptibility to a particular type of effect). They may be heavily concentrated on people living in one small area. Alternatively, as for example with long-lived radioactive isotopes discharged into the atmosphere, there may be a low level of risk affecting very large numbers of people. In the latter situation and in others, a substantial part of the risk to which the activities give rise may affect future generations. Decisions on environmental standards or policies may well turn on this kind of distributional issue, which can be determined only by making value judgements. The commitment to sustainable development strengthens the need for a comprehensive assessment of risks, and emphasises temporal and equity factors which have previously been less prominent.

Public acceptance of risks

4.30 As already noted, the measure most often used in risk analysis is the probability of human death. There has been much debate about the differences in the risks of death which the general public accept in practice from different activities. The report of the second Royal Society Study Group (4.9) was intended as a contribution to that debate. Its terms of reference read in part:

> To consider and help bridge the gap between what is stated to be scientific, and capable of being measured, and the way in which public opinion gauges risks and makes decisions;

To compare the decisions taken on investment by society in the reduction of risks and the allocation of resources implied on risk-benefit criteria.

4.31 It will be clear that many differences in the risks of death the public is apparently prepared to accept from different activities are likely to stem from factors discussed in the previous section: the extent to which particular activities have other adverse consequences as well as human deaths, including effects on the natural environment, the different social meanings of different categories of risks, and whether there are seen to be associated benefits, and the ways in which risks are distributed. Public acceptance of risks will also be affected by other factors, such as the way in which people perceive probabilities, the information that is provided to them in a particular case, and the credence they place on the source of information.

4.32 On the whole, people's perceptions of the probability of a specified event, though often differing from the actual probability, are of roughly the same order as the actual probability. However, people attach a higher probability than is justified statistically to striking or unusual risks, and under-estimate the risks of death from common causes such as heart disease or stroke.

4.33 It may not be easy psychologically to distinguish one low probability from another. Even with high probabilities, some studies show that people's responses to scenarios involving identical probabilities may depend on how the descriptions of them are worded.[35]

4.34 There is extensive media coverage of environmental and scientific issues, and this provides an invaluable source of public information. At the same time the media are well-attuned to the types of hazard about which people are most likely to be concerned or in which they are most likely to be interested. Style and content also reflect the values and assumptions of the editors.[36] These factors often result in particular types of information about the environment receiving disproportionately large coverage in the media (for example news about sudden or violent events) and being presented in a way that emphasises drama and conflict. Some people in the media are making efforts to redress the balance by giving more attention to longer-term environmental issues, and to placing these in context.

4.35 There have certainly been cases in which the media have played a part in amplifying people's perception of a particular risk with considerable practical consequences. It has been suggested that reporting of the malfunction in the nuclear power station at Three Mile Island in the USA is one such case. Although death or physical injury had not occurred, there were devastating financial consequences for the utility which owned the plant, nuclear reactors worldwide were operated at a reduced level, and the policy response placed enormous costs not only on the nuclear industry but on society generally.[37]

4.36 Conflicts and dilemmas such as those over the siting of hazardous facilities have made governments, regulators and industries look for methods of providing information about risks which might contribute to gaining public acceptance for proposals. Moreover, there are increasing pressures on government and industry to inform people about risks to which they may be exposed. New information may suggest grounds for concern about the safety or environmental impact of an industrial plant, or that a medicine has hitherto unknown dangers. In such cases governments, regulators or companies are often faced with conflicting goals, because they typically wish to warn the public about a risk while at the same time offering reassurance that it is tolerable and under adequate control.

4.37 To the extent that the public may have imperfect information about the scale and nature of environmental risks, or needs to be given new information, what is the most effective way of communicating such information? Traditionally, communication of information to the public about risks was seen in terms of the technocratic, or top-down model, in which an expert transmits a message to a non-expert audience. There is no evidence that giving people raw statistics is an effective method of changing their attitudes towards different human activities. There is now wide recognition that risk communication is a much subtler and more complex process, and in particular that it must be a two-way process.[38] The context of the message must be sensitive to the frames of reference within which a particular audience views a particular problem. It is a complex task to achieve that because there are so many different world views and frameworks for approaching risk problems. The interdepartmental working party on risk assessment (4.15) has considered ways of improving risk communication and commissioned research on some aspects of the subject.

4.38 People's reactions to information about risks are considerably influenced by the circumstances in which it is presented to them. Attempts to persuade people that particular risks are acceptable by comparing them with other risks may backfire. They may appear to be trivialising the issues, or to be patronising in implicitly devaluing the perspectives and knowledge of those who are being asked to accept the risks. Such attempts will also be counter-productive if they are seen as glossing over political aspects of many of the risk conflicts in society and ignoring differences in the social meanings of risks, for example by equating voluntary with involuntary risks.

4.39 Another respect in which information provided about risks may be patently inadequate is in glossing over uncertainties: a statement that the probability of an event is 1 in 1,000,000 needs to be accompanied by information about the degree of certainty attaching to the estimate. In relation to any risk, but especially in relation to environmental risks subject to large uncertainties, the reception accorded to information depends on the credibility of the person or organisation providing it. There is good evidence that the credibility of communicators is critically dependent on the trust placed in them. Professional networks and informal networks of family and friends are far more trusted as sources of information than scientists, the media or government. Where trust has to be built up, that can be done only through open and honest communication over a continuous period.

4.40 In the case of environmental risks a crucial aspect of credibility and trust is the perceived intentions, competence and effectiveness of those (whether government, regulator or companies whose activities give rise to them) who are seen to be responsible for controlling the risks. A further proviso attached to HSE's characterisation of the acceptability of a certain level of risk (4.28) was that 'proper precautions are taken'. Recently there appears to have been an erosion of public trust in environmental regulation, and we discuss the reasons for that in chapter 8.

The precautionary principle

4.41 We have referred already in previous chapters (1.33, 2.71) to what can best be described as a change in the burden of proof on environmental issues. This change is expressed in general adoption of the precautionary principle. This principle is acknowledged by the European Union in the Maastricht Treaty, where it is closely linked with 'the principles that preventive action should be taken, that environmental damage should as a priority be rectified at source and that the polluter should pay' (1.25). In the 1990 Environment White Paper it was expressed in the following terms:[39]

> Where there are significant risks of damage to the environment, the Government will be prepared to take precautionary action to limit the use of potentially dangerous materials or the spread of potentially dangerous pollutants, even where scientific knowledge is not conclusive, if the balance of likely costs and benefits justifies it.

Other expressions of the precautionary principle have appeared in many international conventions and declarations in the 1980s; examples are given in box 4A.

BOX 4A **INTERNATIONAL EXPRESSIONS OF THE PRECAUTIONARY PRINCIPLE**

Marine pollution

1984 Bremen Ministerial Declaration of the International Conference on the Protection of the North Sea – States 'must not wait for proof of harmful effects before taking action'

1987 London Ministerial Declaration of the Second International Conference on the Protection of the North Sea – 'in order to protect the North Sea from possibly damaging effects of the most dangerous substances, a precautionary approach is necessary'

1992 OSPAR Convention – preventive measures are to be taken 'when there are reasonable grounds for concern ... even when there is no conclusive evidence of a causal relationship between inputs and their alleged effects'

Atmospheric pollution

1980 EC Council Decision 80/372 concerning chlorofluorocarbons (CFCs) in the environment – '... a significant reduction should, as a precautionary measure, be achieved in the next few years in the use of CFCs ... giving rise to emissions'

1985 Vienna Convention for the Protection of the Ozone Layer – '... mindful also of the precautionary measures for the protection of the ozone layer which have already been taken at the national and international levels'

1987 Montreal Protocol – although aware that measures should be based on 'relevant scientific knowledge', the Parties are 'Determined to protect the ozone layer by taking precautionary measures to control equitably total global emissions of substances that deplete it'

1992 Climate Change Convention – 'Parties should take precautionary measures to anticipate, prevent or minimise the causes of climate change and mitigate its adverse effects'; 'Where there are threats of serious or irreversible damage, lack of full scientific certainty should not be used as a reason for postponing such measures, taking into account that policies and measures to deal with climate change should be cost-effective so as to ensure global benefits at the lowest possible cost'

Nature conservation

1992 Biodiversity Convention – 'where there is a threat of significant reduction or loss of biological diversity, lack of full scientific certainty should not be used as a reason for postponing measures to avoid or minimize such a threat'

1994 Fort Lauderdale Resolution to the 1973 CITES Convention – when considering proposals for amending the lists of endangered species within the Convention, Parties 'shall apply the precautionary principle so that scientific uncertainty should not be used as a reason for failing to act in the best interest of the conservation of the species'

General international law-making

1990 Bergen Ministerial Declaration on Sustainable Development in the ECE Region – 'In order to achieve sustainable development, policies must be based on the precautionary principle. Environmental measures must anticipate, prevent and attack the causes of environmental degradation. Where there are threats of serious or irreversible damage, lack of full scientific certainty should not be used as a reason for postponing measures to prevent environmental degradation'

1992 Rio Declaration on Environment and Development (Principle 15) – 'In order to protect the environment, the precautionary approach shall be widely applied by States according to their capabilities. Where there are threats of serious or irreversible damage, lack of full scientific certainty shall not be used as a reason for postponing cost-effective measures to prevent environmental degradation'

4.42 The precautionary principle has been one of the most controversial principles of environmental protection, and there has been much uncertainty about what it implies. It was suggested in evidence to us that it requires policy-makers to 'adopt an approach which ensures that errors are made on the side of excess environmental protection'[40] and that it is 'not so much a practical guide to decision-making as a moral injunction *not* to ignore possible environmental impacts which cannot be proven'.[41] The expression of it in the 1992 Rio Declaration has been described as entailing 'a bias towards safety and caution'.[42]

4.43 Described in this way the precautionary principle might seem to be simply the reflection of a particular set of attitudes and beliefs with which people approach environmental issues, and more generally questions about acceptability of risks, what cultural theorists of risk have called 'cultural biases'.[43] It would merely represent one among several possible views of nature (as robust, as fragile, as forgiving but only within limits, as unpredictable and threatening) which are simultaneously held by people in society.[44]

4.44 We emphasise that we do not regard it in that light, but as a rational response to uncertainties in the scientific evidence relevant to environmental issues and uncertainties about the consequences of action or inaction. We have indicated that even the best scientific assessment may not provide a clear basis for taking a decision on an environmental issue (2.73). The rational response to such a situation will depend on the seriousness of the possible consequences of action or inaction, the time it would take for those consequences to emerge, the time-scale over which remediable action could be taken, the prospects for reducing the scientific uncertainties, and the time it would take to do that. Thus, if the possible effects which are of concern could be corrected quickly, and it is reasonable to suppose that the scientific uncertainties can be reduced within a short time, it may be sensible to defer a decision rather than take precautionary action. If on the other hand the possible effects would be serious and irreversible, precautionary action is likely to be justified, and might be shown to be so even on a statistical analysis of costs and benefits.

4.45 The precautionary principle originated in Germany in the 1970s as the *Vorsorgeprinzip*.[45] An essential complement to it in German administrative law is the principle of 'proportionality' of administrative action and the prohibition of excessive actions. The guidelines produced by the Federal German government state that:

> The determination of measures for *Vorsorge* requires a balancing which takes into account on the one hand the economic and other effort involved and on the other the achievable maintenance and improvement of environmental quality.

4.46 Although we have emphasised that the precautionary principle itself is of general validity and not a matter of choice, its interpretation and application, like many issues about risk covered earlier in this chapter, inevitably raises questions about values. This applies for example to terms like 'serious or irreversible'. There is also scope for different interpretations of terms like 'full scientific certainty' and 'cost-effective'. (All these terms are used in Principle 15 of the 1992 Rio Declaration, quoted in box 4A). Decisions about the interpretation and application of the precautionary principle are part of a political process; and 'There are different world views that determine how different groups cope with the universal experience of potential outcomes of actions and events.'[46]

4.47 The safety factors used in assessments of toxicity (2.35) and ecotoxicity (2.47) are in a sense precautionary. However, they are used when there is already evidence of an effect in order to estimate the size of the effect. The true application of the precautionary principle is in cases where there is reason to think there may be an effect, but no evidence has yet been obtained for its existence or the evidence is inconclusive.

4.48 **Whatever action is taken in the name of precaution (from use of worst-case scenarios and safety factors in assessments through to application of the precautionary principle in decision making) should be transparent and subject to review in the light of development of understanding. Relevant data should be collected and reviewed on a continuous basis; and if a standard has been set, it should be revised up or down as necessary.**

Output from assessment of risk and uncertainty

4.49 We conclude this chapter by considering the form that an assessment of risk and uncertainty should take in order to provide the most useful input to decisions about environmental policies or standards. The scientific assessment will itself indicate the uncertainties and limitations associated with the data used and cover all the possible interpretations of the scientific evidence (2.80). **We see the assessment of risk and uncertainty dealing with two important components:**

looking at broader uncertainties about the current issue which extend beyond the available scientific evidence and considering a wider range of possibilities;

where sufficient data are available, quantifying and analysing the risks associated with the issue under consideration.

The relative importance of these two aspects will vary according to circumstances, and in any given case one of them may predominate.

4.50 **Risk assessments prepared in support of decisions on environmental policies or standards should start with information about the nature of the hazard which the policy or standard seeks to address and the extent and quality of the evidence available for assessing the risks it poses. This part of the analysis should indicate whether the hazard is of a relatively well-understood type; if it is unfamiliar, an attempt should be made to identify the most nearly analogous hazards and the aspects which are not understood.**

4.51 In cases where the precautionary principle is relevant, the risk assessment should assess the potential scale and nature of the consequences of the hazard so that this information can be considered in a later stage of the decision procedure alongside the conclusions from the other components of the analytical stage.

4.52 Numerical estimates often convey an unwarranted sense that the precise extent of the risk is known. Estimates should therefore be accompanied by qualitative information about the uncertainties involved. **The limitations and uncertainties in any estimates of risk must always be made clear in ways which are meaningful to people without particular specialist knowledge.**

4.53 **Risk assessments should identify the uncertainties which have the largest implications and the actions that would need to be taken to reduce or resolve them. However, it would be inappropriate and misleading to attempt to incorporate into risk assessments estimated probabilities for the correctness of particular scientific theories or interpretations.**

4.54 **If there are sufficient data, and sufficient knowledge of the underlying processes, quantitative risk assessments should cover not only risk of human deaths but risks of other harmful outcomes. For each estimate the assumptions made should be explicit and clearly stated.**

4.55 Where different estimates of risks from the same hazard have been made by different people the assessment should include all the estimates with the assumptions on which they were based. It would be useful to explore making greater use of techniques for setting out the sensitivities of risk assessments to divergent assumptions in order to provide a clearer view of the political and ethical implications of different decisions.[47]

4.56 **As well as distinguishing between different types of effect from a hazard, risk assessments should also:**

a. **indicate the distribution of risks (whether they are especially high for people in certain localities, age groups or occupations, or people with certain medical conditions or genetic predispositions);**

b. characterise as far as possible the respective perceptions of the risks held by relevant groups, the meanings the risks will have for them, and their views about the tolerability of the risks.

Quantitative information on these points should be provided where it is available, otherwise qualitative assessments should be given.

4.57 For risks of the same general type, and where data are available and the processes sufficiently understood, direct comparisons between options may be useful in informing decisions, for example:

a. between the risks from the hazard being addressed and other risks of the same general type affecting the same group of people or compartment of the environment, so that estimates can be made of the total risk of that type to which these will be subject;

b. between the risks from the hazard being addressed and the risks from different sources or pathways for the same pollutant or different pollutants from the same source, in order to identify any options for risk reduction that might obtain a larger benefit for a similar cost.

However, making comparisons between risks which the public does not perceive as comparable can undermine the credibility of regulators and governments.

4.58 Risk assessments cannot establish a relationship on any objective basis between risks of different types or between risks imposed on different groups of people, because to do so raises value questions. It has been generally recognised that public perceptions of risks which diverge from expert estimates are not necessarily irrational but may well reflect different values from those underlying the expert assessments. Pursuing and resolving these differences in perceptions and values will demand better methods of communicating about risk. The kinds of procedure we discuss in chapter 7 may be appropriate for that purpose.

4.59 Government Departments and other regulators should not seek to set environmental standards, or other forms of standard, on the basis of risk assessments considered in isolation. They are only one of several essential components of the decision procedure required, which we discuss and describe in chapter 8.

Chapter 5

ECONOMIC APPRAISAL

Economic appraisal aims to facilitate the choice between alternative policies by providing an assessment of their respective costs and benefits. Practical problems can arise when an attempt is made to place valuations on some of the consequences of environmental policies. Issues of principle may also be raised. There are differing views on what assistance economic appraisals can provide when decisions have to be made on environmental policies.

5.1   Economic appraisal is a further component of the analytical stage of the policy process, as described at the beginning of this report. It utilises information from other components, including scientific assessments of the effects which particular human activities have, or would have, on human health and on the natural and built environment and analyses of the technological options available for avoiding or minimising such effects. The natures and limitations of these forms of analysis were discussed in chapters 2 and 3. Chapter 4 discussed the contribution risk assessment can make to decisions about environmental policies or standards. Quantitative risk assessments may also provide an input to economic appraisal.

5.2   In this chapter we first describe a conceptual framework provided by economics for assessing the benefits arising from an environmental standard and the costs which it imposes (5.4–5.9). We touch briefly on defining policy objectives and the significance that should be accorded to prior constraints in deciding whether an economic appraisal should be undertaken (5.10–5.12). We then summarise the main features of guidance on best practice in economic appraisal published by UK government Departments (5.13–5.22). We describe briefly multi-criteria analysis, a technique to establish weightings for different factors which are not expressed in money terms (5.23–5.24). We consider the application of discounting (5.25–5.27). We summarise current use in the UK and the European Community of economic appraisal and other approaches for taking costs into account in decisions on environmental matters (5.28–5.37). We review the debate about the role of economic appraisal in relation to decisions on environmental policies (5.38–5.48). Finally, we discuss the form in which the findings from economic appraisal should be presented in order to provide the most useful input to decisions (5.49–5.53).

5.3   The definition of economic appraisal given by the UK Treasury, and its definitions of other relevant terms, are in box 5A.[1]

Economic analysis and environmental standards

5.4   The theoretical framework for economic appraisal of an environmental standard can be explained by considering the consequences of imposing a limit on emissions of some form of pollution. To simplify, the example taken is of a single industrial plant at a given location producing an output which confers material benefits on those who purchase it, but which also gives rise to some form of pollution. The people incurring costs as a result of damage caused by the pollution need not be, and probably will not be, the same as those who derive benefit by purchasing the product. Different groups of people are, therefore, likely to have different views about the benefits of imposing a limit on the pollution emitted and the costs that will be incurred as a result of doing so.

| **BOX 5A** | **TREASURY DEFINITIONS OF SOME ECONOMIC TERMS** |

economic appraisal: a process of defining objectives, examining options, and weighing up the costs and benefits and risks and uncertainties which takes into account a wide range of *welfare costs and benefits* (see below). How wide depends upon the context. It may include all welfare costs and benefits, or all those which affect gross domestic product, or all those which can be valued in money terms

cost-benefit analysis: analysis which seeks to quantify in money terms as many of the costs and benefits of a proposal as possible, including items for which the market does not provide a satisfactory measure of economic value. The term is sometimes used to describe analysis which is confined to costs and benefits quantified in money terms and sometimes to describe an analysis of all the *welfare costs and benefits*

cost-effectiveness analysis: the comparison of alternative ways of producing the same or similar outputs, which are not necessarily given a monetary value

present value: the capitalised value of a stream of future costs or benefits. The term 'net present value' is often used to refer to the difference between the present value of a stream of costs and the present value of a stream of benefits

welfare cost or benefit: any effect on human well-being

resource costs: payments for goods or services

existence value: the value placed by people on the continued existence of a thing of environmental value for the benefit of present or future generations

---

5.5   The firm operating the plant can be assumed to have a choice between alternative production processes which vary both in cost and in the extent of pollution emitted. The total amount of pollution received by the population vulnerable to it, and the damage caused by that pollution, therefore depend on the production process chosen by the firm, as well as varying with the level of its output. Imposing a limit on the amount of pollution permitted from the plant will cause the firm to choose a different, less polluting production process rather than the one it would have chosen in the absence of such a limit. There is sometimes scope to adopt innovations which reduce pollution without increasing costs, but in many cases the new production process will have higher resource costs.

5.6   The imposition of a more stringent limit on the pollution emitted by the plant is, therefore, likely to raise the resource costs of production. This increase in costs will lead to a higher price being charged for the product, which will mean somewhat less of it is bought (and, if more of people's income is then being spent on this item, there may be less money left for buying other goods and services too). If less of the product is bought, output of the product will be reduced, reducing further the amount of pollution and the associated damage costs. But there will also be less material benefit for the people who want to buy and enjoy the product.

5.7   There is thus a *trade-off* between the material benefit derived from production and use of the product and the amount of disbenefit arising from the pollution caused in its production. The decision about the level of the limit will determine the point on this trade-off that the firm will choose. (A limit is needed only if the point chosen by the firm when left to its own devices is deemed inferior to others available.)

5.8   One way of formulating the problem of deciding at what level to set the limit on pollution is to note that the welfare of people depends on both the damage likely to be caused by the pollution and the material benefits they enjoy, and that both of these are affected by the level at which the limit is set. On this formulation, the best outcome will be achieved if the limit is set at the level which, given the available technology of production, maximises people's welfare.

5.9   When the limit is high, the damage done by pollution is more extensive but the output produced by the firm is relatively cheap in terms of resource costs. As the limit becomes more stringent, the production process becomes progressively more expensive in terms of resource costs and so its output becomes more expensive, but the damage costs fall. The limit imposed on emissions in this simple example is analogous to an environmental standard. The purpose of economic appraisal of a possible standard is to inform whoever is responsible for setting the standard about the position of the trade-off between the damage resulting from pollution and the material benefits of the activities giving rise to that pollution.

Prior constraints

5.10 Before appraising any proposed policy, the first step is to define the objectives and identify any prior constraints. The objectives for an environmental policy are sometimes defined only in very general terms. In other cases, however, there will be significant prior constraints on the choice of policy. Such constraints take various forms, including international conventions, European Community (EC) Directives, domestic legislation, previous political commitments and political pressure.[2] They may reflect principles of an ethical kind.

5.11 The existence of constraints should not be generally accepted without question. In relation to an individual case the existence of a relevant environmental standard will itself be a prior constraint, possibly legally binding. Standards themselves, however, need to come under critical scrutiny. We have emphasised that proposals for new environmental policies or standards need to be subjected to rigorous analysis in which economic appraisal is a component. Moreover, existing policies or standards, whether or not they are incorporated in legislation or an international agreement, ought to be periodically reviewed, using similar methods of evaluation.

5.12 Some prior constraints are of a more fundamental character than a pre-existing standard, and need to be acknowledged by policy-makers, whether or not they are in a legally binding form. To the extent that it is accepted that there is a constraint which determines what kind of policy is to be adopted, or excludes a particular option from consideration, there can be no point in carrying out an appraisal of that policy or that option.

Best practice in economic appraisal

5.13 Appraisal as characterised by the UK Treasury involves, first, defining the objectives (5.10) and then normally going through the following sequence:

   i.   consider the options;

   ii. identify, quantify and where possible value the costs, benefits and risks and uncertainties associated with each option;

   iii. analyse the information;

   iv. present the results.[3]

We summarise in this section Treasury guidance on best practice in economic appraisal and advice which the Department of the Environment (DOE) issued in order to ensure that environmental effects are fully considered during policy appraisal.[4] We pay particular attention to difficulties that may arise where the option or options under consideration are for an environmental policy or standard.

Specifying the base case

5.14 In order to assess an option it has to be compared with an alternative scenario. Often the comparison will be with a case defined as 'do nothing' or 'do the minimum possible'. In the economic appraisal described in box 5B a set of possible air quality standards was compared with the legislation already in existence or planned to improve air quality.[5] Even a 'do nothing' case has to be carefully specified because there may be changes in prospect in technology or in other policies. For example, the costs and benefits of achieving air quality targets would be affected by changes in energy policies.

BOX 5B   **ECONOMIC APPRAISAL OF AIR QUALITY STANDARDS**

In a study for the European Commission three research institutes analysed the costs and benefits of achieving in 2010 the limit values likely to be set for concentrations of nitrogen oxides, sulphur dioxide, particulate matter (PM_{10}) and lead. Costs and benefits which could not be readily assessed in terms of market prices were assigned money values, largely based on individual willingness to pay to avoid damage. A sensitivity analysis was included.

The estimated costs represented the direct costs of measures to reduce emissions from fixed and mobile sources. For vehicles these included use of low sulphur fuels, road pricing, and the introduction of clean fuels for buses. The set of measures was identified by the consultants and was different to that which the European Commission in fact proposed on the basis of other studies (5.22).

The only benefits considered were avoidance of effects on human health and on materials. Some health impacts could not be quantified. Nor were benefits to crops and ecosystems included. Indirect effects on ozone levels were not taken into account.

The base case included the impact of some expected legislation (for example, on sulphur content of fuels), but the estimated costs and benefits would be affected by other possible developments, such as energy policy initiatives to reduce carbon dioxide emissions.

The table below shows that, except for lead, the quantified benefits of achieving these air quality standards considerably exceeded the estimated costs. For lead, quantifiable benefits were lower than estimated costs. When the limit value for lead was published as a formal proposal in October 1997, the European Commission noted a possible source of under-estimation in the benefits and argued that 'The relatively low costs seem to justify the limit value'.

	required reduction in emissions %	estimated annual costs (million ECU)	quantified annual benefits (million ECU)
sulphur dioxide	10	4–48	83–3,783
oxides of nitrogen	8	5–285	408–5,900
PM_{10}	50	50–300	5,007–51,246
lead	not quantified	12–40	3.2–5.8

Identifying the consequences

5.15 To obtain a full picture, all the significant consequences of an option have to be taken into account. There is no fool-proof way of ensuring that all the consequences have been identified. Scientific assessment and analysis of technological options provide the basis. It may be necessary to obtain supplementary assessments, or commission research, if an option and its consequences have not been specified in sufficient detail. DOE guidance on identifying the environmental impacts of policies provides a useful check-list: examine all stages of policy implementation, examine indirect effects as well as direct effects (a reduction in one form of pollution may be accompanied by an increase in another form of pollution), look for wider effects, consult widely with others who may have a different perspective.[6]

5.16 An initial assessment should be made of each significant consequence of an option in order to determine whether:

> that consequence should be perceived as a gain (benefit) or a loss (cost);

> it is likely to be an important factor in the decision;

> it is likely to be subject to a wide range of uncertainty;

> it can be valued or measured.

This preliminary assessment enables the remaining stages of the appraisal to be sensibly designed and structured, so saving time and money. The extent and type of the uncertainties associated with the options affect the manner in which an economic appraisal should be carried out, including what sensitivity analyses (5.51–5.52) ought to be conducted.

Quantifying the effects

5.17 The next step is to assess the impact of an option more precisely by quantifying, wherever possible, those effects which seem likely to be significant in relation to the decision whether or not to adopt the option. Although quantification of effects can sometimes be relatively straightforward, there is a substantial degree of uncertainty about the consequences of most policies, particularly standards relating to the environment, or to health and safety.[7] If the scientific assessment has provided reasonably precise estimates of the exposure of people to a pollutant and of the dose-effect relationship (2.32–2.37), it may be possible to estimate within a reasonably narrow range the improvements in health that a given standard or policy would achieve. As chapter 2 showed, however, those conditions are unlikely to be satisfied in practice. Although it is often easier to quantify the actions required to achieve compliance with a given standard, there may be uncertainty on that side too in practice because of the difficulty of predicting the impact of technological innovations, perhaps stimulated by adoption of the standard (5.5).

Valuing the effects

5.18 Some of the consequences of a possible policy or standard are of such a kind that they can be valued relatively easily in money terms, for example the costs of installing and operating pollution control equipment or the administrative costs of regulation. In economic appraisal goods or services that have alternative uses should be costed at their full value in the most valuable alternative use to which they could be put (that is, at their *economic* or *opportunity cost*). The starting-point for estimating economic costs is generally market prices.[8]

5.19 Nearly all environmental policy options have important consequences for which there is no market price. These may include implications for human health or for the conservation value of particular areas of land. The appraisal either has to use a method of valuing such consequences in money terms or represent them in terms of quantities other than money or provide a clear verbal description of them. Some of the techniques used to impute money values to non-marketed consequences of environmental policies are listed in box 5C.[9] A Department of Health committee is currently considering the range of possibilities for putting money values on health benefits. Another source of evidence is the money value for a similar factor that can be regarded as implied by a previous decision about another policy. Another possible approach is to consider, for each factor in turn in the present case, the money value that would have to be imputed to that factor in order to swing the decision.[10]

BOX 5C METHODS FOR PUTTING A MONEY VALUE ON ENVIRONMENTAL DAMAGE

OUTPUT-BASED METHODS – an example of an output loss is the money value of a reduction in crop, forestry or fishery yield caused by environmental damage. A focus on output effects may disregard other impacts over which people are concerned. In particular, ill health may stop people from working, but may also cause pain, grief and suffering.

PREFERENCE-BASED METHODS seek to take explicit account of the preferences, constrained by available income, of those people who will be affected by a particular policy decision. Broadly speaking, they are of two kinds:

revealed preference methods
preventive expenditure: the amount paid to prevent or ameliorate unwanted effects, for example expenditure on insulation and double-glazing to keep out noise (sometimes a community valuation can be inferred, as when governments provide grants towards such expenditure)

replacement/restoration cost: the amount individuals spend on, for example, the restoration of damaged buildings or landscapes

property valuation: differences in the market value of similar properties that reflect differences in the local environment, for example the amount by which the price of a house is lower because it is next to a busy road

compensating wage differentials: the premia in wage rates in occupations that are riskier or have above average health hazards, from which money values for preventing fatal and non-fatal health effects can be inferred

expressed preference methods
contingent valuation: asking people to say either how much money they would be willing to accept to compensate for unwanted effects *or* (which tends to produce lower valuations) how much money they would be willing to pay to avoid unwanted effects (but the amount people say they would be willing to pay may differ from the amount they would be willing, or able, to pay in practice)

conjoint analysis: asking people to rate or rank alternative bundles of attributes of a good, service or policy option (for example, bundles comprising specified amounts of environmental damage; health effects; effects on wildlife; etc.) and eliciting from their rankings or ratings the implied rates at which they trade off one attribute for another. If one of the attributes is money, implicit money valuations can be inferred

relative valuation: determining the *relative* value people place on a good or service by comparing it with another good or service for which a money value has already been established, for example deriving money values for preventing non-fatal road injuries of different severities from the money value previously determined for preventing road fatalities

---

5.20 The purpose of imputing a money value to something which is not traded is, not to estimate what its 'price' would be if it were traded, but to communicate evidence about 'the relative values which society places on different uses of resources'.[11] Although money values are often used to communicate information which an economic appraisal has assembled about the trade-offs between alternative non-marketed consequences of an option, and between non-marketed and marketed consequences, that is not always the case. Some consequences may be quantified in their own units or on an *ad hoc* scale.[12] Others, for example ethical issues, might simply be identified as relevant considerations.

Distributional effects

5.21 One aspect of the consequences of policies which is, by its nature, incapable of being traded in a conventional market is their distributional effects. Many environmental policies have different implications for people of different incomes, ages, health states or locations. As in the hypothetical example described at the beginning of this chapter (5.4), the benefits of such a policy often accrue to one group of people while the costs are borne by another group. Where appropriate, an economic appraisal should elucidate these distributional effects by disaggregating the analysis of costs and benefits according to the groups affected.[13]

Cost-effectiveness analysis

5.22 It is sometimes appropriate to use a limited form of economic appraisal, known as cost-effectiveness analysis, in relation to environmental issues. This compares alternative options for obtaining the same or similar outputs. For example, if standards for air quality are taken as given, a cost-effectiveness analysis can be carried out to provide information about alternative methods for achieving them, and the results can then be taken into account in setting emission and product standards.[14]

Multi-criteria analysis

5.23 A group of methods have been developed for the formal analysis of complex decision problems without imputing money values.[15] Some of them are regarded as tools to be used in economic analysis,[16] others have been developed by management scientists and operational researchers. Multi-attribute analysis (5.34) is one such method, and we describe briefly here multi-criteria decision making (MCDM). The purpose of this is to transform imprecise goals into a set of criteria which are relatively precise, although they may be in conflict with each other.[17] The attributes on which the selection should be based are established, usually by discussion with or between the parties to the decision, together with weights to show their relative importance. The relative performance of each option is then scored against the attributes. There are various methods by which the weights and scores can be elicited.[18] A widely-used approach is the 'analytic hierarchy process'. In this, each major attribute is subdivided into contributory attributes, thus defining an attribute tree (sometimes called a 'value tree'). Each stakeholder is then asked to compare the options in pairs against the lowest-level attributes. From these pairwise comparisons a set of scores can be calculated to show the performance of each option against the main attributes. The weights attached to the attributes and the scores for each option reveal which option is preferred.[19] It is possible to calculate from the pairwise comparisons whether the preferences thus elicited are consistent. The results obtained can also be examined to reveal whether, for example, different groups of stakeholders show preferences which are sufficiently different to lead to different decisions, and whether the decision is sensitive to small changes in the weights or scores.

5.24 It is a feature of the various forms of multi-criteria analysis that the weights and scores elicited have no significance outside the context of the immediate decision. It is not, therefore, possible to use this approach to address issues of consistency between decisions. These forms of analysis are most useful when there is an overall objective which can be taken as given and the decision involves choosing between alternative ways of achieving it.

Application of discounting

5.25 An integral part of economic appraisal is to take into account trade-offs between things enjoyed today and things enjoyed at some future date. Just as people's valuation of traded goods and services is reflected in their relative prices, so people's valuation of tomorrow's enjoyment of basic consumer goods relative to today's is reflected in the market interest rate. The method adopted for taking into account this form of trade-off is to apply a discount rate to future costs and benefits.

5.26 A discount rate of 1% will reduce by more than one-third the value today of benefits obtained in 50 years' time and reduce by nearly two-thirds the value today of benefits obtained in 100 years' time. A higher discount rate will lead to even greater reductions in the value today of future benefits.

5.27 **When performing an economic appraisal it should be borne in mind that the *relative* values of the things under consideration may change over time.** If some thing of environmental value were to become scarcer as the years go by, the people who enjoy it would value it relatively more highly. The relative values of increasingly scarce things will rise over time. Although such changes in relative values are difficult to predict with any accuracy, the direction of the change may be uncontroversial.

Current use of economic appraisal

5.28 We now review briefly the ways in which economic appraisal is currently used in the UK and the European Community.

5.29 In the view of the UK Treasury 'The identification and, where possible, valuation of environmental costs and benefits has become still more important with the acceptance of a policy of "sustainable development".'[20] As to the valuation of impacts for which there is no market value, it has summed up the present position in UK central government as follows:[21]

> Sometimes these impacts can be valued, in ways which are widely enough accepted to be used as a basis for policy decisions. This applies routinely to, for example, the valuation of working and of leisure time in the calculation of the costs and benefits of a road scheme. It may apply in some appraisals to specific environmental impacts, or for example to the value placed by people on changes in the standards of some public amenity. Appraisal which makes substantial use of valuations of this kind ... is however not the norm even in public sector appraisal and evaluation. More often than not, all of the non-marketed costs and benefits are compared on the basis of quantitative and sometimes only qualitative assessment, with no valuation, and this is often the best approach.

There have been relatively few formal appraisals of environmental policies substantially based on imputing money values to environmental factors, although their number is said to be increasing.[22]

5.30 There has been quite widespread use of cost-effectiveness analysis, which does not in general require evaluation of environmental impacts. One reason for its use is that so much of the environmental legislation applying in the UK now comes from the European Community where the UK has less say over the setting of environmental standards. While it may be desirable for the European Commission to carry out full analyses of the costs and benefits of alternative standards, there would be little point in the UK carrying out such an analysis on its own if the dynamics of negotiation mean that this is unlikely to influence the outcome. In such circumstances, a cost-effectiveness analysis, directed to identifying the least-cost method of achieving a given standard, may be a more useful input to the UK's negotiating position, especially as it is relatively simpler and can be carried out more quickly to meet the demands of a fast-moving negotiation.[23]

5.31 There is a long-standing requirement that, when primary or secondary legislation is submitted to the UK Parliament, an assessment must be published of the financial costs that compliance with it will impose. The justifications for this requirement were described in the context of the last government's Deregulation Initiative as, first, to inform Ministers, Members of Parliament, business, and other interested parties of the effect on them of complying with new or amended legislation; and, second, to identify unnecessary burdens on business well before a decision is taken on whether or not to go ahead with the proposals.[24] Requiring preparation of a compliance cost assessment exerts pressure for costs to be taken fully into account when legislation is being prepared. An assessment of compliance costs is also included in the explanatory memoranda which the UK government submits to Parliament on proposed EC legislation as part of the scrutiny process described in appendix D.

5.32 The requirement for UK regulators of emissions from the more significant industrial processes to take costs into account in their decisions is long standing. While this was implicit in the concept of 'best practicable means' (BPM) introduced in the 1874 Alkali and Clean Air Act, it became explicit in the concept of 'best available techniques not entailing excessive cost' (BATNEEC) which replaced BPM in 1990. We have discussed previously how process standards are set by the Environment Agency on the basis of BATNEEC and how 'excessive' is interpreted (3.12–3.18 and box 3A).

5.33 The Environment Agencies have a statutory obligation, in making decisions about the exercise of any of their powers, to take into account 'the likely costs and benefits' of either exercising or not exercising those powers. However, the other statutory duties of the Agencies, including their conservation duties, and any specific environmental objectives set by Ministers or contained in legislation (appendix C, C.61), are treated as prior constraints (5.10). Furthermore, the duty to take into account costs and benefits does not apply if 'it is unreasonable for it to do so in view of the nature or purpose of the power [being exercised] or in the circumstances of the particular case'.[25]

5.34 In circumstances where the statutory duty to take into account costs and benefits applies, it does not necessarily require the Environment Agencies to carry out a cost-benefit analysis (box 5A). The Environment Agency's internal guidance on interpretation of the duty is that a fully quantified cost-benefit analysis should be carried out only 'where there is a reasonably acceptable way of putting monetary value on the non-financial costs and benefits of the alternatives'; and that, 'where there are additional features which mean that monetary valuation is inappropriate or unacceptable, (for example a wide range of diverse costs and benefits or a wide range of people involved)', multi-attribute analysis (5.23) may be used. Because of the expense involved, a fully quantified analysis of costs and benefits, or multi-attribute analysis, is regarded as justifiable only if a policy would involve the Agency and those affected by it, in estimated total expenditure of at least £1 million.[26]

5.35 In the health and safety field the Health and Safety Executive (HSE) takes account of costs and benefits by applying the principle of 'as low as reasonably practicable'. Both the use of this concept and the way it is interpreted depend on the level of risk. It is applied in what HSE calls the 'tolerability region' of risks, the middle band of risks which are neither unacceptable nor possible to disregard (4.13). The significance attributed to costs depends on the level of risk within that region: '... the higher or more unacceptable a risk is, the more, proportionately, employers are expected to spend to reduce it.'[27] Just below the limit of tolerability they are expected to spend up to the point at which further expenditure would be grossly disproportionate to the reduction in risk obtained; where risk is lower, and close to being broadly acceptable, they are not expected to obtain a further reduction in risk if the cost of doing so would exceed the improvement gained.[28] There is thus an implicit and informal comparison between the (financial) costs of a particular course of action and the benefits it will bring.

5.36 The Environment Directorate-General of the European Commission in evidence submitted to us in 1995 said it did not regard use of cost-benefit analysis as appropriate in the environmental field. It has nevertheless commissioned cost-benefit analyses of proposed standards (box 5B) and wider policies (see box 5E later). The Maastricht Treaty requires the European Union, in preparing action relating to the environment, to take into account, among other things, 'the potential benefits and costs of action or lack of action'.[29] The versions of the Treaty in other languages, however, use different terms because of a concern that 'benefits and costs' might be interpreted to cover only benefits and costs to a company.[30] Despite a commitment by the European Commission to prepare *fiches d'impact* for legislative proposals, compliance cost assessment appears to be not much used at European level.[31]

5.37 In certain contexts it has been held that costs are not a relevant factor in relation to EC legislation. The European Court of Justice has taken the view that economic considerations are not relevant in taking decisions about the designation of special protection areas under the Wild Birds Directive. Even in this context, however, selection of the population size at which a species is to be maintained has to take account of 'economic and recreational requirements' as well as 'ecological, scientific and cultural requirements'.[32] Legal systems often recognise a more general principle of proportionality, that the costs of any action a person or body is required by law to undertake must not be wholly disproportionate to its beneficial effects.

The role of economic appraisal

5.38 Economics is conventionally defined as 'the science which studies human behaviour as a relationship between ends and scarce means which have alternative uses'.[33] In those terms, use of economics is intrinsic to the task of devising policies so as to channel human resource use to meet chosen ends, including sustainable development and more specific environmental goals.

5.39 There is much debate about how useful economic appraisals can be in supporting decisions on environmental policies. The main focus of debate has been that form of appraisal (cost-benefit analysis) which imputes money values to those costs and benefits of a policy for which the market does not provide a satisfactory measure of value. The debate is at two levels. One level is about the difficult practical problems of ascertaining those values on the basis of little or divergent information and of the very considerable uncertainty involved in quantifying some of the effects of an environmental policy (5.17). Second (although it is beyond the scope of this report to explore that aspect fully), there is a deeper critique of cost-benefit analysis in particular and welfare economics in general. This critique argues that cost-benefit analysis does not properly take account of values associated with the environment, and further that the attempt to aggregate such values is objectionable.

5.40 Practical problems arise over valuation because, although there are various methods that can be used to set a money value on environmental effects (box 5C), such estimates are often not robust in the sense of being repeatable. While use is made of contingent valuation, there are doubts about the validity and reliability of the answers people give in surveys of this sort.[34]

5.41 Because of uncertainties about their effects and the practical problems of setting money values on non-marketed effects, cost-benefit analyses may give very wide ranges of money values for the costs and benefits of environmental policies. The report summarised in box 5B provides examples. Another consequence of the uncertainties involved is that different studies of the same issue may produce widely different valuations of costs and benefits. One example is the different estimates of the quantified environmental and social costs of road transport in Britain.[35] Another is the estimates made of the external environmental cost of obtaining electricity from coal-fired power stations.[36] In some cases different parts of such wide ranges may have quite different implications for decisions. In other cases a cost-benefit analysis may impute a specific money value to a given factor but the effect of changing one assumption is to produce very different implications for the decision: box 5D[37] describes a recent case about the effects of abstracting water from a river in which different assumptions about the number of people who give it a 'non-use value' or existence value (box 5A) had very different implications for policy.

5.42 As with scientific assessment (2.74), there are two separate questions that need to be addressed when considering the process of economic appraisal and its output. The first question is whether the appraisal has been done well, and whether the uncertainties and limitations are properly accounted for and made explicit. Whether the appraisal is helpful to those taking policy decisions is a separate question. If the conclusions are subject to great uncertainty, that uncertainty may stem from the intrinsic difficulties and complexities of the issues under consideration. Even in such cases, economic appraisal can make valuable contributions by clarifying the issues which may be important in relation to a given decision, for example, in the case described in box 5D, by indicating the significance of determining the groups of people for whom a particular river has an existence value.

BOX 5D	**EXISTENCE VALUE: THE RIVER KENNET**

A public inquiry in 1996 considered a dispute about the amount of water Thames Water should be allowed to extract from boreholes at Axford, close to the River Kennet in Wiltshire. The Environment Agency had proposed licence conditions designed to bring about a phased reduction over ten years in the amount of water abstracted by Thames Water. This was part of a plan to protect river flows and the natural ecology of an important stretch of the River Kennet. Thames Water appealed, resulting in the subsequent public inquiry.

Each side in the dispute prepared cost-benefit analyses to support its case. Two elements of these analyses were relatively uncontroversial:

the costs of using alternative sources of water, estimated by Thames Water as £6.2 million;

the benefits to other users of the river if Thames Water's abstraction was reduced as proposed by the Agency, estimated by the Agency as £67,000 a year (or £0.4 million as a net present value discounted over 30 years).

The major discrepancy was over estimation of the 'non-use' or 'existence' benefit of the River Kennet, the benefit of the river to people who do not directly use it for economic or recreational purposes. The Environment Agency examined the increase in the existence value of the River Kennet if abstraction was reduced and estimated the net present value of such benefits discounted over 30 years as £13.2 million, much higher than the cost of alternative sources. However, the Inquiry Inspector estimated it as £0.3 million, much less than the cost of alternative sources.

The two analyses used similar figures for the average amount households who did not use the River Kennet would be willing to pay each year to counter low flows. The Agency transferred estimates from a separate opinion survey of willingness to pay carried out for the River Darent in Kent, which showed that people up to 60 km away would pay an average of 32 pence per household per year per river to counter low flows. The Agency then applied this figure to the 3 million households or 7.5 million people in Thames Water's supply area. Using previous results in this way (a practice known as *benefit transfer*) saves the cost of new surveys, but may be misleading if factors in the original study are poorly matched at the new site.

The Inquiry Inspector, in assessing the benefits of improving the River Kennet, used an approach which assumed that only a relatively local population (of 100,000 people) could be included in the wider benefit calculations.

The Secretary of State accepted the Inspector's recommendation that Thames Water should be allowed to abstract the same amount of water for the next ten years, subject to a higher minimum flow in the river. He accepted the lower figure for the population which placed an existence value on the river. The basis for his recommendation, however, was his conclusion that the environmental evidence did not support a reduction in abstraction to the extent sought by the Agency, although there was some evidence that the Kennet's ecology was being harmed by low flows.

5.43 One approach to economic appraisal is to make the best attempt possible to quantify in money terms as many as possible of the costs and benefits of a proposal, including items for which the market does not provide a satisfactory measure of economic value; to calculate the net present value as the difference between the present value of those costs and the present value of those benefits (box 5A); and to explain what has been left out of the calculation, giving as much information as possible about the items left out and noting any particular issues relevant to the items included (uncertainties, variations with changing assumptions, and so on). The usefulness of this exercise as an input to decision making will vary from case to case; where it is less useful, that will reflect the features of the particular case rather than the limitations of economic appraisal.

5.44 Simply adding together all the diverse costs and benefits of an environmental policy is controversial. This is illustrated by the study of options for household waste management summarised in box 5E.[38] Financial costs tend to be relatively well-defined whereas valuations of environmental impact are much less certain. In this case treating the two categories as if they were equivalent led to contentious findings about policy. The consultants emphasised that the conclusions should be treated with caution. They have not led to any changes in policy.

BOX 5E	**OPTIONS FOR HOUSEHOLD WASTE MANAGEMENT**

A study carried out by Coopers & Lybrand for the European Commission analysed the costs of recycling, incineration, composting and landfill as options for management of household wastes.

Coopers & Lybrand argued that waste management policy should be deciding by adding together the financial and environmental costs of each method to give what they called its 'total net economic costs' and choosing the methods with the lowest costs. They collaborated with the Centre for Social and Economic Research on the Global Environment to make life cycle assessments of the environmental burdens which each option caused or avoided.

The clear conclusion was that recycling is the best form of management for household wastes (apart from organic waste and plastic film) in both urban and rural areas. Another conclusion was that landfill is preferable to either centralised composting or incineration (with or without energy recovery). This implies a different hierarchy for waste management methods to that incorporated in the European Community's 1991 Framework Directive on Waste or in the UK government's 1995 White Paper *Making Waste Work*.

The technique used was controversial in making direct comparisons between well-defined financial costs and much less certain valuations of environmental impact. The analysis omitted several environmental costs and some benefits which can only be meaningfully assessed at local level, including the impacts of landfills and incinerators on amenity; the report warns that 'The limitations ... mean that it is more difficult to be sure that the conclusions regarding landfill, incineration and composting would hold if a more comprehensive assessment were possible.'

The consultants emphasised that the conclusions should be treated with caution. They have not led to any changes in policy.

5.45 Another approach is to interpret economic appraisal in a broader and less formulaic way as providing a framework for analysing the consequences of a policy. This will take into account the money values of resources where they have a market value. It will also use the available techniques, where appropriate, to impute money values for those costs and benefits of a policy which are not marketed. But it will not aim to impute money values to all consequences. A variety of means of description can be used to explain all the identified consequences of an option or options (5.20).

5.46 Another view which has been taken is that economic appraisal often does not provide a helpful or appropriate framework for dealing with many of the issues raised by environmental policies. One argument advanced in support of such a view is the scale and nature of the uncertainties typically associated with public policy issues: in some cases the degree of uncertainty will simply be a reason for caution in the presentation of the results of such an analysis, but in others it is seen as a reason against attempting such an analysis.[39] Guidance from government Departments has taken the view that 'there will always be important environmental assets which cannot be valued'.[40] Some people consider this is not only for practical reasons but for theoretical reasons:[41] treating things of environmental value as if they are tradeable, and thus characterising decisions about environmental issues as trade-offs, fundamentally misrepresents valuation of the environment and the choices to be made. Those who take this view of economic appraisal argue that treating people's views about public policy and moral issues as if they belonged to the same logical type as their views about marketed goods and services is a category-mistake. In other words, certain moral obligations have a character and logic which is different in kind to the character and logic of preferences.[42] A commitment to sustainability, concerned as it is with matters such as equity between present and future generations, arguably involves a duty to protect the environment for the sake of subsequent generations. This is not a matter of balancing costs and benefits and discount rates, but a fundamental obligation and a constraint on other policies.

5.47 Current practice in the use of economic appraisal (5.28–5.37) reflects these differing views about its role. Appraisals which seek to value in money terms as many as possible of the costs and benefits of an environmental policy or standard (cost-benefit analyses) are often not regarded as appropriate if there are significant uncertainties about the consequences of a policy or there are substantial non-marketed consequences of such a kind that their valuation in money terms would be problematic, either for practical reasons or because commitments of an ethical kind are at stake.

5.48 We regard economic appraisal as one of several complementary components in the analytical stage of the policy process (1.35). To the extent that people's values (as expressions of fundamental commitments to the environment or to equity, whether within society or between present and future generations) are regarded as not answerable to economic appraisal, the question then arises whether there is any other approach that could provide additional assistance to decision making in that respect. In chapter 7 we explore novel approaches for obtaining information about people's values which might provide a component of environmental policy making, and which take into account as an essential feature of people's values that they are not typically preformed and may be in conflict with each other. Such approaches are not intended to replace the need to consider the economic implications of choices concerning standards. Like cost-benefit analysis, they will be more appropriate in some cases than others, or will be given greater prominence in some areas than others. What is important, however, is a recognition of the need to develop new kinds of approach to assist in the increasingly complex choices involved in determining environmental policies and setting environmental standards.

Output from economic appraisal

5.49 **Economic appraisal should be regarded as an aid to making decisions which also take other factors into account. Formal techniques such as multi-criteria analysis should likewise be regarded as aids to decision making.**

5.50 **An economic appraisal of an environmental policy or standard should identify the objectives of the policy or standard and the options to be considered; summarise and analyse all the consequences of the options; and indicate what that analysis implies for the decision that has to be made. It should cover consequences which cannot easily be valued in money terms, as well as those that can easily be valued in money terms. Where consequences are not valued in money terms, they should be represented either qualitatively or in terms of other quantities. It should indicate the timing of the costs and benefits.** Information should be given on the steps taken in the appraisal. The underlying assumptions and calculations should be clearly presented, including the discounting procedures applied. If a net present cost or value has been calculated, its main components should be listed separately.[43]

5.51 To the extent that the report of an economic appraisal values the consequences of a policy in money terms, it should not appear to put precise values on quantities which cannot themselves be precisely estimated. **The report of the appraisal should describe the major uncertainties. It should include a sensitivity analysis showing the effects of changing key assumptions.** This might take the form of a table summarising the results in an appendix. Uncertainties will affect a number of different aspects of the appraisal, including for example the dose-effect relationship and the future relativities of market prices and other valuations.

5.52 If an unnecessarily stringent standard is applied to some form of pollution, the improvement obtained will not be sufficient to justify the costs incurred. However, there are also dangers in the other direction. If a form of pollution turns out at a future date to be more damaging than is at present believed, and companies have made large investments on the basis of the present assessment, the costs of switching to a different technology in order to reduce emissions might be extremely high. The sensitivity analysis should cover that possibility in appropriate cases.

5.53 **The report of an appraisal should normally incorporate a description of the information that will need to be collected to enable a retrospective evaluation of the policy or standard to be undertaken at a later date.**

Chapter 6

IMPLEMENTING ENVIRONMENTAL POLICIES

The effectiveness of environmental standards in modifying the actions of companies or individuals derives from the methods used to implement them. One influence on the choice of method is the geographical scope of standards. For the most familiar forms of standard, compliance is supervised by a government agency and failure to comply may be a criminal offence. Other approaches to implementing environmental policies are receiving increasing emphasis. Those approaches have both advantages and limitations. In order to be effective and acceptable, they may themselves require new forms of standard to be set.

6.1   The purpose of environmental policies is to influence human behaviour in order to avoid or limit damage to the environment. In this chapter we consider the main methods used to implement policies and their effectiveness in influencing behaviour; the extent to which that effectiveness depends on standards being set; the support which those methods receive from sanctions, rewards and values; and their respective advantages and limitations.

6.2   Human behaviour is determined by complex sets of individual and social factors. These include the perceptions individuals have, the judgements they make, the rights and liabilities enshrined in the legal system, and civic and organisational cultures. Sociology, anthropology, social psychology, economics, political science, and socio-legal studies have developed extensive understanding of patterns of social behaviour and the forces that give rise to them. In some cases those forces tend to protect the environment; for example, some structures of property rights have that effect. In other cases such forces may make it more likely that the environment will be damaged, or constrain the effectiveness with which environmental objectives can be pursued.

6.3   The values people hold are an important determinant of human behaviour, and ultimately shape the policies that are followed towards the environment. The adoption and implementation of policies based on particular values have a powerful effect in reinforcing those values, as well as bringing about their practical realisation. We discuss in chapter 7 how people's values relevant to environmental policies can be articulated, and their evolution facilitated.

6.4   The social factors determining human behaviour vary from country to country, and in some cases between different communities within countries. Some environmental problems are localised, but the response to other problems involves taking measures over much wider areas. There is a crucial relationship between the geographical scope of an environmental standard and how it can be implemented most effectively. The tendency has been for more and more environmental standards to be set by the European Community (EC) or by international conventions. The effect may have been to reinforce the approach traditionally adopted for implementing environmental policies, which we call 'direct regulation'. That particular pattern will not necessarily hold for the future.

6.5   Direct regulation involves banning activities which are potentially damaging or allowing them, normally subject to conditions, only under some form of administrative permit from a government agency, and supporting those controls by imposing criminal penalties. Many environmental standards are being enforced in that way. Analysis of what happens in practice shows that the behaviour of regulators and permit-holders is less simple and straightforward than might be assumed at first sight. It also throws light on some limitations of this traditional approach.

6.6   Environmental policy making has been affected by wider pressures to reduce the scale and scope of government regulation, especially as it affects companies. At the same time many of the environmental problems now of most concern stem directly or indirectly from deeply rooted and strongly reinforced patterns of behaviour among people generally, as energy users, as travellers, or as consumers of other goods and services. These trends have focused attention on other ways of influencing behaviour that do not rely directly on legal compulsion, especially economic instruments, campaigns to influence the general public, and encouragement of environmentally responsible behaviour by companies. It can be argued that, where regulator and regulated share a common purpose, more flexible and sophisticated approaches to setting and implementing environmental standards, with less reliance on bureaucratic procedures and criminal sanctions, is likely to be more effective and acceptable in an era in which industry, trade and information have become globalised, the environmental agenda has a different character, and the aim is to achieve sustainable development. Direct regulation will also continue to have an essential role in securing protection of the environment, however, because those conditions will not apply in every case.

6.7   This chapter begins by examining the geographical area over which environmental standards should be set, and some ways in which the decision on that point can influence the method of implementation (6.9–6.33). It then examines the advantages and limitations of three approaches to implementing environmental policies: direct regulation (6.34–6.55), use of economic instruments (6.56–6.69) and what we call 'self-regulation' (6.70–6.92). We consider how the different approaches can complement each other (6.93–6.95). We discuss whether self-regulation removes the need to set standards, or whether its successful use will in itself be dependent in one or other way on setting standards; and, if so, what form those standards should take, and how they should be set. We examine briefly how implementation analyses of projected environmental policies should be conducted and the conclusions presented (6.96–6.100).

6.8   An important part of the social context for environmental protection stems from other government policies. Policies in other fields may lead to patterns of behaviour that are damaging to the environment. For example, they have at some periods encouraged the transport of freight by road rather than rail or subsidised the use of forms of energy that have harmful effects. A crucial contribution to achieving sustainable development is to integrate environmental considerations into other government policies. How that can best be done in specific areas of policy has been a central theme in recent Commission reports and will be further pursued in our forthcoming study of energy. We do not therefore cover it in this report, beyond emphasising its importance.

Geographical scope of standards

6.9   We drew attention in chapter 1 to the major role the European Community now has in developing (and likewise ensuring the implementation of) environmental policies and standards (1.24–1.25). More generally, there has been a marked trend over the past 30 years for more and more of the environmental policy process to take place internationally, and in many cases globally. Sometimes this has involved clarifying the scientific basis for environmental policies (appendix C, C.87–C.88). In some fields international co-operation has been necessary in order to set environmental standards, either through publication of authoritative guidance (appendix C, C.86, see also for example 2.21) or through an international convention. There have been several reasons why states have regarded an international convention as an appropriate response to a given environmental problem (appendix C, C.83). Some of the environmental problems being tackled affect the whole globe, or a large part of it, and are therefore beyond the capability of any single state to solve on its own. In other cases, action has been prompted by damage caused by human activities which are themselves international or by the desire to protect aspects of the environment which are regarded as of common concern to the human race. There are now some 200 'multilateral environmental agreements' (MEAs) in the form of international treaties or other agreements on environmental matters.[1]

Multilateral environmental agreements and free trade

6.10 The issue about the geographical scope of environmental standards which has recently caused most concern globally is the relationship between about 20 of the present MEAs, which contain trade provisions,[2] and the rules on international trade contained in the General Agreement on Tariffs and Trade (GATT) and enforced by the World Trade Organization (WTO). The GATT commits signatories to reducing tariff and non-tariff barriers to trade and not discriminating in trade matters. There are two main aspects to non-discrimination. The 'most favoured nation' principle requires that:

> any advantage, favour, privilege or immunity granted by any contracting party to any product originating in or destined for any other country shall be accorded immediately and unconditionally to the like product originating in or destined for the territories of all other contracting parties.[3]

The 'national treatment clause' provides for non-discrimination between imported and domestically produced products. States are allowed to discriminate against imported goods, however, if that is necessary to protect the health of humans, plants or animals within their boundaries or in pursuit of measures relating to the conservation of their exhaustible natural resources.[4]

6.11 The best known of the MEAS which include trade provisions are the Convention on International Trade in Endangered Species of Wild Fauna and Flora; the Montreal Protocol on Substances That Deplete the Ozone Layer, which, among other provisions, bans imports of such substances from states which are not parties to the Protocol (appendix C, C.73); and the Basel Convention on the Control of Transboundary Movements of Hazardous Wastes and their Disposal. There is no specific exemption in the GATT for trade restrictions required by the provisions of MEAs. If a trade-related provision of an MEA does not clearly fall within the explicit exemptions in the GATT mentioned above and a party to the MEA sought to apply it to a WTO member, a problem might arise, more particularly if the latter state is not itself a party to that particular MEA. The latter situation is one that could easily occur in practice, even for MEAs such as the Montreal Protocol, which has more states as parties (161) than WTO has members (132).

6.12 **Despite attempts to resolve the situation, there is still a need for an internationally agreed set of principles to deal with the potential difficulties caused by the overlap between the GATT rules and trade provisions contained in MEAs, and for ambiguities in the operation of the GATT to be clarified. Greater effort is needed by the international community to resolve the difficulties.** The agreed principles should emphasise caution in the use of trade measures against non-MEA members and should stress that trade measures should always be considered a last resort. They should also state that, in cases where an MEA enjoys widespread support among WTO members, the GATT rules must not be permitted to frustrate the attainment of its objectives. Where they do come into conflict, environmental objectives must be given a high priority.

6.13 The effect of the GATT rules is to prevent an individual state discriminating against like products on the ground that particular methods were used to produce or process them. There has been considerable debate about what constitutes a 'like product' in this context because some states have wanted to ban imports of products obtained in ways that they consider environmentally harmful (for example, tuna caught by certain methods).

6.14 Enforcement by a government of an environmental standard based on the life cycle of a given category of product would normally involve discriminating against products in terms of the methods used to produce or process them, and would therefore be contrary to the GATT rules. Some developing countries contend that even voluntary life cycle-based standards (3.43) create significant barriers to trade. They argue that the monitoring and auditing required under a credible and effective labelling scheme make heavy demands on administrative resources of kinds that are scarce in many developing countries. **There is a need to clarify the relationship between labelling schemes and the GATT rules. More needs to be done to ensure that ecolabelling schemes do not disadvantage developing countries.**

Subsidiarity in the European Community

6.15 Within the European Community the key issue about the geographical scope of environmental standards is the interpretation that should be given to the principle of *subsidiarity.* This principle was originally enunciated in the First Environmental Action Programme in 1973 and was therefore specific to environmental policies, but it has now been applied by the Maastricht Treaty to the EC's policies in all fields.[5] By raising institutional questions, the prospect of further enlargement has reopened the debate about subsidiarity. There is now a wider political interest than previously among Member States in applying the subsidiarity principle in ways which would decentralise decision making and bring decisions as close as possible to the citizen. In some expressions of this point of view, environmental policies are explicity excluded.[6]

6.16 In the first formulation of the subsidiarity principle in 1973 the emphasis was on taking action according to functional effectiveness: that is, action by the tier of government which could most effectively meet the goals of policy. In this context, those goals include not only tackling pollution but also the wider economic and social objectives expressed in the Treaty. There is no bias towards any particular tier in this interpretation of the subsidiarity principle.

6.17 In the revisions to the Treaty agreed at Maastricht, the Community moved towards an alternative view which suggests there should be a bias towards the near or local – in other words that standards should be set locally unless there is a compelling reason for them to be set by a different tier. Following Maastricht, Article 3b of the Treaty establishing the European Community reads:

> The Community shall act within the limits of the powers conferred upon it by this Treaty and of the objectives assigned to it therein. In areas which do not fall within its exclusive competence, the Community shall take action, in accordance with the principle of subsidiarity, only if and in so far as the objectives of the proposed action cannot be sufficiently achieved by the Member States and can therefore, by reason of the scale or effects of the proposed action, be better achieved by the Community ...

6.18 The Edinburgh Summit of December 1992 approved guidelines to be used in examining whether Community action is justified in a particular case. These included:

> issues having transnational aspects which cannot be satisfactorily regulated by action by Member States;
>
> cases where action by Member States alone or lack of Community action would conflict with the requirements of the Treaty (for instance by failing to correct distortion of competition); and
>
> cases where action at Community level would produce clear benefits by reason of scale or effects compared with actions at national level.

6.19 The respects in which environmental standards have in the past been regarded as having the potential to distort competition within the Community are if Member States set different standards for the characteristics of traded products (which might represent non-tariff barriers to trade) or are laxer than other Member States in regulating the environmental impact of industrial processes. In the latter case it is arguable what constitutes distortion of competition. While the first of the Edinburgh Summit's criteria is relatively straightforward, the third criterion leaves room for interpretation. The Community's explicit goals for sustainable development and environmental protection have been used to justify setting many standards at Community level, such as quality standards.

6.20 The question arises, particularly with enlargement in view, whether more environmental standards should be set nationally or sub-nationally rather than for the whole Community, in cases where that would not conflict with other current objectives and commitments of the European Union (EU), such as maintaining the integrity of the internal market. Following the approach taken at the Edinburgh Summit, the Parliament requested that 'the Commission and Council, under the present or future Presidency, protect existing environmental ... protection legislation from any attempt to apply a retrospective subsidiarity test.'[7] This position may of course evolve, as may the position of Member States. The *acquis communautaire* is in any case preserved by the Maastricht Treaty. It has, however, been argued that the need for the Commission to justify more fully action at Community level led it to withdraw certain proposals and initiate many fewer after 1992.[8]

6.21 Often, a more interesting question than the tier by which action should be taken, is how responsibility should be shared between different political and administrative tiers. This is a point recognised by the EC's Fifth Environmental Action Programme. In the recent revision of the Drinking Water Directive, responsibility for drinking water quality is shared between the EC and Member States, in that the setting of standards for aesthetic parameters which do not have a health significance (for example, the colour and taste of water supplied) has been transferred back to Member States. Recent Framework Directives have emphasised the building of capability for environmental management in Member States through the establishment of procedures for investigation, planning and implementation. In the case of the Framework Directive on Ambient Air Quality Assessment and Management there will also be Daughter Directives setting precise standards for air quality and dates for their achievement. In the case of the proposed Framework Directive on water resources the essential requirement on Member States is to bring waters not at present in good condition to 'a good ecological state' by 2010.

6.22 An alternative approach to the sharing of responsibility lies in mutual recognition procedures. For plant protection products and biocides, active ingredients are approved at Community level by standing committees of experts, and authorisation of products containing the approved ingredients is carried out by Member States. Mutual recognition means that a product approved by one Member State is authorised for use in any Member State.[9] Another approach, used for new and existing chemical substances, is for all decisions on substances to be taken at Community level but with the task of producing assessments for individual substances divided between Member States.[10]

6.23 Where EC environmental legislation was adopted under Article 100a of the Treaty of Rome with the aim of establishing the internal market, there is provision for Member States to have more stringent national standards if they deem this necessary on specified grounds, which include protection of the environment or of the health of humans, animals or plants. Such national measures have to be confirmed by the European Commission after it has verified that they are not a disguised means of discrimination. The only two cases in which that exemption has been successfully invoked involved bans by Germany and Denmark on use of the timber treatment chemical pentachlorophenol, despite a Directive permitting its use subject to certain conditions.[11] At the 1997 Amsterdam Conference, Article 100a (which will be Article 95 in the post-Amsterdam consolidation) was amended so as to give Member State a specific right to introduce stricter national laws based on new scientific evidence relating to the protection of the environment or the working environment on grounds specific to the Member State arising after the adoption of the harmonisation measure. It contains important qualifications and it remains to be seen how difficult it will be for a Member State to persuade the European Commission that such measures can be permitted in practice.[12] The accession of Austria, Finland and Sweden has raised the problem of stricter pre-existing controls, particularly on a range of chemicals, that has yet to be resolved.

Enforcement of EC law

6.24 In contrast to the position under international conventions, EC legislation can be enforced on Member States through judgements of the European Court of Justice; since the Treaty of Maastricht there can be financial penalties for non-compliance with such judgements.

6.25 Some EC legislation has direct effect in Member States, in the sense that it can be invoked directly before national courts. EC Regulations (such as those relating to the transfrontier movement of wastes), for example, by their definition in the Treaty have such effect. In contrast, EC Directives, the usual instruments for environmental policy, normally require transposition into national law to have internal effect, but in accordance with principles developed by the European Court of Justice, provisions of Directives which are considered sufficiently precise and certain may be invoked in national courts against government Departments and other public bodies even where transposition has not taken place. Furthermore the European Court has insisted that wherever possible national law must be interpreted by national courts in a way that is consistent with Community obligations. These principles give Community law a status before UK courts quite distinct from international law.

6.26 There has been concern (acknowledged, for example, in the Fifth Environmental Action Programme) that, even when transposed into national legislation, EC environmental legislation is not being enforced consistently or with equal stringency in all Member States. The European Commission has power to bring action where failures of enforcement occur and has done so in a number of controversial cases. But its investigative powers and resources for doing so are severely limited. In its October 1996 Communication on Implementing Community Environmental Law, the Commission indicated that it would concentrate on ensuring that the formal transposition of Directives into national law was correctly carried out, but emphasised that national courts and other enforcement procedures would have to play a greater part to ensure that legal obligations were respected in practice. Other initiatives (such as setting up the informal network for the Implementation and Enforcement of Environmental Law (IMPEL)) have been taken to ensure greater consistency in implementation. Some flexibility in implementation is required for detailed legislation to be applied successfully to Member States with such a variety of geographical and social conditions. It has yet to be seen whether provisions in such general terms as the proposed Framework Directive on water resources will be so ambiguous as not to be credible.

Responsibilities for environmental regulation in the UK

6.27 Over the past 25 years there have been many changes within the UK in the location of responsibilities for environmental regulation. Some functions have been transferred from the national level to the European Community, but others have been transferred from local or regional bodies to national agencies or central government.[13] A concern to bring adequate technical competence to bear on industrial pollution across all environmental media has been a significant influence. There has been some increase in the functions of local authorities, but that trend has been less marked. Centralisation has not accompanied the growth of EC legislation in every Member State: in France, for example, there has been an emergence of local initiatives and powers in environmental policy making. The apparent explanation for this divergence lies in the earlier traditions of strong local authorities in Britain but highly centralised powers in France.[14] In federal states, EC legislation has strengthened the federal government in relation to the sub-national units. In Germany, where the Länder are particularly jealous of their powers, we were made aware of the tension which can exist between a desire for consistency across the whole country in setting and implementing standards and the need for flexibility to take account of local circumstances. The fear that variations in emission standards between Länder could be detrimental to industry had, we were told, led the federal Ministry to prefer uniform standards for each industrial sector.

6.28 Because of the diversity of geographical and social conditions in the European Community, the nation state is not necessarily the most effective sub-Community tier at which to adopt environmental policies. It is argued by some that recent Community activity has placed an increasing importance on sub-national regions and the Committee of the Regions is endeavouring to increase its influence on policy making. The UK government has strengthened its English regional offices (a move which some, however, have seen as evidence of further centralisation[15]).

6.29 Despite the existence of separate legislation for Scotland, and delays in implementing policies in Northern Ireland, there has been a recent trend towards identical standards in all four parts of the UK. This may now be set to change. The responsibilities of the Scottish Parliament and the

Welsh Assembly will include environmental protection, and the Scottish Parliament will be able to pass primary legislation. The UK government will remain responsible for international and European negotiations. To the extent that the framework for environmental protection is set in EC legislation, it will continue to be common across the UK; but, to the extent that EC legislation leaves discretion, it is probable that some differences will come to exist, including differences in the environmental standards applying in different parts of the UK.

6.30 Two other developments may encourage greater emphasis on local regulation. The first is the Local Environment Agency Plans being drawn up by the Environment Agency in England and Wales, which take account of local topography, land uses, and a range of pressures on the environment, and set out targets in appropriate cases. Some of these reflect standards set by other bodies and apply nationally or internationally but others, for example the non-statutory water quality objectives, are proposed by the Agency after local consultation. The second is the duty of local authorities to establish air quality management areas under certain circumstances and, where necessary, to prepare action plans to achieve air quality standards. Local authorities might be able to secure some action by means of agreements with polluters but they are likely to be restricted in effectiveness. Otherwise, as the law stands at present, local authorities would have to have recourse to direct regulation, but the government has announced that it intends to introduce legislation to help them tackle congestion and pollution by giving them powers to charge road users and introduce levies on workplace parking, initially in pilot schemes.[16]

Area for which standards should be set

6.31 In our view, there is no automatic rule for deciding the geographical or political level at which standards for most pollutants should be set. As a matter of practicality, it may be easier to improve transparency and openness and to take account of people's values at a more local level; but, for reasons already outlined, some standards will continue to be set at international or European level. **We consider environmental standards should be set for the smallest area for which it is sensible and effective to do so.**

6.32 The geographical scope of standards can strongly influence the form they take, and this will in turn have repercussions on the way in which they are implemented. International agreements may have symbolic as well as practical significance and this may predispose negotiators towards traditional forms of regulation, which typically embody a quasi-regulatory requirement in the substance of the international agreement. Often this has taken the form of a percentage reduction in emissions of a substance over a specified period. It is for the contracting parties to fulfil the obligation as it relates to each of them by appropriate means in their own territory. An obligation which takes the typical form indicated above may predispose policy-makers to use analogous instruments to achieve it: in other words they may rely on direct regulation as the surest way of achieving the required reduction in emissions by the required date. In such a case, voluntary action or reliance on economic instruments to secure reductions may not be thought a feasible means of delivering the agreed result with sufficient certainty unless there are reliable indications that other factors (such as a major shift in production methods) will reinforce their effect.

6.33 The predisposition to use direct regulation is equally strong when policies are determined by the European Community. The desire to lay clear and comparable obligations on each Member State, the difficulty of designing EC measures which respond to local environmental differences, and the unwillingness of states to extend Community competence to taxation matters, have resulted in a predominance of specific standards set out in Directives. This tendency has been reinforced by the European Commission's reliance on existing national legislation as the starting-point for its proposals, and the desirability of easily monitoring transposition by Member States. Nevertheless, as the Community has expanded, there has been doubt over both the efficiency of uniform requirements and their effectiveness in securing a high level of environmental quality across an increasingly diverse range of geographical conditions. **We consider that, where a standard is set at European or international level, it should be set in a form that allows as**

much discretion about the methods of implementing it as is feasible without undermining its effectiveness.

Direct regulation

6.34 The traditional approach to implementing environmental policies was characterised above as involving permits from government agencies backed by criminal sanctions. In the USA this approach has come to be known as 'command and control', and it has been the focus of what has been described as a 'crisis of legalisation'. In the UK on the other hand direct regulation has been more flexible, and more administrative than legal in character. We believe the situation that has arisen over regulation in the USA is largely the result of factors other than the inherent limitations and disadvantages of direct regulation, and that conclusions drawn from analyses of it do not necessarily apply to Europe. Certainly in a UK context, the words 'command and control' give a misleading impression of the power a regulator normally has over the activities being undertaken, and for that reason they are not used in this report.[17]

6.35 It is not practicable to make compliance with an environmental standard subject to legal sanctions if the standard is in such a form that no company or person can sensibly be held responsible for breaches. Of forms of standard set on environmental pathways (box 1A), it is only to emission standards and product standards that criminal sanctions can be applied in any straightforward way. Criminal sanctions are also used to secure compliance with some forms of standard not set on pathways, especially process standards and use standards. Quality standards for air cannot be enforced on any person or company, although at a strategic level the imposition on governments of statutory duties related to such standards may be an important element in establishing an effective system of air quality management. To some extent the same arguments apply to water; pollution of an inland water may give rise to a civil action or prosecution but, as the law stands at present, neither would be related to an explicit standard for quality of the water. Establishing responsibility for pollution of groundwater may be an especially difficult task. Even in the case of land, allocating responsibility for attaining quality standards can raise similar difficulties, largely because pollution may have occurred a considerable time ago, and was not unlawful at the time when it occurred. In the USA allegations of responsibility for such pollution have led to enormous amounts of civil litigation. Difficulties in assigning responsibility have also contributed to the delay in bringing into force new UK legislation.

6.36 We focus here on control of emissions. Legal sanctions associated with a numerical standard for emissions, or with limit values for emissions derived from a process standard, can take several forms. The simplest is that non-compliance with the standard is in itself a criminal offence. More frequently, the offence is failing to observe the conditions of a permit. Or the offence may be described in general terms, for example causing pollution, and breach of a standard may constitute evidence that an offence has been committed. Non-observance of a standard may also be a material factor in civil litigation over damage allegedly caused by pollution. In other contexts legislation provides that observance of a standard, or the conditions of a permit incorporating the standard, is a defence against prosecution for an offence defined in general terms. Any of these sanctions will help ensure that a standard has its intended effect on behaviour.

6.37 For criminal sanctions to be effective, not only must there be somebody who can be identified as responsible for any breach of legal requirements, there must also be a reasonable prospect that the regulator will detect such a breach and will be able to gather sufficient evidence to mount a prosecution with reasonable chances of success. **An essential condition for effective direct regulation is that there should be adequate inspection and adequate monitoring of compliance with limit values.** It may be expensive to meet those requirements. In practical terms, however, the stringency of a standard depends not only on the level at which it is set but on the frequency with which compliance is monitored. For some parameters continuous monitoring may be feasible at an acceptable cost. At the other extreme, measuring some parameters may be so difficult and expensive that it is done only very infrequently.

6.38 For monitoring to be valid, there must be consistency in the procedures used for taking samples and subjecting them to chemical or biological analysis. Deficiencies in this area may well mean that monitoring results are not comparable. Not only may results vary by up to several orders of magnitude if different analytical methods are used, there may be large discrepancies between the results obtained by different laboratories using the same method. **Numerical standards for concentrations of substances should always incorporate protocols for sampling and the analytical techniques or methods by which compliance is to be measured, and should require analyses to be carried out in laboratories which are participating in appropriate accreditation and proficiency testing schemes.**

Specification of standards

6.39 The appropriate way of specifying a standard for a substance depends on the nature of its effects and of the consequences if the standard is exceeded. A standard can take the form of:

> *an average*, if occasional high levels of the substances do not cause damage so long as they are offset by low levels at other times or locations (the averaging period must be related to the length of time within which low levels have to occur in order to have that effect);

> *an absolute limit*, if occasional high levels are a particular cause for concern;

> *a limit that must be met during a specified proportion of a specified time period (a percentile)*, perhaps combined with a *lower running average*, if the effect of a high level is reversible provided high levels occur only rarely.

6.40 Effective monitoring of compliance with a standard presupposes that the standard is specified with sufficient precision. With any form of numerical standard there are problems in applying a single number to complex reality in which there are variations over time and between locations. These problems are thrown into sharp relief when a numerical standard provides the basis for criminal sanctions. For most standards the verification procedure for achievement or breach is not unambiguously defined. This was an issue raised in some of the submissions we received.[18] Having identified this as a topic requiring special attention, we asked Professors Barnett and O'Hagan of the University of Nottingham to prepare a report on how it should be approached and resolved from the statistical point of view. That report has been published elsewhere,[19] and we therefore confine ourselves here to summarising its main conclusions.

6.41 The report drew a distinction between ideal and realisable standards. What is often specified within environmental policies is an *ideal standard* that applies throughout a period of time or to the totality of a particular compartment of the environment such as a river. An example of such an ideal specification would be a standard that the concentration of nitrates in a section of river should not exceed a particular limit. Such a standard cannot be verified objectively by sampling. The concentration in the whole section of river cannot be measured at any one time and, for most substances it is not possible to take continuous measurements over time. Such a standard is described as ideal, in the sense that it is not directly verifiable. A *realisable standard* is one that is expressed in such a way that one can determine without uncertainty whether it is satisfied at any location. An example of this would be a standard which specifies that nine out of ten samples taken at any given site must not exceed a specified concentration of a substance.

6.42 An ideal standard may be expressed in terms of a percentile of a distribution, but may still not be realisable in the sense defined above, because compliance has to be verified from sample data rather than from knowledge of the actual distribution.

6.43 Barnett and O'Hagan argue for the use of *statistically verifiable ideal standards*. These would combine a statistically-based ideal standard for levels of pollutants or effects (recognising natural variation and uncertainty) with a separate but complementary standard for the quality of statistical verification required to demonstrate compliance with the ideal standard. For example, the verification standard might specify that a certain number of samples should be taken over a specified period at a certain number of locations and that no more than a specified number of samples exceeding the primary, ideal standard must be found within a specified period of time. It is preferable that the standard for statistical verification should set out the statistical techniques to be used, together with the underlying assumptions or statistical models, but leave open the details of the sampling scheme and statistical methods, so that there is scope for improvement in the light of experience.

6.44 Every numerical standard should be specified in a way that takes full account of the nature of the substance to which it relates, the extent of statistical variation in the parameter to which it relates and (where it is legally enforceable) the requirements for verification. Some existing numerical standards go some way to meet these criteria, for example, those in the EC Drinking Water Directive, which are accompanied by detailed mandatory programmes for monitoring. **Many current environmental standards are defective in terms of these criteria, most often in not being verifiable. Where that is the case, it should be remedied by setting a supplementary standard for verification, with the aim that environmental standards should be, wherever possible, statistically verifiable ideal standards. Reviews of exisiting standards should pay particular attention to this aspect.**

Flexibility in practice

6.45 The legal limits placed on emissions in a particular case may or may not coincide with the relevant standard, depending on the flexibility the regulator has to take other factors into account in drawing up the conditions attached to a permit. Exercising control through issue of a permit makes it possible to tailor regulation to the circumstances of a particular site. Moreover, reasonableness is an essential part of credible, effective regulation and regulators have discretion over the way they enforce compliance with legal requirements. The existence of discretion in these respects brings considerable benefits, but may also create certain tensions over the relationship between regulator and regulated companies. In the case of policies intended to influence the behaviour of individuals, there is normally much less scope for discretion because of the number of cases involved.

6.46 Although enforcement style is partly a matter of choice, it can be influenced by the provisions of the legislation itself. For instance, strict liability rules imposing absolute duties limit the extent of discretion allowed to the regulator, provide simple tests for enforcement action and largely determine the nature of that action (and can appear attractive to inspectors for those very reasons). They can, however, lead to problems of 'creative compliance'. Broader-based rules involving tests of reasonableness may achieve more profound behavioural change and therefore more effective environmental improvements but may be more time-consuming and difficult to enforce.

6.47 Although direct regulation carries the threat of criminal sanctions there are different views about the significance such sanctions should have in practice. Law is not simply a static creation which is externally imposed and then left to run its course. It is given meaning and reality in social interaction.[20] As far back as 1878, in the early years of the Alkali Inspectorate, two contrasting strategies had been identified:

> There are two modes of inspection, one is by a suspicious opponent, desirous of finding evil, and ready to make the most of it. The other is that of a friendly adviser, who treats those whom he visits as gentlemen desirous of doing right.[21]

6.48 The aim of a compliance strategy is 'to prevent a harm rather than punish an evil. Its conception of enforcement centres upon the attainment of the broad aims of legislation, rather than sanctioning its breach'.[22] In line with this view, some commentators have argued that prosecution is often an inefficient method of enforcement compared to negotiated compliance-seeking (where negotiation, education, and warnings are used and prosecution is a last resort). More generally, it has been suggested that the regulator's role is one of bargaining to achieve compliance.[23] On the other hand, advocates of prosecution-led enforcement have seen negotiated compliance-seeking as providing inadequate environmental protection and offering evidence of regulatory capture. Such criticisms were levelled at the former Her Majesty's Inspectorate of Pollution (and the Alkali Inspectorate from which it had inherited this approach), whilst the former National Rivers Authority (NRA), with powers virtually limited to controlling the discharges leaving a site, and in order to mark a clear break with the practice of the water authorities, adopted a deterrence strategy of strict enforcement and prosecution of offences. This was supplemented by some successful education campaigns, for example on dealing with farm waste. The Environment Agency has produced guidelines setting out the circumstances in which it would normally expect to prosecute.[24] The intention is to take action which is proportionate to the risks to the environment and the gravity of any breach of the law, consistent, transparent, and well-targeted. This can be regarded as an attempt to reconcile the two approaches outlined above by combining flexibility with deterrent action when that is merited.

6.49 Studies of regulation suggest that the adoption of enforcement practices will vary according to the background of regulators, the organisational culture of an agency and its legal powers. The choice of strategy will be affected by a range of other factors. These include the seriousness and nature of the offence (strict liability or otherwise); an agency's own perception of itself as adviser and educator; limited resources in terms of money, people and time; the likely effects of enforcement on the reputation of the regulator (for example the NRA's higher public profile after the 1989 Shell prosecution); the nature and speed of the prosecution process; and the range of penalties available, which although higher than previously, often fall far below what non-governmental organisations (NGOs) and regulators would like to see.

6.50 It is often moral values about just deserts which prompt enforcement – yet it is often difficult to judge whether a breach was accidental, negligent or wilful. A challenge which a regulator may therefore have to resolve, irrespective of the general enforcement style adopted, is to establish when a breach is morally reprehensible and thus deserving of punishment. The morally problematic nature of enforcing standards is particularly acute where there is no obvious victim and a breach is not an easily identifiable and isolated event, or where acts are not individually very serious but have harmful cumulative effects. The result is that, unlike enforcers of certain other more obvious crimes, the authority of regulatory agencies is not always based on a moral and political consensus about the harms they seek to regulate. The attitude of the polluter may be as important a factor in deciding how to proceed as the damage (real or potential) being done. While the criminal law in this area does not normally admit accidental cause as a defence, regulators, who are often unenthusiastic about prosecuting contraventions that arise out of ignorance or are genuine accidents, are placed in an invidious position. In such cases, improving management systems to prevent a repetition can lead to a better environmental and social outcome than prosecution.

6.51 Under integrated pollution control (IPC), monitoring of emissions from a prescribed process is carried out by the operator in accordance with approved procedures, and all the results reported to the regulator. A programme of check monitoring is in place to test every self-monitoring scheme, unannounced, over a five-year period. There is no explicit basis for such self-monitoring in the Environmental Protection Act 1990, but there is in the EC Directive on Integrated Pollution Prevention and Control. Under the terms of IPC licences stipulating self-monitoring, withholding of results is a breach of the licence and continuing to operate would then be a criminal offence. This seems to be a practical solution to the potential enforcement difficulty which would arise if a company withheld data which it had gathered in order to avoid self-incrimination.

6.52 Flexibility in direct regulation has considerable advantages, but there is a tension because the advantages of uniformity, practical and symbolic, are also signficant. Traditional regulation has long been at the core of environmental policy. Its strengths are that it can impose fixed standards, based on the best available expertise and wide consultation, which prohibit activity not conforming to the standards; reflect the public interest; provide reassurance to the public that the law is being used to protect them; and impart a symbolic significance in legally declaring some forms of behaviour to be unacceptable.

6.53 Regulatory bodies which exercise considerable discretion have sometimes been accused of 'regulatory capture', undue deference towards the activity they are regulating. Criticisms of this kind were made in the mid-1970s against what was then Her Majesty's Alkali and Clean Air Inspectorate.[25] It has been suggested that capture can be successfully avoided, while maintaining discretion and co-operation, in circumstances where the following conditions are fulfilled: the regulatory body deals with a large number of companies and with diverse industries; not all inspectors have a background in the industry they are inspecting and regulating; and the same inspectors do not always visit the same companies.[26]

6.54 The more flexible regulation seeks to become, the greater the demands for expertise and judgement on the part of inspectors. Attempts to make regulation pro-active, by setting technology-forcing standards or stimulating adoption of clean technology, may also require considerable expertise on the part of regulators. An external regulator may be as well-informed about the technical choices open to a manufacturer as most manufacturers are themselves, but cannot be as informed about other aspects of the business which may be relevant. Reliance on process standards and, in future, identification of best available techniques at European level go some way to overcome the difficulties but are far from eliminating them (3.52–3.53).

6.55 **The drawbacks of direct regulation and the tensions to which it may give rise mean there are considerable attractions in complementary approaches which seek to internalise environmental considerations within the decision procedures of potential polluters.** We discuss two ways in which that can be brought about, which are not mutually exclusive:

> internalisation in *financial terms* through use of economic instruments to internalise the external costs which the activities of either companies or individuals impose on the environment;

> internalisation in *cultural terms*, for example through voluntary action of various kinds, and the establishment of environmental management systems within companies.

Use of economic instruments

6.56 Environmental policy aims to discourage polluting activities. One way of doing that is to encourage producers and consumers to choose less damaging processes and products by modifying market prices. This might take the form of taxing products and services which are to be discouraged on environmental grounds or subsidising those which are to be encouraged.

6.57 Pollution is frequently caused in situations where there are unpriced external costs associated with particular activities. The exhaust gases produced when fuel is used in motor vehicles illustrate the argument. It is clear, if the starting-point is taken as a situation of free and untaxed markets, that a tax on motor fuels will tend to improve the situation. Revenue raised from introducing taxes which reflect the existence of unpriced external costs can be used to cut other taxes which distort the operation of markets, such as income tax or national insurance contributions, or to pay for environmental or other benefits without having to raise other taxes.

6.58 In theory, if it were clear what value should be placed on the external effects caused by use of a product, that might indicate the appropriate rate at which to tax the product. If tax were imposed at that rate, the socially optimal quantity of the product could be regarded, in broad terms, as the amount consumers then chose to use. The value placed on the external effects, and the tax rate, would need to be reviewed and adjusted subsequently, as imposition of the tax would tend to change the relative quantities of products and pollutants, and therefore their relative valuations.

6.59 It is not easy to design and introduce corrective taxes (or subsidies) in the sense described in the last paragraph.[27] The value to be placed on an external effect may not be obvious. A pollutant emitted today may have effects for centuries to come. The external effects of using fuel in a motor vehicle will vary with weather conditions and with the condition of the particular engine in which it is being burnt; it would be impracticable to adjust the rate of tax on motor fuel to reflect such variations. **While economic instruments are not a panacea, and administrative controls may be required as well, economic or financial incentives should be used wherever possible to reinforce the effect of direct regulation.**

6.60 One factor that has limited the use of environmental taxes is a concern for income distribution. If for instance tax is raised on motor fuel, and offset on average by a reduction in vehicle excise duty, the effect will be that those who drive above average mileage will lose out and those with below average mileage will gain. This may be regarded as objectionable to the extent that some of those who lose out are poor and have to drive above average mileage for essential reasons such as getting to work, for example, if they live in the country. Imagination and ingenuity are needed to identify ways of compensating losers, for example, by changing patterns of social security support to those most dependent on cars because of disability, or on domestic heating because of age or ill health.

6.61 Another form of economic instrument is particularly likely to be applied where the cause of concern is the total emissions of a substance, either globally or within a defined area, and the issue in this case is how reductions in that total should be allocated between those producing the emissions. Quantitative limitations of this kind are most likely to arise in international environmental agreements (see appendix C, C.90–C.91).

6.62 Where the number of emitters is known and manageable, and especially if the scale of their respective emissions in a given period is known, one way of fulfilling a commitment to halve total emissions is to require each emitter to do so. This is demonstrably inefficient as the marginal cost of achieving a 50% reduction may well vary from site to site. Reductions should be concentrated where they are most easily achieved. A regulator might attempt to achieve such a result through administrative discretion. But it is what would be expected to happen if each company were to receive permits for half its base period emissions and were allowed to buy and sell permits in trading with other permit holders.

6.63 Trading should be expected to establish a price for a traded permit which equals the marginal cost of reducing emissions by the amount covered by the permit. A company should then be indifferent, at the margin, between reducing emissions further or buying a permit to legitimise them. The price mechanism will have equalised the marginal cost of reducing emissions across all the companies to which the trading system applies, which is a necessary condition for achieving the specified reduction at least cost.

6.64 A system of tradeable permits for emissions of sulphur dioxide operates in the USA, where the inflexibility of direct regulation made this approach attractive. Such a system is optimal in the simple form described above only if there is an active competitive market, and the exact location of emissions, and the circumstances in which they occur, make no difference. In order to achieve a specified reduction in total emissions of sulphur dioxide in England and Wales, while at the same time preventing local damage, the Environment Agency has given the electricity generators two kinds of limit on emissions: one is a specific limit for each generating station, the other is a 'bubble' covering the whole of each company's emissions. Allocating permits without charge to companies making emissions in the base year would give windfall gains to companies which are reducing emissions for other reasons and inhibit competition by raising the cost of entry to the industry (a new entrant would have to buy a permit as well as building a new factory). These problems can be overcome if permits are auctioned rather than given exclusively to established polluters.

6.65 In principle, a reduction in total emissions could be achieved as efficiently by a uniform tax on emissions as by a system of tradeable permits. It has been suggested smaller companies would find a tax much simpler and therefore less burdensome.[28] The effect of a permit system on emissions is more predictable however: it would take some time to discover, probably by trial and error, the rate of tax that will achieve the required reduction, and that rate might vary significantly as old technologies are retired and new ones introduced. With either approach, uncertainty about the position in future years (the rate of tax or the price of permits) might be a deterrent to investment in an industry.

6.66 Proposals for environmental taxes have been opposed on the ground that there would be an adverse effect on the competitiveness of particular industries or of a whole country. Certainly companies are likely to have to meet higher costs in order to purchase cleaner technology or materials, and this may lead to higher prices, reduced sales volume, possibly reduced sales revenue, and reduced profits. These outcomes follow from the decision to adopt a given environmental standard or accept an obligation to reduce total emissions by a given amount. They will be the same in principle for a uniform tax as for a system of tradeable permits. If a tax is imposed, companies will face the additional cost of making payments to the government but this cost can be offset by reductions in other taxes. Hence, while the higher costs imply a loss to the competitiveness of the industry in question, they do not necessarily do so for UK industry as a whole. The tax revenue could, like the greater part of that from landfill duty, be used to reduce employers' National Insurance contributions, thus lowering labour costs and raising international competitiveness generally (other things being equal).

6.67 In general, we do not find the zero sum concept of international competitiveness very useful. In particular it is unlikely to be conducive to international co-operation. Productivity in generating material consumption is more general and more useful in international discussion. A decision to accept an environmental standard or limit on emissions represents a decision to sacrifice material consumption in pursuit of environmental benefits. It is material consumption which may have to be sacrificed in pursuit of higher environmental standards. Efficiency in trading off material consumption against higher environmental standards entails minimising the amount of material consumption that has to be forgone in order to achieve a given environmental improvement. That in turn means that the marginal cost of achieving reduced pollution must be equalised across all relevant polluters. Only uniform taxes and tradeable permits can provide the conditions for meeting this goal.

6.68 **Well-designed economic instruments should be capable of achieving a better overall result for the environment, by providing incentives for the introduction of clean technology and other innovations, although improvements are likely to be differently distributed and the environmental outcome in some areas might be inferior to that which would have been brought about by direct regulation. Use of economic instruments should also limit the cost of environmental protection, both in resources used and in transaction costs. They are especially valuable in controlling pollution from diffuse sources. Use of economic instruments does not dispense with the need for legislation, monitoring and criminal sanctions because a legal framework is required for their operation.** The Environmental Protection Agency told us that they regarded tradeable permits as having been successful in the United States even though little trading had taken place. We received other evidence (from the statutory conservation agencies in Great Britain) that the detailed rules governing the operation of trading had important repercussions on the cost of pollution control and the environmental effects. An examination of actual permit systems operating in the USA did not show that trading schemes were systematically preferable in terms of either cost or reduced pollution. The agencies concluded that to control sulphur dioxide emissions in the UK a weather related tax might be more appropriate.

6.69 In France, Germany and the Netherlands charges are levied on emissions of effluent to water and the income is used to fund investment in measures to improve water quality.[29] In its Sixteenth Report in 1992 the Commission argued that there was a convincing case for introducing a similar scheme in the UK and it made detailed recommendations on how such a scheme might be implemented and the revenue used. We do not discuss this form of economic instrument further here, save to note that subsequent work suggests that the success of such schemes depends heavily on their detailed design within the framework of national policy styles and the interest coalitions established as part of the operating procedures for regulation.

Self-regulation

6.70 In the last few years there has been widespread interest in *self-regulation* as an approach to environmental policy. This term has been applied to a very wide range of things. An attempt to provide a general definition of what is meant by the term in the environmental field has resulted in the following: 'all (partly) voluntary individual and group activities that contribute to the realisation of a common interest within the conditions agreed with, or provided by, a government or non-government organisation'.[30] In the case of companies, mechanisms which can be regarded as forms of self-regulation include environmental management systems, product labelling going beyond statutory requirements, 'negotiated agreements' entered into with governments or government agencies, and release of information to the public about the environmental impact of company operations. There is also great scope for individuals to limit or redirect their own activities in ways that will reduce damage to the environment.

6.71 The definition quoted above refers to self-regulatory activities as 'voluntary', but has to qualify that description. They are voluntary in the sense of not being undertaken in direct response to legal requirements. But they take place in a social context which includes a variety of external sanctions and rewards besides legal compulsion. Some actions which can be included under this heading bring financial savings to companies or individuals. Companies may take other actions that benefit the environment because they believe they thereby gain a marketing advantage that will retain existing customers or attract new ones. In other cases, actions may be taken, especially by companies or industries, to avert a threat, explicit or inferred, that some form of compulsion will otherwise be applied.

6.72 Nevertheless, **many actions that benefit the environment are taken primarily or exclusively because individuals, either on their own account or as company managers, place a high value on protecting the environment.** In recent decades there has been a significant shift of values in this direction. This discussion of self-regulation is confined to mechanisms, and takes existing values as given. Achievement of sustainable development may well depend on the extent to which the principle of reconciling environmental protection, material well-being and equity becomes an internalised value. There is some evidence that this is already happening to a significant extent.[31] How people's values about the environment can be better articulated is considered in chapter 7.

Individual and community action

6.73 Several government-funded campaigns are publicising ways in which individuals can help the environment (box 6A[32]). The adoption of less aggressive driving styles illustrates how actions by individuals can reduce environmental damage, in this case by reducing fuel consumption and emissions of pollutants.[33] Various other organisations are encouraging people to help the environment by pledging themselves to take or avoid specified actions.

6.74 Some forms of action, for example setting up recycling schemes, can more appropriately be taken by local communities. Community action for the environment is being promoted through the Local Agenda 21 movement, which aims to implement at local authority level the principles adopted at the Earth Summit in 1992 and is being carried forward enthusiastically in many areas of the UK. Successful ways have been devised to empower the public at grass-roots level to deal with matters of local concern. In some areas, neighbourhood groups have been established which have been able to take full control of their own agendas and activities following facilitation during an initial period by an external moderator. Their main purpose has been to decide how they wish to see their local environment improved and ensure that the necessary measures are carried out with the financial help of the local authority.[34]

BOX 6A   **CAMPAIGNS TO INFLUENCE THE GENERAL PUBLIC**

Going for Green was launched in February 1996 as part of the government's commitment to sustainable development and is jointly funded by the Department of the Environment, Transport and the Regions and the private sector. It promotes the Green Code, which has five elements:

   cutting down waste: reducing the amounts of packaging; re-using carrier bags, bottles and containers; recycling paper, cans, bottles, plastics and rags; repairing things instead of throwing them away;

   saving energy and natural resources: turning off electricity and gas when not needed; using water wisely; insulating the home;

   travelling sensibly: making fewer car journeys and sharing cars; walking and cycling more; using public transport more; keeping cars properly tuned and maintained;

   preventing pollution: careful disposal of chemicals and oil; not dumping waste; not burning waste which gives off fumes and gases – especially plastics;

   looking after the local environment: clearing up litter; helping to keep and create special areas for wildlife; composting and organic gardening methods; seeking out local projects which need help.

The philosophy of this awareness campaign is that small actions by individuals can make a huge difference to the environment if everyone adopts them. A variety of publicity strategies have been used. Sustainable Communities Projects have been launched throughout Britain to test the effectiveness of the Green Code and examine the factors that encourage or prevent responsible environmental behaviour by households.

Other government-funded campaigns with a similar philosophy are *Are you doing your bit?* launched in March 1998 and *Energy Efficiency – It's clever stuff.*

6.75 A danger with individual or community initiatives is that, although actions may be intended to benefit the environment, there may not have been a sufficiently rigorous assessment to confirm that they are likely to bring a net benefit, nor sufficient control over subsequent stages to ensure that they do so in practice. Some people will be reluctant to take action individually to benefit the environment unless they can be sure that this is part of a broader effort that will have a worthwhile overall effect. One of the purposes of government publicity campaigns is to give them that assurance. But publicity may have to be accompanied by more tangible measures by government if voluntary action is to be stimulated to achieve its maximum potential. For example, a driver may be more willing to give up the car for a less environmentally damaging form of transport if there is some assurance this will not simply leave more road space for other cars to occupy.

Green consumerism

6.76 **One form of action that many people take is to buy products which they believe to have been produced in ways that are environmentally sustainable or to be less damaging to the environment than competing products.** Many producers and retailers make environmental claims for their products, and a variety of labelling schemes purport to endorse such claims. Environmental labelling is a form of self-regulation in which both companies and individuals are directly involved. The response of consumers to the claims made is the crucial factor determining its effectiveness.

6.77 Some companies or industries have established schemes which, rather than publicising or selecting existing features of products or the ways in which they are produced, aim to use market power to bring about changes in methods of production. For example, major UK supermarket chains place requirements on farmers and growers about the way crops are grown; three-quarters of Sainsbury's UK-sourced produce is grown under integrated crop management, which embraces a range of 'lower-input', 'less-intensive' and 'sustainable' farming systems.[35]

6.78 For certain types of product global standards are being set for methods of production in ways designed to avoid conflict with the GATT rules (6.14). The pioneer has been the timber certification scheme organised by the Forest Stewardship Council, described in box 6B.[36] The key feature is that this is a joint initiative by logging companies and international environmental groups. Unilever and the World Wide Fund for Nature are establishing a Marine Stewardship Council on similar lines to promote sustainable methods of fishing.

BOX 6B	**CERTIFICATION OF GREEN CLAIMS: FOREST PRODUCTS**

Since the end of the last century there has been concern over the rate with which forests have been used to meet the demand for timber and the slow rate of replanting. In due course, awareness in the industry itself led to higher rates of replanting.

At the Earth Summit in Rio de Janeiro a series of principles for the conservation and sustainable use of forests was adopted. A 1993 conference of European Forestry Ministers in Helsinki defined sustainable forestry management as 'the stewardship and use of forests and forest lands in a way, and at a rate, that maintains their biological productivity, regeneration capacity, vitality, and ... potential to fulfil, now and in the future, relevant ecological, economic and social functions, at local, national and global levels, and ... does not cause damage to other ecosystems.'

Companies realised that there would be a market advantage in describing their products as 'environmentally friendly', but after some time, consumers began to mistrust such descriptions. A certification scheme was launched through the newly formed and independent Forest Stewardship Council (FSC), with the aim of harmonising certification on the basis of a set of principles and guidelines. Retailers have welcomed the reassurance the scheme offers their customers; and companies selling 14% of the UK's wood and paper products are now committed to selling FSC-labelled products. Some organisations have included FSC-certified timber in their purchasing policies.

The scheme applies more readily to large forests and the FSC is now examining the problems experienced by small private forest owners with a view to including them in the scheme.

6.79 Whilst schemes such as these use well-defined criteria to qualify for the award of labels, **many environmental claims for products are made in very vague terms, and may have only a flimsy basis.** Few private labelling schemes look at the life cycle of a product (3.24). A product for which environmental advantages are claimed may even be more damaging to the environment than competing products (3.24). It would be unfortunate if the whole notion of environmental claims for products became discredited because this would remove an important route by which consumers can make their preferences known. Yet it may be very difficult to assess whether a given product has overall advantages for the environment, let alone whether it is produced, processed and transported in a manner that ensures those advantages are routinely realised. The information costs are therefore very high. Government-backed ecolabelling under the voluntary EC scheme has had only a very small impact so far. The Department of the Environment thought 'publicity and peer pressure' might be sufficient to prevent companies making their own misleading claims,[37] even though consumer and trading standards bodies have pressed for UK legislation for that purpose. In February 1998 the government published a code of practice on the making of 'Green Claims'.[38] **To be effective, standards for making environmental claims will have to be established on a European or global scale**: the International Organization for Standardization (ISO) has published a draft standard (ISO 14021) on environmental labels and declarations used by manufacturers.[39]

The responsible company

6.80 Over the last ten years there has been a marked change in the attitudes to environmental issues in the company sector, especially (but not exclusively) among large companies. Companies have recognised that they have responsibilities, not only to their shareholders or as contractual obligations, but to 'stakeholders', a term which can be interpreted to include anyone who could be affected for good or ill by the company's impact on the environment. An increasing number of companies now publish environmental reports alongside their annual reports to shareholders. Some are preparing complex assessments of their overall effects on the environment (3.29). Such reports and assessments are directed in part to outside observers, but also serve the purpose of helping central management direct and monitor the company's environmental programmes.

6.81 There has also been a rapid spread of environmental management systems complying with the ISO 14001 standard. These developments can be regarded as part of a wider movement, encouraged by insurers, towards the systematic management of the risks facing businesses. To establish further control over risk, and in response to green consumerism, companies certificated to ISO 14001 are likely to make it a condition of their contracts with their suppliers that they too become certificated. Recognition of environmental responsibilities is also consistent with general acceptance of the 'polluter pays principle'. The Environment Agency has a preference for company certification under both ISO 14001 and the EC Eco-Management and Audit Scheme (EMAS), in order to secure the benefits of the validated information on environmental performance which EMAS requires to be made public.

6.82 A company's stakeholders include its employees as well as those who might be affected by the environmental impact of its operations. A few companies publish reports that cover both health and safety and the environment, most keep the two issues separate. A responsible management attitude, committed to reducing risks, is likely to bring about a reduction in the risk of catastrophic accidents, with benefits on both fronts; and may encourage the adoption of cleaner technologies which reduce the exposure of employees, as well as the public and the natural environment, to toxic substances. There can also be circumstances in which reducing risks to employees and reducing environmental damage come into conflict with each other, for example, if a choice has to be made between storing radioactive substances on site and dispersing them at very low concentrations in the environment.

6.83 It is sometimes suggested that companies which have adopted an environmental management system should benefit from a reduced frequency of inspection by the regulator. The argument is that the frequency of inspection should be related to potential risk, level of managerial control and track record. It has been claimed by the Confederation of British Industry that EMAS can indicate to inspectors that the identified risks are being controlled, and that therefore the burden of regulation should be reduced for companies with good management systems.[40] Because there is some overlap between the requirements of the IPC regime for industrial processes and formal environmental management systems such as ISO 14001 and EMAS, a reduction in inspections might seem logical.

6.84 Accreditation of environmental management systems, however, is intended to ensure that a company follows a structured approach to managing environmental performance. It is not designed to secure any particular level of environmental performance. The Rover company was fined for pollution over a period of time despite being accredited under British Standard (BS) 7750, as were Akzo Nobel and ICI Runcorn in other high profile cases.[41] The Environment Agency has said that, while an externally certified environmental management system is one relevant factor, it would be simplistic to rely solely on such accreditation in assessing the risk presented by a site.[42] The Agency prioritises regulatory action by combining a performance appraisal of the operator and a pollution hazard appraisal to produce an Operator and Pollution Risk Appraisal (OPRA) for a site. Environmental management systems are relevant to this appraisal but, until there is much stronger evidence that they significantly reduce the risk posed by accredited sites, they will not provide a reliable short-cut to indicate which companies need the greatest inspection effort.

6.85 The wider adoption of environmental management systems brings advantages primarily to the bodies which adopt them. They are likely to bring advantages to the environment in terms of improved compliance with other environmental standards, and they can make a useful contribution towards the achievement of broader environmental goals. **Firms should be strongly encouraged to instal environmental management systems; in due course all firms above a certain size might be required to operate such systems, in a form which involves regular publication of information about their environmental performance.**

6.86 However, environmental management systems, and related forms of self-regulation, are not designed to be, and cannot be, a substitute for direct regulation. Environmental management systems are merely procedural; they presuppose that there are other standards against which a firm can calibrate its environmental performance. In a system which attempted to rely wholly or largely on self-regulation it is likely that the pattern of environmental improvement would be distorted by factors which are not related either to what is desirable in environmental terms or to what would be most efficient in economic terms. Moreover, achieving the biggest feasible reduction in emissions from one firm or one industry does not necessarily lead to the best overall result for the environment on a life cycle basis (3.25).

Negotiated agreements

6.87 Agreements between industry and government are another important aspect of self-regulation. By 1996 more than 300 environmental agreements had been concluded at the national level in the EU but about two-thirds of these are in the Netherlands and Germany. They can be divided into two categories: those where a company or industry enters into an informal understanding with government but sets its own targets, and those where there is a form of contract and negotiated targets with specific commitments and time schedules.[43]

6.88 In the Netherlands negotiated agreements were introduced in the context of environmental strategy defined in the National Environmental Policy Plan (NEPP), which is updated regularly (see box 6C[44]). The original plan identified key target groups whose contributions were crucial to its success. The system is backed up by legislation. There may be distinctive national social and industrial characteristics which would make it difficult or impossible to apply an identical scheme in other countries but, with imagination, it may be possible to extract some lessons for application elsewhere.

6.89 Extensive use has been made of agreements in controlling pollution in Japan. These are local agreements which prefectures or local authorities or residents' groups enter into with companies operating, or proposing to operate or expand, facilities in their areas. They set limits on emissions which are more stringent than national, prefectural or municipal standards; and also set limits for some substances (for example, from high technology industries) for which there is no standard. One objective of such agreements is to protect particular ecosystems; for example, they might prohibit use of some pesticides and chemical fertilisers on a golf course. In other cases an agreement might be reached to reduce emissions of, for example sulphur dioxide from a power company's plants. Agreements are seen as a way of adjusting regulation to local circumstances and as a method for resolving conflicts between companies and local people. Specific agreements of this kind originally evolved as a means of reducing industrial pollution at a time when national laws were unequal to the task; local power over planning applications helped persuade firms to accept emissions restrictions. Information exchange between local authorities has over the years created a

---

BOX 6C   **NEGOTIATED AGREEMENTS IN THE NETHERLANDS**

The National Environmental Policy Plan (NEPP) identified ten target groups (one of which was industry) which were expected to contribute towards meeting the goals set out in the Plan. Industrial sectors were subsequently identified and NEPP targets set for each sector. The preferred method for achieving them was a series of voluntary agreements between the government and industry sectors. Both parties welcomed the flexibility these would provide. Industry was also keen to eliminate uncertainty about possible future targets and the agreements were originally designed to be legally binding. In view of the government's unwillingness to have its freedom to act curtailed, the agreements ended up as a declaration of intent. If operators fail to meet their targets voluntarily, however, their authorisations can be tightened and normal enforcement mechanisms would apply.

The declarations include demanding targets, formalised in sectoral plans, and task forces have been established to assist in their implementation. To avoid the problems of free-riders, pressure is put on non-participating companies by the regulator who may discriminate between participants and non-participants in the agreement. Participants are given some flexibility providing the sector as a whole meets its targets; this flexibility does not extend to non-participants whose authorisations require them to meet each target by a specified date.

---

powerful ratcheting effect on emissions levels across a wide range of processes and pollutants. The combination of dialogue between policy-makers and firms and the use of voluntary measures, both as stepping stones to further regulation and as part of the learning process generally required for effective regulation, appears characteristic of the Japanese approach to pollution control.[45]

6.90 A survey of environmental agreements in EU Member States carried out by the European Environment Agency found that although there had been improvements in environmental performance, these could not be attributed specifically to the agreements. Many agreements did not include monitoring and reporting requirements; this damages their credibility, undermines accountability and makes it extremely difficult to evaluate their effectiveness. Only in the Netherlands were data partially available to demonstrate some effectiveness. The European Commission has issued a Communication setting a general framework for environmental agreements between public authorities and industry at both Community and national levels;[46] and a Recommendation containing guidelines on the use of voluntary agreements by Member States to implement EC Directives.[47]

6.91 **Basic issues arise over how transparency and openness can be increased, and accountability maintained, in a system in which there is a substantial measure of self-regulation.** Accountability for the state of the environment might be difficult to locate, and the system for protecting the environment might become less objective. Existing legislation on freedom of access to environmental information would need to be supplemented by the publication of much more information about releases of substances by companies, probably by revising the Environment Agency's Chemical Release Inventory to make it more effective.

6.92 From a legal perspective some critical issues about self-regulation have been identified.[48] One question relates to the compatibility of such an approach with principles in other areas of contemporary law. Competition law is one such area. Before introducing a system of self-regulation in a sector, action needs to be considered to deal with the problem of free-riders. Although it has been claimed that this could be reduced by binding agreements with a particular sector, sanctions need to be in place to penalise the culpable company rather than the entire industry sector. A second issue arises out of the co-existence of forms of self-regulation with a legal framework of regulation. This is one of several concerns about the role of public law principles and the shift away from formal regulatory machinery. Principles such as a fair hearing to those affected by the decision need to be dealt with carefully.

Combining approaches to implementation

6.93 Even if self-regulation were a viable alternative to direct regulation for larger companies, there would still remain the numerous medium and small companies for which direct regulation is the only sensible option. Representatives of large companies told us in evidence that they prefer to operate within a framework of statutory regulation. **We believe that self-regulation and the use of economic instruments should be regarded, not as alternatives to direct regulation, but as complementary to it.**

6.94 Regulatory legislation can be framed in such a way that it stimulates cultural changes which involve the internalisation of new values, especially if these changes reinforce elements within the culture which already exist. Occupational health and safety in the UK provides a good example of cultural change brought about by legislation (see box 6D[49]). Experience has also confirmed, however, that for cultural change to be effective, it must be underpinned by adequate resources devoted to inspection and enforcement. Under the twin pressures of cuts in resources and government policies favouring deregulation, the proportion of major injuries in the workplace investigated by the Health and Safety Executive fell from more than 15% in 1994 to 4% in 1996.[50] This trend has been accompanied by an increase in fatalities at work after a long run of years in which they had fallen: from 258 (1.2 per 100,000 workers) in 1995/96 to 302 (1.7 per 100,000 workers) in 1996/97.[51]

BOX 6D	**LEGISLATION INTENDED TO CHANGE ATTITUDES**

When, in 1970, the Robens Committee investigated existing health and safety legislation, it found a haphazard mass that was complex, difficult to amend, and out of date. People were conditioned to think of health and safety at work as a matter of detailed rules imposed by external agencies. They placed too much reliance on state regulation and too little on personal responsibility and voluntary, self-generating effort.

The Committee believed that health and safety law should establish a framework within which self-regulation could flourish and industry itself could take responsibility for health and safety matters.

The Committee suggested that the basic function of state inspection should be the provision of advice and assistance towards better safety standards. Prosecution was not to be the first priority. It advocated a mixture of statutory regulations and voluntary codes, which was 'constructive rather than prohibitory', with clearly stated, intelligible principles. This was to be supported by self-regulation, occasional monitoring by government agencies and greater use of administrative sanctions (such as improvement and prohibition notices) rather than criminal penalties.

The system operated by the Health and Safety Commission and Executive today contains a hierarchy of legal rules. There is a single standard of care ('reasonable practicability') set out in the Health and Safety at Work etc. Act. Subsidiary legal instruments of different kinds spell out how that standard is to be, or can be, met. There is also a good deal of non-statutory guidance, some of which is produced by companies (for example, specialist manufacturers of certain hazardous substances).

6.95 **New forms of standard, possibly in some cases with legal force, can help to make self-regulation function more effectively.** For company environmental reports to be credible records of stewardship of the environment, for example, standards will have to be set for them. These will need to cover the contents of such reports, arrangements for independent verification of their contents, and the methodologies used for measuring a company's overall effects on the environment. It may well be that, perhaps through amendment of the Companies Acts, formal obligations should be placed on companies to reflect their now widely recognised responsibilities to protect the environment and contribute to sustainable development. To the extent that company policies come to be based on methodologies such as life cycle analysis and assessment of total burden on the environment (and both their investment decisions and public presentation of their environmental effects will increasingly be based on such analyses), there is a strong case for developing standards for the application of such methodologies. There is also a case for exploring whether a consensus could be reached about the relative weighting of different environmental impacts (at present assigned by companies themselves under such concepts as 'environmental load units' or 'potency factors'). Not all these tasks need necessarily be undertaken by governments or intergovernmental bodies, provided sufficiently authoritative standards can be set elsewhere. In view of the extent to which company operations and product cycles span national borders, what is necessary, if such standards are to be effective, is that they should be set at a minimum for the European Union, and possibly by a global body such as the International Organization for Standardization.

Output from implementation analysis

6.96 How are policy-makers, faced with complex problems, incomplete information, disparate pollution sources and possibly conflicting goals, to choose the most appropriate instrument to achieve specific environmental goals? Within the framework of increasing internalisation of environmental values, economic instruments and self-regulation are likely to increase considerably in importance. In assessing whether either economic instruments or self-regulation would be acceptable, or preferable, as an alternative to direct regulation in particular cases, at least three considerations are relevant:

whether the alternative approach would achieve superior results in environmental terms;

whether it would achieve a given benefit for the environment at a lower cost (taking into account both transaction costs and other costs);

whether it would lessen or increase the problem of erosion of public trust in environmental regulation which we discuss in chapter 8.

6.97 **In seeking to deploy the wide range of legal and quasi-legal instruments available in order to control pollution and enhance the environment, policy-makers should identify those strategies which will be most effective in influencing behaviour and the legal status that will best complement those strategies. To ensure transparency and openness, self-regulation and use of economic instruments should take place within the framework of clear published targets for environmental quality set by government after taking into account all relevant considerations and on the basis of wide participation of all relevant interests.**

6.98 The key requirement is to assess the extent to which different strategies are likely to achieve legitimate objectives in a way that is efficient, technically competent, accountable and fair. Assessments sometimes focus too narrowly on the efficient achievement of objectives. There are other questions to be answered about, for example, the accountability of those who devise and apply devices such as liability rules or marketable permits; and about the fairness and openness to representations of the procedures involved in devising and applying the schemes.[52]

6.99 In the context of this report we have focused on analysis of implementation as an exercise carried out prior to the decision to adopt an environmental policy or standard. In this, as in other areas of public policy, an essential requirement is for implementation plans which can accommodate adaptive strategies.[53] Equally important is careful evaluation of the success of policies against the objectives they were designed to achieve. It has to be recognised, however, that there are difficulties in practice in assessing the success of economic instruments or self-regulation because there is frequently no clear base-line for evaluation and it is difficult to tell what changes would have occurred in a similar direction in the absence of the measures that were taken.

6.100 **Use of a combination of approaches in setting and implementing environmental standards is the best way to further general adoption of clean technology, whilst not putting at risk compliance with numerical standards set to protect humans and the natural environment against specific hazards.**

Chapter 7

ARTICULATING VALUES

Values are an essential element in decisions about environmental policies and standards. People's environmental and social values are the outcome of informed reflection and debate. To ensure that such values are articulated and taken into account, less familiar approaches need to be used to extend and complement present procedures for consultation and participation.

7.1   Previous chapters have dealt with the components that make up the analytical stage in reaching decisions about environmental policies. We identified important questions of value which can be crucial to such decisions and cannot themselves be resolved by technical analysis. This chapter examines ways of articulating the values that are potentially relevant to a particular decision. Chapter 8 will outline a procedure which seeks to combine all the various elements essential to decisions on environmental policies, and will explain why we consider a procedure on those lines is likely to provide the most robust basis for reaching such decisions in a democratic society.

7.2   We begin this chapter by indicating what we understand by 'values', and why there are competing values that bear on environmental issues (7.3–7.7). Established methods for seeking the public's views about such issues are briefly assessed (7.8–7.18). We then look at some less familiar, and in some cases experimental, ways of eliciting people's values that have been developed on local and national scales (7.19–7.34). We consider whether similar tasks can be undertaken at European or global scales (7.35–7.39). Finally, we consider the contribution these newer approaches to eliciting values might make in practice (7.40–7.47).

Values and environmental policies

7.3   We understand *values* to be beliefs, either individual or social, about what is important in life, and thus about the ends or objectives which should govern and shape public policies. Once formed, such beliefs may be durable. It is also characteristic that they may be both formed and modified as a result of information and reflection. Environmental and social values, in particular, are not necessarily preformed or fixed but, for many people, emerge out of debate, discussion and challenge, as they encounter new facts, insights and judgements contributed by others. The implications of this characteristic feature of values are explored in this chapter.

7.4   Any individual may have several reasons for regarding the environment as important. Concern for the environment in general, or for a particular part of it, may relate to one or more of the following considerations:

the environment is a vital resource for human livelihood and an essential condition for human health and well-being;

the rich diversity of species, ecosystems and habitats deserves protection not because of its usefulness to the human race, but for its own sake;

the environment has a cultural, historical or social significance, and may deserve protection on this account alone (for example, a landscape which has resulted from industrial or mining activity may signify a history of which a community may be proud or highly conscious).

7.5 Alongside values about the environment, an individual is likely to have other values. These will have implications for the way environmental values are pursued, and *vice versa*. Adopting the principle of sustainable development, for example, implies that concern for the environment has to be co-ordinated with concern for equity, both equity between generations and equity between different countries and groups within countries.

7.6 Because there are different reasons for valuing the environment, and because this range of environmental values is part of a much wider set of commitments, there are many situations in which different values are competing with each other, and there may, therefore, be difficulty in choosing the right course of action. As such dilemmas occur even for individuals, they are bound to be a significant feature of societies made up of individuals with contrasted backgrounds and sets of commitments. In such circumstances, finding the best way forward involves considering a range of policy options and identifying the one which comes closest to satisfying the values relevant to a particular decision. It is very unlikely that one policy will be the best by all criteria. As well as facilitating the emergence of values, processes of debate and discussion may be vital in resolving such situations of competition between values, both for individuals and for communities. In this way they may be able to play an important role in creating or identifying policy choices which will command wide support.

7.7 People's values are not the same thing as the interests of stakeholders. Rather than seeking to articulate and challenge values, the stakeholder model places the emphasis on negotiation between interested parties with the aim of reaching an expedient compromise. Stakeholders, for example employees or affected residents, certainly have to be considered in decisions about environmental policies or standards, but so must the values of people in their capacity of citizens. Valuable as the concept of a 'stakeholder' is in other contexts, we do not believe it is useful or appropriate to stretch it to cover the concerns ordinary citizens have about the environment.

Established methods for seeking public views

7.8 Those directly affected by an environmental matter should always have an accepted right to make their views known before a decision is taken about it. Giving them that opportunity is also likely to improve the quality of decisions; drawing on a wider pool of knowledge and understanding (lay as well as professional) can give warning of obstacles which, unless removed or avoided, would impede effective implementation of a particular decision. Over and above these considerations, those taking a decision may well want to ensure there is the widest possible consensus in favour of what they decide, all the more so in the case of important or sensitive decisions which are taken by politicians rather than officials. They may also feel that people who believe their views have been taken into account are more likely to have confidence in the decision-making process and the policies it produces. These factors have brought about commitments by governments to wide public participation in decision making on environmental matters, now enshrined in a pan-European Convention, although its terms are too vague to affect procedures for setting standards.[1] The four most familiar methods used to discover and take into account people's views about environmental issues are public opinion surveys, consultation exercises, public inquiries and Parliamentary procedures.

Public opinion surveys

7.9 The simplest method for discovering the views of large numbers of people is a public opinion survey. A well-designed survey of a properly representative sample of a population provides a useful way of capturing the views of that population; a random sample will give unbiased results provided that a high response rate is obtained. A quota sample is unlikely to give an unbiased result because the criteria used to define quotas will not cover all the dimensions on which people differ and the sample obtained may well not be representative of the population about which the information is sought. Surveys are mostly devoted to investigating responses to specific questions; qualitative methods such as focus groups (7.30 and box 7A) can be used to identify people's concerns so that these can be investigated subsequently through surveys.[2] The wording of questions can influence responses in a particular direction. Experts in the field consider that survey research can measure not only knowledge, behaviour, opinions and attitudes, but also values.[3] However, we do not believe survey research can provide useful information about values in the sense in which we use that term.

7.10 The difficulties of using survey techniques to help resolve dilemmas of environmental policy are illustrated by the current controversy over the capital investment programme that should be assumed in setting limits on water prices in England and Wales for the next five years. This is described in appendix E.

Consultation exercises

7.11 Consultation exercises are part of the stakeholder model. Most often they are based on some form of consultation document sent direct to those with a known interest in an issue or a proposal. This may be supplemented with meetings, either bilateral or with wider groups. Sometimes an attempt is made to find out the views of the general public through public meetings and/or exhibitions, distribution of popular leaflets, and possibly public opinion surveys. Consultation documents typically supply a significant amount of information about problems and policy options, and may provide a much wider opportunity than a public opinion survey for suggesting and developing alternative approaches.

7.12 The contribution a consultation exercise makes to opening up decision making depends on prior decisions about its scope. The problem which is giving rise to the consultation exercise will have been placed within a particular frame, and that may exclude some options from consideration. In some cases the options have been narrowed considerably in private consultation with experts at an earlier stage; if so, the choices presented to the public will be determined by the values of the limited group of people who have previously been involved. Often it is not revealed who these were. Some consultation exercises are so narrow or technical in nature that it is difficult or impossible for members of the public to respond unless they have followed the issue from the earliest stages. Exclusion from the initial framing of the problem disempowers people.

7.13 **Consultation has an important role to play in publicising proposals, stimulating critical debate, and eliciting a broad range of comments on the practicability and desirability of proposals.** Formal consultation can take a variety of forms; the stage at which it is undertaken, the breadth of responses encouraged, and the receptiveness to new suggestions and criticism vary considerably. An open and extensive consultation procedure should welcome scrutiny which explores wider issues and goes beyond points of practicability and relative detail. In order to secure a broad response, consultation documents should be publicised widely and written in a way comprehensible to lay people. Comments expressed in non-technical language should not be dismissed for that reason alone, as has sometimes happened with potentially important information from the public.[4]

Public inquiries

7.14 Public inquiries are a familiar method of discovering and clarifying views about controversial issues. In the UK they are held for a variety of purposes including the hearing of objections to local development plans, appeals against refusals of planning permission for new development, and those applications for permission for new development, including some road proposals, which are 'called in' for decision by the Secretary of State. They are not used directly in the setting of environmental standards. In the USA, on the other hand, confirmation of proposed standards frequently involves a regulatory hearing. The scope of public inquiries differs according to their purpose: any objector to local plan proposals has the right to be heard at an inquiry, but inquiries into road proposals have been criticised for excluding issues of national policy and hence the value questions which underlie those issues. Public inquiries are valuable ways of settling differences between particular interests but, partly because of their often adversarial character, they are not attuned (or designed) to elicit people's deeper values.

7.15 At a more strategic level, examinations in public (EIPs) are held to consider the general issues which arise in drawing up structure plans (which provide the strategic framework within which the more detailed local plans are set). The local authority and the chairman of the EIP establish the list of issues for discussion. Participants are selected who, between them, represent a broad range of viewpoints and have a relevant contribution to make. The format and procedures are less adversarial than many public inquiries and constructive debates may take place but again they are not designed to elicit public values directly. Insofar as these are reflected in discussion, it is generally through the representations of participating councillors, or particular representative bodies.

Parliamentary procedures

7.16 The UK and European Parliaments have important functions in relation to decisions on environmental policies and standards. Some of these are described in appendix D. The roles of Members of Parliament include representing the views of their constituents. Parliamentary committees look in detail at specific issues or at proposed legislation. They issue invitations to submit evidence to the world at large, as well as to organisations and individuals already known to be involved with a subject. In view of resource and time constraints, they do not themselves seek to conduct full consultation exercises, and committee inquiries are not in practice a primary means of eliciting lay opinion direct from the public. More often than not, committees have to rely on evidence from non-governmental organisations (NGOs) and pressure groups, and it can be problematical deciding how far these can be taken as proxies for the wider public. Committees can nevertheless perform an important task in weighing up opposing opinions; for example the Science and Technology Committee of the House of Lords did that in relation to the views of the Natural Environment Research Council and Greenpeace on the environmental implications of the Brent Spar case.[5] Not all issues are considered there, however, and the range of viewpoints taken into account may not be comprehensive or representative.

7.17 **Parliaments can have a significant influence on environmental standards by requiring Ministers and others to explain and justify their proposals on the basis of objective criteria, by independently seeking advice from experts, and in debate if proposals are laid before them. Parliaments are able to express public attitudes and values to some extent. Nevertheless, governments should use more direct methods to ensure that people's values, along with lay knowledge and understanding, are articulated and taken into account alongside technical and scientific considerations.**

7.18 Devolution within the UK is creating new bodies in which views about environmental issues can be given effective expression. The proposed Scottish Parliament will have full legislative responsibility for environmental matters. The proposed Welsh Assembly will be responsible for secondary legislation relating to Wales. Environmental matters are among the responsibilities of the Northern Ireland Assembly.

More effective procedures for articulating values

7.19 Established methods for participation and scrutiny must continue to play an important role. The opinions and attitudes elicited by public opinion surveys, consultation exercises or public inquiries may reflect deeper, underlying values; in cases where values are shared across society, these methods have been effective in highlighting areas of public concern. They do not expose such values to informed reflection and debate, however, yet this is critical if they are to evolve and be modified. In cases where there is no obligation on the responsible body to report the results in detail and explain the outcome, it may be impossible for outsiders to know what consideration has been given to their views.

7.20 The failure to provide an opportunity for interaction, and for clarifying the values underlying the responses made, is a major shortcoming of traditional forms of consultation. There is little scope for opinions to be developed as a result of exchanging views with others and considering issues in the light of growing understanding. It is unrealistic to suppose that values are fixed, and waiting to be uncovered by questionnaires or other types of analysis. For most people it is more accurate to think of their values emerging or taking shape as they are brought to face important choices between competing options. **When environmental standards are set or other judgements made about environmental issues, decisions must be informed by an understanding of people's values. Traditional forms of consultation, while they have provided useful insights, are not an adequate method of articulating values.**

7.21 Although Parliamentary procedures involve debates and discussions on questions of value relevant to environmental issues, most Parliamentary committees recognise that the process of articulating values extends beyond Parliament. One House of Lords Committee has seen its role in the following terms: 'As [European Council of Ministers] negotiations customarily lack openness on the scientific basis on which the prescriptive standards in a Directive have been arrived at, it is for national parliaments and the European Parliament to elicit the data on costs and on health risks which must be *publicly debated* before a new bathing water Directive can command public assent' (*emphasis added*).[6]

7.22 The other major shortcoming of established methods is that public involvement is generally deferred to a relatively late stage in the policy process, after the problem has been defined and a particular framework established. Yet it is often in determining and clarifying the issues, and the way these should be pursued, that values would be particularly relevant. Of the established methods, it is again Parliamentary scrutiny which sometimes applies at an early stage. **Values should be articulated at the earliest stage possible in setting standards and developing policies. The public should be involved in the formulation of strategies, rather than merely being consulted on already drafted proposals.** Openness at this framing stage allows people to question assumptions about the character of environmental issues and the scientific understanding upon which analysis is based. Framing of the issues to be subjected to scientific and technical assessment needs to be more socially intelligent.

7.23 In complex and controversial cases, existing procedures should be supplemented by new procedures. **A more rigorous and wide-ranging exploration of people's values requires discussion and debate to allow a range of viewpoints and perspectives to be considered, and individual values developed.** We now explore possible new approaches on different geographical scales, starting at the local scale. We draw on examples related to various aspects of environmental policy. There are no examples known to us up to now of similar methods being used in the UK to set environmental standards. Because many of the new methods are still at an experimental stage, there is only limited evidence available as yet about usefulness and effectiveness.

Experience at local scale

7.24 While local authorities have little involvement in setting environmental standards in the sense used in this report, they are responsible for many aspects of environmental management. They are directly accountable in the sense that councillors are elected. The role of elected representatives can be enhanced if new approaches help build consensus about local issues on which there would otherwise be considerable disagreement. By engaging local people in discussion and debate, a range of viewpoints can be explored and people can develop understanding informed by views other than their own. For involvement of local people to be meaningful, it must start in the early stages of policy development.

7.25 Local Agenda 21 has been mentioned already (6.74) for the stimulus it has provided to community action. It has also led to the setting up of broadly-based community fora to debate issues of local importance. In some cases targets and indicators have been developed to express the priorities and goals of a particular community.[7] Good practice is being disseminated through a joint central/local government project in the UK[8] and through a website at European level.[9] The Open Forum in Bradford on Avon, aimed at participation in decisions about traffic in the town, is described in appendix F (F.2–F.4). It identified community objectives and brought about transport policy initiatives by the county council.

7.26 Faced with conflicts about waste management policies and the siting of new disposal facilities, Hampshire County Council set up a community forum process, with a wide range of viewpoints represented. Three fora were asked to consider management of household waste, with a strong presumption against exporting it from the county. The extensive and innovative programme (described in more detail in appendix F, F.5–F.8) increased awareness of waste management problems, and the credibility of the council's officials, among those directly involved, but to a lesser extent in the general population. The county council gained an understanding that public responses to proposals for waste disposal facilities which had previously been categorised as 'NIMBY' (not in my back yard) should not be dismissed as irrational, subjective and based on self-interest, but masked issues that had to be addressed about inequities in risk sharing and lack of trust in decision-takers. The fora reached a consensus that an integrated waste management strategy was required, though not about its content or implementation. Another important conclusion was that stakeholders should be involved in the formulation of waste strategies and plans, not merely consulted about already drafted proposals. The three fora were replaced by a single forum with a watching brief while the waste disposal contract for the county was being tendered.[10] Following the award of the contract, and as part of the siting process for three new incinerators, community involvement is continuing through 'contact groups', which are discussing elements of the environmental assessment, and through an outreach programme.[11]

7.27 Local authorities should review existing provision for public participation in relation to their environmental functions, and seek to extend this as appropriate. Greater use should be made of community fora to create consensus on local issues. The aim should also be to expand the local partnerships established through Local Agenda 21 initiatives to embrace consideration of policy issues.

7.28 The former National Rivers Authority undertook extensive consultations at local level for the purpose of setting water quality objectives in catchment management plans. Those plans are now being superseded by Local Environment Agency Plans covering the exercise of all the Environment Agency's functions within a given river catchment.[12] The consultation procedures used in each case are outlined in appendix F (F.9–F.13). **The Environment Agencies should explore ways of stimulating public input into policies relating to all aspects of their work at the earliest stage possible. Local Environment Agency Plans are a welcome innovation. The Environment Agency should consider how procedures can be introduced which will be more effective in articulating the values of all sections of the relevant communities.**

Experience at national scale

7.29 Although national governments are elected and accountable, and Parliamentary procedures play a vital role, there is a recognised need for other methods of obtaining information about people's opinions, attitudes and values. The UK government is establishing a People's Panel for this purpose as part of its *Better Government* initiative. This 5,000 strong panel will allow more effective tracking of public opinions and attitudes over time, especially on matters relating to public services. By using a panel it is hoped that research will be better co-ordinated and more cost-effective. Moreover, it will be possible to gain insight into how the views of individuals change and develop over the three-year life of the panel. Sub-sets of panel members, perhaps selected by region, could be used for a wide range of quantitative and qualitative procedures, including citizens' juries and deliberative polls (see box 7A). There is a commitment to publish the results of research and there will be an independent evaluation of the initiative after its first year.[13]

7.30 For specific policy areas in which people's values are important, several methods have been used at national level in the UK, in most cases experimentally, to articulate those values and obtain information about possible bases for consensus. Their key features are described in box 7A.[14] Focus groups are the longest established and most widely used. They have been used by companies to gauge consumer reaction to new products and by government Departments to elicit the views both of the public and of service providers on policy questions. They are also used to test publicity material (for example, on domestic energy saving and sustainable development). Interest in focus groups as a way of supplementing traditional methods of consultation about environmental issues has recently been growing.

BOX 7A	METHODS FOR ARTICULATING VALUES

In a **focus group** up to about a dozen people, randomly chosen or fitting the template of a target population, discuss a subject with the help of moderators. The transcript is analysed to reveal a profile of views and reactions. In a group people express their views more openly and spontaneously than in a one-to-one interview.

A **citizens' jury** is a small group of people, selected either at random or to match the profile of a particular community, who are asked to consider an important question relating to policy or planning. Usually such a jury is commissioned by a body which has power to act on its recommendations. After initial briefing, the jurors are presented with a broad range of evidence over a period of several days and have the opportunity to cross-examine witnesses. Their discussions are facilitated by an independent moderator, and for some of the time they may split into smaller groups. They are asked to make recommendations at the end of their deliberations. The question to be considered, the programme and the choice of witnesses are usually decided by an advisory group of stakeholders. Focus groups may also be used to help refine the question put to the jury. The moderator writes the report incorporating the recommendations and circulates this to the jurors for approval. It is then submitted to the commissioning body. The jury's verdict is not binding. Nor need it be unanimous.

A **consensus conference** is the only form of public consultation devised specifically to deal with technological and scientific issues. Typically, a panel of a dozen or more lay people is recruited through national advertising and given an introductory package. At its first meeting, at which discussion is facilitated, the panel takes control of the agenda. It is responsible for conducting its own investigation and identifies the expert witnesses it wishes to hear. It examines witnesses at a public conference lasting several days. Following its investigation, the panel writes a report and presents this in public.

Deliberative polls have been devised as the counterpart of a town meeting, with the aim of giving everyone in the community a chance to participate, regardless of social cleavages. As many as 300–400 people are recruited by quota sampling to be representative of the relevant population. They are invited to a central location for several days, and paid expenses and a nominal fee. The participants are first divided randomly into small groups, which select the questions that are subsequently considered in public debate by the group as a whole. The participants therefore set the agenda. The shifts of opinion that take place as a result of the debate are measured from questionnaires completed at the beginning and end by all the participants. Discussion is facilitated by a moderator, whose performance is evaluated after the event to ensure that the moderator's own views have not been imposed on the participants.

7.31 Consensus conferences were devised in Denmark by the Board of Technology, an agency of the Danish Parliament. They have been used occasionally in the Netherlands, New Zealand and Switzerland. The first held at national level in the UK was used to stimulate wider debate on plant biotechnology and is described in box 7B.[15] The usefulness of consensus conferences can be shown by contrasting UK and Danish experience over food irradiation. The Danish Parliament had available a very negative report by a lay panel and decided that irradiation of food should not be approved for general use. In the UK the Advisory Committee on Novel Foods and Processes decided that the process should be introduced. There was a hostile response from the public, and industry was unable to use plant it had installed. That outcome might well have been avoided if there had been appropriate public debate before the decision was taken.

BOX 7B   **CONSENSUS CONFERENCE ON PLANT BIOTECHNOLOGY**

The first attempt to apply the Danish model of consensus conference in the UK was funded by the Biotechnology and Biological Sciences Research Council and organised by the Science Museum, London. A lay panel was recruited by placing advertisements in regional newspapers throughout the UK and selecting from respondents to achieve a representative cross-section of the public. A steering committee of six was recruited to oversee the initiative and a professional facilitator appointed. The lay panel was sent background information and attended two preparatory weekends. The Conference took place over three days in November 1994 and was attended by 300–400 people.

The aim was to contribute to public debate and policy making on plant biotechnology. Reactions to the Conference suggested that it generated considerable interest and influenced some government Departments and Members of Parliament, despite the absence of a formal link with the policy process.

7.32 Citizens' juries have been used over the last 20 years in the USA. Box 7C describes the use of such a jury in Wales to explore views on genetic testing for common disorders.[16] This confirmed that lay people have the capacity to discuss complex issues and can come up with practical suggestions. A broadly similar method which is being used extensively in Germany is *Plannungzelle* (planning cells).[17] In order to structure the views of members of such a cell, multi-criteria analysis (5.23–5.24) is sometimes used.

7.33 Four general characteristics appear important in order to ensure that the methods described in box 7A provide a reliable indication of the values an informed lay person is likely to hold on the issue under consideration:

lay participants who are either randomly chosen or demographically representative;

access to a range of authoritative information through written evidence and expert witnesses;

time for the participants to discuss the issues thoroughly and debate the main points of concern which have emerged. Some discussion should take place in small groups to encourage contributions from all the participants. By considering knowledge and judgements from a range of perspectives, better understanding can develop;

independence of the organising body, to eliminate any suspicion of bias.

BOX 7C   CITIZENS' JURY ON GENETIC TESTING FOR COMMON DISORDERS

A citizens' jury was organised by the Welsh Institute for Health and Social Care in November 1997 to consider 'What conditions should be fulfilled before genetic testing for people susceptible to common disorders becomes available on the NHS?' This question was derived from a series of seven focus groups involving 70 lay people in total. A steering committee selected the evidence and witnesses to be presented to the jury.

Bids were invited from market research organisations and university departments to undertake recruitment of the jury. People were randomly selected and interviewed in 19 primary sampling locations throughout Wales and then invited to attend a group meeting. Of the people who attended a group meeting, 24 expressed an interest in participating, and 15 of these were selected to form a jury which corresponded with the demographic profile of Wales.

An independent moderator was employed to facilitate discussions. After an introductory afternoon, the jury met for four days in the following week. It examined evidence, questioned expert witnesses, debated the issues, and at the end presented a series of recommendations to decision-makers. The witnesses represented a broad range of perspectives including clinical genetics, sociology, general practice, psychiatry, nursing, National Health Service management, private sector interests, public policy-makers and patients.

The Citizens' Jury on Genetic Testing for Common Disorders illustrates how lay perspectives can be used to inform policy choices when a complex issue is at stake. The jurors proved to be competent in dealing with a wide range of technical material and grappling with difficult moral and social issues. The jury's recommendations have been circulated to a number of key bodies, including health authorities and trusts, Royal Colleges and patient organisations, and each of these bodies has been asked for a formal response.

7.34 Another way of promoting interaction between expert knowledge and people's values is to introduce lay membership into expert bodies. In this context 'lay' should include anyone from outside the disciplines associated with a particular expert body. Department of Health medical committees now have a lay member, as do government advisory committees on food and food-related subjects.[18] Lay members provide an alternative viewpoint, and can suggest alternative ways of framing issues, or of how issues can be communicated in a meaningful way to a wider audience. There is, however, a danger that they may be appointed for presentational reasons, and may not provide a sufficiently effective or representative reflection of people's values. Appointment of lay members is certainly not a substitute for making expert bodies more transparent and open in their working methods. The real requirement is that expert bodies themselves should develop a sensitivity to questions of values. Given such sensitivity, they may find it more productive to mount exercises of the kind described above, with a wide range of lay representation, than to rely on input from a token lay member.

Experience at European scale

7.35 Most environmental policies and standards affecting the UK now stem from, or are dependent on, proposals for legislation put forward by the European Commission (1.24). There is a general impression that the European Commission has not undertaken enough consultation in the past before submitting formal proposals to the Council of Ministers. There are guidelines for legislative policy containing a section on consultation; the explanatory memoranda to proposed legislation must give an account of the procedures and outcome of external consultations.[19] In the environmental field the European Commission has been more forthcoming, and has said that it 'will consult as widely as possible on the formulation of new proposals for Community environmental measures. Consultations will include the full range of actors who will be concerned with a particular measure.'[20] The European Commission prefers to deal with Europe-wide representative bodies (for example, Eureau for the water industry or the European Environment Bureau for environmental groups).

7.36 The problem of ensuring that decisions on environmental matters are informed by people's values is even greater on a European scale because of the complexity and lack of openness of the decision-making procedures (appendix D) and the greater diversity of circumstances across the Member States. It can be expected that governments will seek to reflect the values of their electors in the Council of Ministers. It can also be expected that Members of the European Parliament will seek to represent the values of their constituents. These may be difficult tasks, however, both for Ministers and Members of Parliament, unless people's values have previously been articulated in relation to the issues under discussion. The European Commission has had since 1996 the General Consultative Forum on the Environment drawn from industry, business, regional and local authorities, professional associations, unions, and environmental protection and consumer organisations. However, this is made up of 'eminent personalities' rather than representative members of the public.[21]

7.37 **Improving the mechanisms for articulating values should be high on the agenda for the future development of European institutions.** Suggestions recently put forward include simultaneous use of deliberative polls (see box 7A) in all Member States, a Europe-wide interactive communication network for political participation, and use of Europe-wide referenda both for popular initiatives (with the Council and Parliament as filters) and to provide the possibility of cancelling newly enacted legislation.[22] We do not believe referenda are a suitable method for deciding difficult environmental issues, either nationally or in Europe, because it is unlikely that they would be accompanied by the processes of challenge and dialogue needed if values are to evolve and develop.

Experience at global scale

7.38 Articulating people's values to inform environmental decisions taken on a global scale is a still greater challenge. Certain features of international negotiations produce favourable conditions for identifying and debating questions of values. One is the involvement of a wide range of governments with different perspectives and different interests to protect. Another is the frequent presence at negotiations of NGOs which have observer status and can ensure their viewpoints are heard. Those viewpoints, however, are not necessarily an adequate reflection of the full range of people's values. It may sometimes be desirable to promote a more broadly-based dialogue. National governments could use one or other of the methods described in box 7A to test out questions of values, as part of preparing their positions for international negotiations.

7.39 The World Wide Web has aroused great expectations about the potential for global debate on environmental issues. It is already used extensively by NGOs and others to inform, consult and lobby. Key current documents are starting to appear on the World Wide Web (for example, the negotiating text for the Kyoto Conference of the Climate Change Convention in December 1997), so making international negotiation a much more transparent process, though not necessarily a more open one. Quality of information and debate on the Web is often low, however, and cannot measure up to the criteria we identified (7.33) for the effective functioning of methods to articulate people's values. The participants are not representative of the whole population nationally, still less globally. And they may well be afflicted by 'rational ignorance': if they have no reason to think their views expressed on the Web are going to make any difference, it is not worthwhile for them to devote effort to obtaining reliable information on a subject.

Scope for using new methods to articulate values

7.40 The decision whether to use one of the new methods for eliciting people's values in any given context should depend on the nature of the issue under consideration. Special measures to articulate values are not required in connection with all decisions, for example on detailed technical matters, on environmental policies. Many such decisions are made within established frameworks reflecting a broad consensus on values, without there being any reason to suppose that values have changed. On the other hand, in highly contentious fields such as genetically modified organisms (GMOs) or radioactive discharges, or in relation to hazards which pose a complicated or unpredictable threat, use of a more elaborate and thorough procedure to elicit people's values may well be justifiable, indeed may be a necessary condition for making progress. In intermediate cases, such as national air quality standards or some European Commission proposals, some use of new methods to probe people's values may well be helpful.

7.41 In setting environmental standards, these new methods should be used primarily in connection with issues which are both complex or controversial and of broad scope. Rather than attempting to cover every proposed standard, efforts to elicit values should focus on general questions of principle or procedure. Areas to consider might include the framework governing a whole group of standards, the choice of instrument for implementing standards, the tolerability of risks, and the communication of possible hazards.

7.42 No method for determining or articulating people's values, whether traditional or novel, provides a guaranteed solution. Novel approaches should be evaluated for their ability to elicit a full spectrum of values on the issue in question from representative participants, so that the procedures used can be refined in the light of experience and their full potential realised. It is important to avoid arousing unrealistic public expectations about the likely outcomes, which could lead to frustration and disillusionment.

7.43 The usefulness of new types of body such as citizens' juries does not depend on their ability to reach a consensus on the issue they are considering. Nor is it necessarily the case that, if the exercise were to be repeated with a different group, the same conclusions would be reached. People will not react in an identical way to information and debate. The fundamental purpose of these new approaches is, not to produce a 'right answer', but to illuminate the value questions raised by environmental issues in order to identify the policies around which consensus is more likely to form and enable decisions to be better informed and more robust.

7.44 In the case of national issues, the new methods cannot have the same kind of direct impact on the views and attitudes of the wider public as has been achieved at local level by community fora used in formulating local transport policies (appendix F, F.2–F.4) or waste management policies for Hampshire (appendix F, F.5–F.8). It is nevertheless generally a feature of the new methods to promote awareness among the general public of their activities and findings. This is all the more important if subsequent policy reflects the outcomes of the discussions. The final discussion is typically held in public or the report of findings launched at a public meeting (box 7A). Effort should be made and resources directed towards ensuring that the results are successfully disseminated and stimulate a wider public. Research should be undertaken to find out how that can best be done.

7.45 Some preconditions for the successful use of the new methods have been identified already (7.33). If they are to carry credibility with the wider public, it is important that the participants are representative and selected in an open and fair way. This is all the more important if the issues being considered affect particular groups of people in different ways. The procedure must also be perceived to be both competently run and impartial. Ways of helping to achieve that include using an advisory group drawn from stakeholders to help develop the agenda and participate in the selection of witnesses for a citizens' jury and appointing a moderator to prevent a small number of people dominating the discussion and marginalising other groups or individuals.[23] The legitimacy of the procedure may also be compromised if the initial brief is highly specific, or inappropriately framed, or if deliberation is restricted to a narrow range of options.

7.46 The costs quoted for use of the methods discussed in this chapter are £15,000–£25,000 for a citizens' jury, £22,000 for a deliberative poll and £85,000 for a consensus conference. These costs can be compared with the cost of up to £23,300 quoted for a conventional telephone survey of 1,000 people.[24] Use of these methods may also lengthen significantly the time taken to reach a decision. **The cost of methods for articulating public values is significant: a judgement has to be made in each case as to whether gains in the quality and robustness of the decision are likely to outweigh the time and resources required.** Although focus groups are much less effective for articulating public values than the other methods considered, they do provide useful information about people's current values, and their cost is much lower. They could provide a valuable screening device to identify the issues that are of high public concern and so facilitate the decision whether a citizens' jury or consensus conference should be arranged on a particular issue.

7.47 As new methods discussed here are still at an experimental stage in the UK, it would be prudent to extend their use gradually and monitor it closely. **The Department of the Environment, Transport and the Regions, in consultation with other government Departments, should:**

> ***a.*** **consider how the new methods should be incorporated into the procedures for considering envionmental issues and setting environmental standards, including the framing of questions to be addressed in analysis and communicating the results of scientific assessments in a comprehensible form;**

> ***b.*** **collate the experience gained, and draw up a code of practice for use of the new methods, designed both to maximise their effectiveness and preserve their integrity.**

Some bodies may require additional resources for this purpose.

Chapter 8

A ROBUST BASIS FOR ENVIRONMENTAL STANDARDS

The public sometimes mistrusts and rejects official judgements about environmental issues. More attention should be given to defining problems, framing questions and clarifying policy aims. Decisions about environmental policies must be based on the scientific evidence and an analysis of technological options, but they must also take into account risks and costs, and be informed by values. A choice needs to be made whether setting a standard is the most effective method of achieving a given purpose and, if so, what form of standard should be used. How should all these elements fit together in the decision-making process? What are the implications for the bodies that set standards? How can such bodies win and retain public confidence?

8.1   At the beginning of this report we drew attention to the changing nature of environmental concerns, and to changes that have taken place in the policy process. We have considered in turn the analytical components needed in order to respond effectively to environmental problems. We have also discussed the relevance of people's values in defining environmental problems and developing solutions to them, and how such values can be articulated.

8.2   In this chapter we first summarise some of the main messages of earlier chapters (8.3–8.13). We highlight an apparent erosion of public trust in environmental regulation. Some of the factors discussed in earlier chapters throw light on the reasons for this (8.14–8.29). We consider what features need to characterise the procedures for deciding on environmental policies, and in particular for setting environmental standards, in order for them to be both logically satisfactory and generally accepted (8.30–8.70). This study has also prompted reflections on some wider issues which we regard as important, and we go on to set these out briefly (8.71–8.82).

The essential components

8.3   Environmental issues reach the agenda by diverse routes. European and international developments play an ever greater part. Environmental issues normally have a major technical component: expert assessments will continue to be essential but their certainty, precision and objectiveness should be neither over-estimated nor under-estimated. The way issues are formulated, and the choices available to deal with them, generally also raise questions of values, which should be specifically addressed from the outset.

8.4   Once an issue has been identified there should be a clear procedure for handling it which we describe below (8.30–8.50). **The analytical stage of the policy process has several complementary and closely inter-related components:**

 scientific assessment;

 analysis of technological options;

 assessment of risk and uncertainty;

 economic appraisal; and

 analysis of implementation issues, including the geographical scope of standards.

Conceptually, this approach would apply to any kind of environmental policy or standard but the nature of a particular environmental problem will determine the resources which should be devoted to each type of analysis in practice.

8.5   There are well-established procedures for assessing the scientific evidence and determining, for example, dose-effect relationships to inform the decision-making process. The aim must be to indicate clearly where the boundaries of knowledge lie. To avoid the spurious accuracy often implied when only a single statement or conclusion is presented, assessments should present a range of relationships concerning the particular issue, each established under different conditions; indicate susceptibility to change (for example through increased knowledge, or changing priorities); and should acknowledge uncertainties more clearly.

8.6   Technological assessment will reveal opportunities for controlling pollution, as well as new forms of pollution resulting from technological change. Life cycle assessment will usually provide the most satisfactory basis for assessing the environmental effects of industrial products and processes, and environmental standards should not be set in ways which discourage the development of this approach, or obstruct the uptake of improved technology.

8.7   Procedures for risk assessment can help to illuminate the choice between alternative policies or standards and rationalise the choice of substances for priority control. Assessments should identify and characterise the different types and sources of risk in the situation under consideration, together with the uncertainties and their implications. Human factors strongly influence the way people conceive of risks and their tolerance of them, and they should be taken into account throughout the assessment process drawing on the evidence from consensus conferences and similar techniques used earlier in the process. Communication about risks should begin at the outset and inform the framing of the assessment.

8.8   The economic appraisal will value the costs and benefits of different courses of action so far as possible. Great care is needed to ensure that effects for which no price can be established are appropriately taken into account in making decisions. The assessment of the costs and benefits of environmental measures can be problematic when available choices raise value questions.

8.9   The way standards are implemented influences particular patterns of behaviour or courses of action by individuals, business and industry. These should be identified in advance to ensure that perverse incentives are not inadvertently created and that the strategies selected will be those most effective in influencing behaviour. The legal status of standards should be that which will best complement those strategies.

8.10 Value questions are necessarily posed when standards are set and scientific, technological and economic appraisals should be supplemented in ways which allow these questions to be properly considered, in order to elucidate the consequences of setting standards. There is scope for more trialling and experimentation in the methods by which public values may be articulated.

8.11 **The presentation to decision-makers of the results of the analyses referred to above should clearly state the assumptions and limitations of each analysis. It will usually be necessary to offer several options and their implications, so far as these can be gauged.**

8.12 An underlying theme which has run through all the chapters of this report is the need for transparency and openness in all aspects of environmental management, and especially at all stages in the policy process that leads to the setting of environmental standards. The functions and composition of all the bodies involved in setting standards should be public knowledge and all the data, models and assumptions they are using should be readily available to the public. There should be opportunities for the public to exert an influence on what happens at each stage, beginning with the initial recognition of a problem.

8.13 Easy as it is to state these as desiderata, it is hard to achieve them in practice because of the complexity of the issues raised by environmental protection, the consequent problems in presenting information in forms that are both accessible and meaningful, and the complex relationships between the bodies involved. These difficulties have contributed to a lack of confidence by the public in environmental regulation, which we discuss below, but have been aggravated by other factors.

The changed nature of environmental regulation

8.14 Changes in the nature of environmental concerns were discussed at the beginning of this report (1.8–1.13). We have considered some of the implications for the way environmental standards are used and set and the types of evidence that need to be utilised. There are also implications for the whole system of environmental regulation.

8.15 The emphasis in environmental policy during the 1970s and 1980s was on scientific issues, on which the expertise lay with a small group of people mainly in the national or regional control agencies, or in government bodies. Pollution control was primarily exercised by direct regulation through statutory control over emissions. Only two parties were normally involved: the control agency, and the firm making the emissions. Expertise about the technology of the processes giving rise to emissions was confined to the regulators and, predominantly, to specialists in the larger and more technically competent firms in an industry.

8.16 The changes which have occurred in the understanding and perception of environmental problems have been accompanied by increased public awareness of, and concern about, environmental issues. Improved legal rights to environmental information, greater attempts by scientists to promote interest in and understanding of their work, and the extensive coverage of environmental and scientific issues in the news media, have placed in the public domain much more information about pollution issues.

8.17 A far wider circle of people is now recognised as having an interest in regulatory decisions. Expertise on environmental problems is much more widely spread outside the pollution control agencies and the companies causing pollution. This is especially true of universities and environmental groups. It is no longer acceptable for decisions to be negotiated privately between regulator and polluter.

8.18 Whilst there is greater awareness of the complexity of many pollution problems, the availability of so much information does not guarantee accurate knowledge of critical points. People are likely to be more interested in individual cases, particularly in the localities affected, than in more strategic and abstract aspects, such as the setting of environmental standards, which have involved a confusing multiplicity of bodies and often obscure procedures.

Erosion of public trust

8.19 The regulatory system has been modified in response to the trends and forces described above, but has not evolved to the full extent that circumstances will require. Increased awareness of the complexity of many environmental problems makes public trust in environmental regulation critical: but there are signs that it is being eroded. There is a tension here. Trust is demanded particularly where there is ignorance, but ignorance always provides grounds for scepticism or at least caution. And trust may take a long time to build, but can quickly be destroyed.

8.20 In most contexts the public accepts the present system of environmental regulation, including the role of the Environment Agencies set up in 1996 and the environmental legislation of the European Community (EC). There is nevertheless much evidence that trust has been eroded. When major and widely-publicised issues arise (such as bovine spongiform encephalopathy (BSE), the release of genetically modified organisms (GMOs), or the disposal of wastes from the nuclear industry), public opinion about the nature and extent of the risk they pose may turn out to be at sharp variance with the assessments that have been made by those with official responsibility for environmental protection.

8.21 One recent report concludes that 'conventional patterns of official reassurance will lack purchase' when new hazards are identified or risks are re-assessed because public acceptance of the official apparatus of environmental regulation may represent a 'sense of lack of alternatives in circumstances of all-embracing and non-transparent dependency on expert judgements', rather than 'authentically deep-rooted confidence based on positive experience [and] expectation [of being able to ensure] the proper behaviour of official regulators'.[1]

8.22 Public opinion on such issues may differ from country to country, both in substance and in how forcefully it is expressed. Events have demonstrated that in a European single market, and with trade, industry, and communications increasingly globalised, public opinion in other countries may in some circumstances be a consideration of vital importance.

8.23 It has been suggested that there may be a general mistrust of technological changes and their consequences, and of those who purport to regulate them in the public interest, and a fear that the values held by many people are not being protected adequately.[2] Surveys of public opinion about environmental issues show that the general public in Britain has no great trust in government scientists. The proportion expressing confidence in 'scientists working for the government' is well under half, a smaller proportion than expresses confidence in scientists working in industry and a much smaller proportion than expresses confidence in scientists working for environmental groups.[3]

8.24 One direction from which trust has been eroded is through pressure for deregulation. This can prompt fears that protective measures which some people found valuable may be dismantled and that those who profit from this action will not themselves suffer from adverse effects which may ensue. There may also be a fear that the possibly short-term advantages to business will be at the expense of long-term harm to the environment, which will be, at best, difficult and costly to remedy.

8.25 The greater use of numerical standards and formal procedures referred to in chapter 1 might have been expected to boost public confidence in environmental regulation by giving a better assurance that it was set on the basis of precise and rigorous procedures, and was operating objectively, impartially and consistently. In reality, the conjunction of greater quantification and loss of confidence is unsurprising. As we have noted, the two trends reflect common factors such as the growing awareness of the complexity of environmental problems and of the uncertainty which pervades them. Moreover, an emphasis by institutions on quantification is frequently a substitute for public trust, rather than evidence of its existence.[4]

8.26 The experience of the USA confirms that. Fragmentation of political power led to a strong emphasis on both formal procedures and the use of quantitative techniques such as cost-benefit analysis and risk assessment because these 'make it easier to reassure critics within and outside government that policy decisions are being made in a rational, non-arbitrary manner'.[5] That fragmentation also meant that the applications made of quantitative techniques were energetically contested by different groups in the courts and in Congress.[6] This history provides no ground for thinking that greater use of quantification and formal procedures will in itself lead to a rebuilding of public trust.

8.27 Chapter 2 suggested that scientific understanding of environmental issues is frequently subject to large uncertainties. Politicians often play down the uncertainties in the belief that this will reassure the public and increase the credibility of policies and projects. They also sometimes place undue weight on statistical comparisons of estimated risks or quantified comparisons of costs and benefits. This approach is counter-productive in the long run, as both scientists and politicians will be discredited. By fuelling mistaken ideas about scientific certainty, both scientists and the regulatory system are exposed to a damaging loss of confidence from that inevitable proportion of cases in which policies turn out with hindsight to have been based on incorrect assumptions. We return to the interface between science and policy later in this chapter.

8.28 Other factors have undermined confidence in environmental regulation. One is a widespread perception that some regulators are not sufficiently independent and impartial in relation to the activities they regulate. This has been particularly important in affecting public attitudes to the roles of the Ministry of Agriculture, Fisheries and Food in relation to the agricultural and food industries and the Department of Trade and Industry in relation to offshore oil installations.

8.29 Another factor has been a failure to pay enough attention to people's values when taking decisions on environmental policies. As was shown in chapter 7, there is a need to consider how traditional methods for taking account of people's views can be supplemented, particularly for policies concerning highly contentious or emotive issues or with marked implications for life-style.

Standard setting as practical judgement

8.30 There are two reasons why we regard clarification of the procedures that should be followed in setting environmental standards as the most important output from this study. The first is that such decisions are complex ones in which various considerations have to be taken into account, and their nature in this respect has been widely misunderstood and misrepresented. The second is that available techniques can and should be used to articulate people's values and integrate them into each critical stage of decision making about environmental standards. The description which follows of the logic of standard setting defines the direction in which we believe the system of environmental regulation should evolve.

8.31 Setting an environmental standard is an exercise in practical judgement. Judgement is reached by a process of deliberation which seeks ways of meeting a multiplicity of constraints and viewpoints. An appropriately designed deliberative procedure deepens understanding and uncovers any inconsistencies or errors. It enhances decision making by improving the way problems are formulated, determining appropriate uses for controversial analytical techniques, clarifying views, and considering a range of perspectives.

8.32 The steps to be followed in responding to environmental problems are illustrated in figure 8-I. This shows at a conceptual level the broad principles of the standard-setting procedure, and how the various elements required for making a practical judgement should be marshalled and deployed. The sequence is a logical one, not necessarily a chronological one. The duration of the stages will differ from case to case, they may overlap with each other, and there may be iterations. We discuss in the following sections of this chapter some organisational implications of this conceptual structure.

8.33 The starting-point for setting any standard is **recognition of a problem**. In most cases, there will be some existing context. In some cases, the problem will be that actions taken previously have had an unsatisfactory outcome. In other cases, the problem will be an entirely new one. Scientific discoveries (such as the discovery of the effect of chlorofluorocarbons (CFCs) on stratospheric ozone) may lead to the identification or re-assessment of a problem. Recognition of a problem may also come about through changes in public perceptions of a situation, which may reflect shifts in values. Attitudes to the proposed disposal at sea of the Brent Spar oil installation illustrated dramatically one such value shift.

Figure 8-I
Environmental policy process

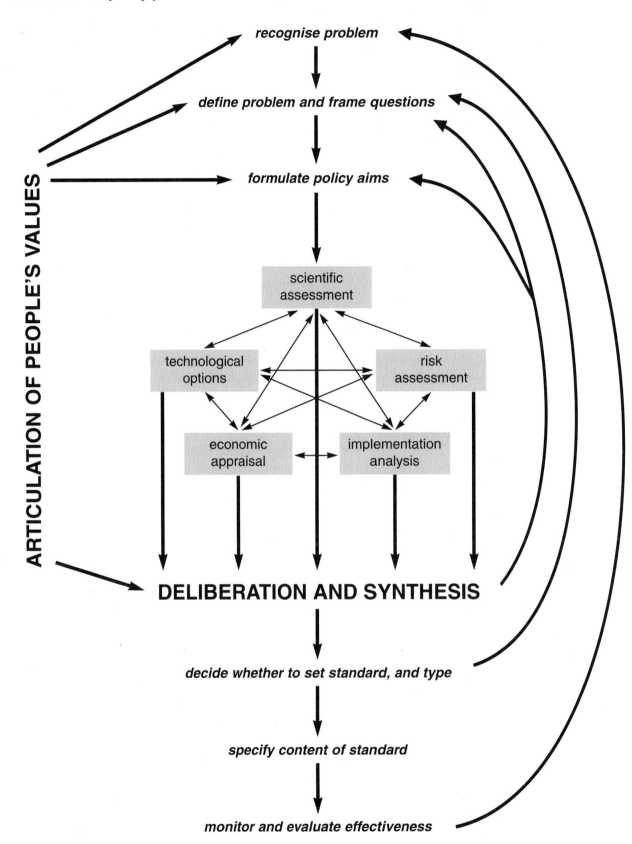

8.34 The second step is **definition of the problem**, not merely identifying that something is wrong, but defining what exactly is wrong. In some cases, the first two stages take place simultaneously. In other cases, further consideration may reveal a wider, more complex situation. When the nature of the problem is uncertain, the values of those who examine it will tend to influence the way they define it and hence the research which is undertaken to elucidate it. That definition may not be universally shared: other people may assess the problem from different perspectives and thus define it differently. The Brent Spar case again provides an example. Was it a question of identifying the best practicable environmental option for an isolated disposal, or establishing a precedent for the disposal of all similar offshore structures? Was dumping at sea an acceptable way of disposing of society's waste products? How were the risks of disposal on land to be compared with the very different risks of disposal at sea? Different groups of people had very different approaches to these issues.

8.35 In some cases there may be different views about what should be protected: human health, the natural environment, or both. Or what degree of protection should be provided: against acute or chronic effects, against long- or short-term effects, or against local or distant effects. Only inclusive procedures can clarify satisfactorily the concerns to be addressed and identify the range of viewpoints to be taken into account, thereby paving the way for effective solutions to the problem. Other examples of incomplete definitions would be considering the intake of lead from the atmosphere without considering the intake from paint or drinking water, or considering the effects of ozone on people without considering its effects on vegetation. As implied by the arrows in figure 8-I which indicate feedback, an environmental problem may undergo redefinition as a result of later steps in the procedure.

8.36 The way the problem is formulated determines how the questions to be considered will be framed, and is crucial to the eventual outcome of the standard-setting procedure. If an environmental problem is first envisaged or composed inappropriately or too narrowly, this may diminish public trust in environmental regulation, may result in defective standards, or have much wider social, political and economic repercussions. It is, therefore, essential to take into account at this early stage the perspectives and values of all those who may be affected by a problem or have an interest in it. This may be a wide or narrow range of people, depending on the circumstances, and their perspectives will often differ significantly. The eventual decision will not necessarily represent a consensus (however desirable that may be) nor a lowest common denominator of acceptability, but it must have taken divergent views into proper account.

8.37 There is no single correct format for articulating values: the mechanism for public involvement should be appropriate to the circumstances of a particular decision. Flexibility and imagination should make it possible to devise ways of taking proper account of the necessary range of factors without producing unwieldy and slow administrative structures. Examples of the kind of forum which might be appropriate for considering local, national, European and global issues are described in chapter 7. Lay people can be involved directly (perhaps through a consensus conference or a citizens' jury) or indirectly, but they are effectively disempowered if they are not included in defining the problem. **Better ways need to be developed for articulating people's values and taking them into account from the earliest stage in what have been hitherto relatively technocratic procedures.**

8.38 The third step is to formulate the **policy aims** which a standard will be designed to achieve. Although this is conceptually distinct from defining the problem, the two steps may not be easily distinguishable in practice. Many environmental problems fall within a framework of established policies and the aims for a standard can be inferred from other policies or established by analogy. Where that does not apply, or circumstances indicate that existing policy aims ought to be reviewed critically, it is vital that lay people should be involved either directly or indirectly. If a consensus conference or citizens' jury is arranged, it could cover both definition of the problem and formulation of the policy aims. As well as issues about the scope of protection to be sought which should have been considered already in defining the problem (8.35), issues to be addressed at this stage include the potentially conflicting concerns, such as equity and material well-being, which the principle of sustainable development seeks to reconcile (1.8–1.10, 7.5–7.6).

8.39 A given environmental problem may require action on several fronts, and may lead to the setting of several different forms of standard. Adequate provision for deliberation about policy aims should ensure that the various actions taken are mutually reinforcing. At this step too the existence of a feedback loop is important: the aims of policy may change as understanding develops.

8.40 The fourth step is **analysis of the problem.** A cluster of analyses is required; the components of the cluster, and the nature of the outputs they should be expected to produce, were discussed individually earlier in this report: scientific (chapter 2), technological (chapter 3), risk (chapter 4), economic (chapter 5) and implementation (chapter 6). The framework for these analyses has been constructed at the second and third steps. They should not be expected to revisit questions of values which have already been considered and resolved. The dominant requirement at this step in the procedure is a high degree of analytical rigour. That can be promoted by subjecting each of the component analyses to peer review within its own discipline.

8.41 It is equally important that there is contact and co-ordination between the component analyses, as shown by the double-headed arrows in figure 8-I. They rely on each other for data and assumptions. In some cases, that may mean they cannot all be carried out simultaneously. The time, resources and emphasis given to each of the component analyses will vary according to the problem being addressed. In some cases, it is the scientific assessment which will pose the greatest challenge. In other cases, the effects of a form of pollution will be familiar (for example radiation), it is likely that the scientific analysis will be relatively straightforward, and greater emphasis may be placed on technological analysis in order to identify the available options and estimate their costs. Other decisions, such as those to deal with vehicle emissions, may depend heavily on economic and implementation analyses to define an effective strategy for influencing behaviour patterns.

8.42 Each component analysis should explore a range of options and scenarios. Some or all of the analyses may be repeated, either because they are not accepted as having been carried out satisfactorily or because new factors emerge which were not originally taken into account. This may happen on the initiative of those conducting a particular analysis or as a result of peer review or because the conclusions of an analysis have been rejected at the following stage, which is discussed below. While iteration may considerably improve the quality of the output, it also adds to the cost of analysis and the time taken. It is therefore desirable to avoid the need for iteration as far as possible by careful attention to the quality of the output from the previous steps and by liaison between those carrying out the component analyses from the earliest planning stage onwards.

8.43 The analytical stage is primarily an activity for experts, within the framework of the questions and policy aims determined at earlier stages. There are circumstances in which other forms of knowledge, possessed by non-experts, can make a crucial contribution to an expert analysis; this may happen with local knowledge, for example of the characteristics of soils in Cumbria (one of the cases discussed in box 2E), but such a situation is perhaps less likely to arise in the context of setting standards. The appointment of lay members to expert committees may be an effective way of ensuring that these have available certain specific kinds of knowledge, but should not be regarded as a substitute either for transparency and openness in the working of such committees or for thoroughgoing measures to articulate the values of people generally at the key framing and decision-making stages (7.34).

8.44 Considering the results from the whole cluster of analyses in the light of the way the problem has been defined and the policy aims previously decided is obviously a crucial step. The name given to it here is **deliberation and synthesis**. Consideration of people's values is an important part of this step. If the procedure has worked effectively, they will have been articulated as part of earlier steps. In other cases, some action may have to be taken at this stage to enable them to be articulated more clearly. If so, advantage can be taken of the much greater volume of information and analysis that will now be available.

8.45 Where there is little difference of view about the solutions to an environmental problem, deliberation and synthesis may be a fairly simple exercise. It is not necessary that it should yield a consensus about the action to be taken. In most cases that will not happen. The essential function of this step in the procedure is to facilitate subsequent decision by identifying areas of agreement and disagreement, and clarifying the nature and extent of differences. That may entail asking for some or all of the cluster of analyses to be repeated.

8.46 The sixth step is **the decision whether or not to set a standard, and the type of standard**; and, if a standard is not set, whether an alternative approach should be adopted. The seventh step is **specifying the content of the standard**. In some cases, the fifth, sixth and seventh steps may be linked together very closely in practice. For example they might all be undertaken within a single international conference. The nature of the standard may have been largely predetermined by the previously agreed policy aims. In other cases, the outcome of the fifth or sixth steps may be that a review is undertaken either of the original definition of the problem or of the policy aims being pursued. The result may then be that the analytical stage is repeated, in preparation for a further round of deliberation and synthesis. This further cycle may happen if the analytical stage has produced a deeper understanding of the problem, for example, or if an adequate degree of consensus cannot be reached about the action to be taken.

8.47 Before a decision is finalised it may be the subject of some traditional form of consultation with interested parties. That may or may not lead to repetition of one or more steps in the procedure.

8.48 The practical application of the procedure described in broad outline above will vary with the circumstances of each case and with geographical scale. Among the differences will be the weight attached to individual elements and the methods by which particular groups of people are involved in the procedures. The time and resources spent on particular methods for eliciting values, and the extent of lay participation, will depend on the nature of the problem to be addressed. Once the procedure has operated to set principles, the setting of subsequent standards within those principles (process standards complying with the principle of 'best available techniques not entailing excessive cost' might be an example) may be relatively uncontroversial. Values must continue to inform the decisions, but the machinery for articulating them might have a narrower scope, perhaps confined to detecting any proposed standard that might raise new value questions.

8.49 The eighth and final step in the procedure is to **monitor and evaluate the effectiveness** of a standard. This will include reviewing new evidence. It will also include some aspects which might also be described as implementation, such as obtaining and publishing compliance data. Performing the activity will often be wholly or mainly for experts, who may for example precipitate a review if significant new scientific data become available. The public will be concerned with the results of evaluation, which may indicate that the manner of implementation should be improved, or ultimately that the whole process of standard setting should be restarted, if the need for a fresh approach emerges.

8.50 The key features which distinguish the procedure described above from what generally happens at present are:

> the explicit separation of functions between analysis and policy;

> the comprehensive description of the forms of analysis required to support decisions and their respective contributions;

> the emphasis on taking people's values into consideration, not only when decisions come to be taken, but in the initial stages of recognising and defining the problem, framing questions, and formulating policy aims. The issues addressed and the methodologies deployed during the analytical stage of the procedure will reflect the values elicited during these earlier stages;

> transparency and openness at all stages.

The interface between analysis and policy

8.51 We have noted previously that a failure to make a clear separation between policy and analysis (which, in the environmental field, has predominantly been scientific analysis) and has had a pernicious effect on trust in the quality and integrity of both expert advice and the decision taken. There are several reasons why a separation of the scientific assessment stage from the policy-making stage is essential. It is important that all the component analyses restrict themselves to setting out the information which will form the raw material of the decision, and do not attempt to displace that decision. Even in cases where the scientific assessment may appear to lead directly to the deliberative procedure from which a standard will emerge, there must always be some consideration of the practicality, cost, legality and morality of the decision, however intuitive this consideration may be in practice. Rigour and accountability are better served if these considerations are kept explicit and distinct.

8.52 A further argument for separation concerns the use and presentation of scientific advice in policy making (see chapter 2). The logic of scientific processes differs from that of policy making, making it inappropriate for both activities to be undertaken simultaneously. There has often been a poor understanding of the nature of scientific investigation and the uncertainty surrounding research results. Politicians often demand certainty from scientists, frame questions in a way that scientists are incapable of answering, and demand answers before sufficient information is available. Where scientists are explicit about the extent of uncertainties, policy-makers may seize upon that as a reason for deferring any action or response.[7] The need to establish clear principles which apply to the use and preparation of scientific advice is especially relevant in cases where there is a large degree of scientific uncertainty, or a significant range of scientific opinion, or where it falls in a highly sensitive area of public policy.[8]

8.53 The knowledge provided by any single discipline is never sufficient to determine the precise level of a standard. By recommending that a distinction be made between analysis and policy making, we are not saying that scientists and other analysts are not qualified to exercise practical judgement, nor that they should not do so. We are suggesting that they should make it clear when they are speaking as scientists (or whatever) and when they are exercising practical judgement.

8.54 We explore the significance of the interface between analysis and policy through some examples. The value of separating the analytical stage from the decision-making stage has been illustrated by the Intergovernmental Panel on Climate Change (IPCC), which has conceived of its task as assessment and not policy making.[9] IPCC's Scientific Assessment Working Group believes that to move into the policy arena would destroy its scientific credibility and usefulness.

8.55 There have been some successful examples of separation of science from policy making at a regional level. A rough separation of scientific from economic and political working groups has been formalised in the approach adopted by the United Nations Economic Commission for Europe Convention on Long-Range Transboundary Air Pollution (LRTAP). There is of course no guarantee (or necessarily any real expectation) that technical groups are immune from political influence since delegates are nominated by their governments. However, the determination of critical loads at international workshops by scientists and other specialists has been kept separate from the setting of standards and targets for emissions, and scientific information collated for the Convention is fairly widely published (for example the various reports by the UK's Critical Loads Advisory Group and Review Group on Acid Rain). Such practices have the potential to improve considerably the transparency of the decision-making procedure.

8.56 The need for a proper separation of functions is illustrated by the criticisms associated with the UK's Expert Panel on Air Quality Standards (EPAQS). The need for an expert body to advise the government on air quality was accepted in the 1990 Environment White Paper *This Common*

Inheritance: EPAQS was set up by the Secretary of State for the Environment in 1991. The terms of reference of the Panel are:

> To advise, as required, on the establishment and application of air quality standards in the United Kingdom, for purposes of developing policy on air pollution control and increasing public knowledge and understanding of air quality, taking account of the best available evidence of the effects of air pollution on human health and the wider environment, and of progressive development of the air quality monitoring network.

Members of the Panel are invited to join on the basis of their expertise in the medical and air pollution fields. There are observers from the Department of the Environment, Transport and the Regions, the Department of Health and the Health and Safety Executive. The Panel is responsible for producing a series of reports containing recommendations on the principal pollutants. Past reports have covered benzene, 1,3-butadiene, carbon monoxide, lead, nitrogen dioxide, particles, ozone and sulphur dioxide. The government incorporated the recommendations made by EPAQS as the air quality standards in the National Air Quality Strategy.

8.57 EPAQS was intended to evaluate toxicological and epidemiological information to arrive at a concentration in air which minimises harm (see box 2D). For pollutants for which there is no safe level of exposure, any recommended concentration other than zero implies that a view has been taken on a tolerable level of harm (see box 2D). Such a decision should not be taken by an ostensibly scientific body and should be made after following the procedure described earlier in this chapter. Whilst EPAQS' approach is no doubt realistic and pragmatic, it demonstrates the desirability of a clear separation of functions in handling scientific, economic, social and value issues in risk assessment and management. This distinction needs to be drawn more firmly and consistently. **Any body involved in setting standards should, in all its pronouncements, draw an explicit distinction between scientific statements and recommendations it wishes to make after considering a scientific assessment in conjunction with other factors; and should identify clearly what those other factors are.**

8.58 The procedures followed by the World Health Organization (WHO) in producing guidelines for air quality and drinking water quality are often cited as a model for the way in which standard setting should be conducted. WHO publishes a detailed justification for each guideline value, summarising the scientific and medical evidence considered, and in recent years there has been a more explicit use of peer review while assessments are being prepared. WHO typically expresses the conclusions of scientific assessments in the form of guideline values (for example, for the concentration of a given substance in air). WHO stresses that its role is to elaborate guidelines rather than set standards, and that these guidelines can be developed into standards by taking local environmental, social, economic and cultural conditions into consideration. In reality, WHO guideline values are often translated directly into legal limits. For example, the European Commission, in putting forward proposals in recent years for legislation on drinking water and air quality, has in practice adopted the WHO guideline value as the proposed standard in almost all cases. This suggests there is a need for more transparent procedures which indicate how a WHO guideline value has been used by other bodies and how other considerations, beyond the remit of WHO, have been taken into consideration. It would be preferable if the conclusions of WHO's scientific assessments were expressed as a range of values representing different levels of risk, as this would draw attention to the policy decision made subsequently by a standard-setting body.

How bodies setting standards should operate

8.59 So far in this chapter we have deliberately concentrated on the logical sequence involved in setting standards, with only incidental references to the institutions through which that task is performed. It will be clear both from this chapter and from the overview of present environmental standards in appendix C that the separate steps in the procedure, and sometimes the separate aspects of a single step in the procedure, are very often the responsibility of different bodies. Setting environmental standards is in general an example of policy being made within a complex inter-organisational network.[10]

8.60 Such networks can have considerable advantages in terms of flexibility, their responsiveness to a plurality of viewpoints and perspectives, and their openness to new information and concepts. The separation of functions which we have emphasised as desirable may be more readily achievable where several separate organisations are involved. On the other hand, it may be much more difficult to manage such a network than to manage the work of a single body. There are certain institutional requirements which are important, not only for the quality of decisions, but for building public confidence, and it is more difficult to ensure that these are met in an inter-organisational setting.

8.61 The first and most basic requirement is that all the steps in the procedure should be covered. **Bodies setting standards ought to take into account the entire range of considerations we have identified as being relevant to such decisions and this should be required by their terms of reference.** To the extent that they do not make detailed assessments of such factors themselves, they must be able to draw on authoritative assessments made by other bodies.

8.62 A second fundamental requirement is that **there should be an audit trail documenting all the considerations taken into account in reaching a decision and how they were taken into account.** The existence of such an audit trail is one of the key advantages of WHO's procedures. It is desirable, not only in the wider interest of transparency (discussed below) but also to provide the basis for review of a standard, either at regular intervals or when something happens to change one of the assumptions on which it was originally based. **All environmental standards should be reviewed at pre-set intervals or earlier if significant new evidence emerges or there is an unforeseen change in circumstances.** The separation of the analytical steps from other steps in the procedure, desirable for other reasons, also facilitates the provision of an audit trail and enhances accountability.

8.63 A basic requirement for public trust which is not in general met at present is that the **bodies setting environmental standards must operate in an open and transparent way. By 'transparent' we mean that there must be full publicity for their existence, their terms of reference, the decisions they take and the reasons for them. By 'open' we mean that there must be adequate opportunities for those outside an institution, especially those with a particular interest in a given decision, to contribute fully to the decision-making procedure.** The nature of the contribution, and therefore the precise requirements in institutional terms, will vary according to the aspect of standard setting involved. For scientific input, for example, the use of peer review and open publication of evidence will be major factors. Both policy-makers and the general public must be able to recognise and take into account the impact of vested interests in the process and the balance struck in the ultimate outcome. **All the analyses should also be subject to peer review and scrutiny.** This is no panacea: whilst transparency is necessary, it is no guarantee that materially good decisions will result. The manner in which communication is undertaken can convey its own message: appearing to disclose information only under pressure does not enhance credibility. And once an agency has become mistrusted, any information from that source will tend to be disregarded.

8.64 A clear principle of the Commission has been that the data justifying decisions should be freely accessible. The Tenth Report[11] contained a full discussion of the justification for this freedom and the ways in which it could be legitimately constrained. It concluded that

> A guiding principle behind all legislative and administrative controls relating to environmental pollution should be a presumption in favour of unrestricted access for the public to information which the pollution control authorities obtain or receive by virtue of their statutory powers, with provision for secrecy only in those circumstances where a genuine case for it can be substantiated.

8.65 In the last decade, changes in UK law and government practice (such as greater willingness to release environmental information) and the work of the environmental pressure groups (such as Friends of the Earth's presentation of information from the Environment Agency's Chemicals Release Inventory in the form of an on-line database of industrial emissions) have in some respects strengthened the right to know and, possibly, the citizen's right to redress. There has been strong pressure to open up the policy and regulatory process to public scrutiny, first in the USA, then in the UK, then throughout the European Union. The World Wide Web is transforming both the amount of information available and the speed with which it becomes available, although the quality of this information varies. Nevertheless, there remain major deficiencies in the accountability of standard-setters.

8.66 Greater openness and more scrupulous attention to accountability also provide a formal means of exposing the misuse of science by politicians. It may provide a means of clarifying the level of uncertainty in scientific assessments and the assumptions underlying scientific and economic analysis. There is a difficult line to tread between openness and scaremongering. Careful, but not unduly simplistic, explanation is one of the means of avoiding reactions of panic to a half-understood story (sometimes seen after announcements about the safety of drugs). Experts need to concentrate on improved explanation and to be better aware of the public's ability to grasp complex issues and cope with uncertainty.

8.67 The decision-making procedures of global bodies that set standards are reasonably transparent and their proceedings relatively open. Direct accountability to national governments facilitates transparency, as they must normally ratify any standards set, and can be expected to have a broader perspective. It is often possible for environmental groups and/or industry lobbies to have a significant effect on decisions by operating in conjunction with sympathetic governments. **It is important that global scientific bodies work transparently, and that their scientific assessments are subject to peer review and published, with the affiliations of the scientists involved made explicit.** Differences of view may arise because of the existence of different scientific communities (differentiated by discipline, by geography or by culture).

8.68 Other institutional requirements are desirable but may be more difficult to meet in practice. **A body setting standards should be able to relate its decisions to decisions about other environmental risks within the geographic area it covers.** The implication is that the body setting standards for a given area should be responsible for all types of pollutant and for all the environmental media. **A body setting standards should also have sufficient resources and continuity of existence to ensure that periodic reviews of standards are carried out, and that there is a fast reaction if new evidence emerges either about a new form of hazard or about the risks associated with a known hazard.** This requirement assumes even greater importance if there have been uncertainties about the scientific evidence of effects or about the technology for reducing pollution.

8.69 The main purpose of this chapter has been to describe how we consider the process of dealing with environmental problems should evolve. We have noted that the credibility of individual environmental standards, and public trust in the whole system of environmental regulation, can be undermined by confusion about the nature of decisions on environmental policies and standards. Whilst trust cannot be created by design, certain procedural characteristics can facilitate trust.

8.70 The separation of analytical functions and the other aspects of the procedures described in this chapter clarifies the different inputs to the task of deciding an acceptable standard. Public involvement in the earlier stages of the procedure, particularly in the problem definition stage, will also help build trust. Openness and transparency will help satisfy the public about the expertise, objectivity and impartiality of the bodies involved in dealing with environmental problems. We believe these features are essential to provide a more robust basis for setting environmental standards for the future.

The new challenges

8.71 Public awareness of environmental problems is now very widespread in most countries and environmental considerations are high on the agenda of governments and large companies. This pervasiveness of environmental concern throughout society will continue to increase. The value of protecting the environment will be appreciated increasingly by individuals, industry, commerce, and governments.

8.72 However great the difficulty of defining exactly what is meant by sustainable development, the concept has taken a firm hold on public and political consciousness. It prompts challenging questions, particularly about the wider and more lasting effects, not just of policy decisions by governments, but of the decisions of companies, and the actions we all take from day to day.

8.73 Associated with these features is a widespread demand for increased environmental protection. An example of this is the current disquiet about the degree of protection afforded by the present regulatory regime against any adverse effects of genetically modified organisms. There is no simple rule for determining the degree of caution which should be applied in particular cases. Sober evaluation of both what is known and what is feared is a prerequisite to policies which are neither unduly restrictive nor heedless of often deeply held convictions about the environment.

8.74 A major conclusion of this report is that much greater use of less traditional approaches is needed to deal successfully with the complexity, widespread distribution and sheer number of pollutants and bring about the life-style changes which are needed in order to tackle some forms of environmental damage. These new approaches will involve much greater use of economic instruments and of the forms of self-regulation discussed in chapter 6. Government should aim to create structures and practices which enable people to achieve environmental goals through co-operation and taking action in common. Some steps have already been taken in this direction, but the road is difficult and much more needs to be done to remove perverse incentives.

8.75 We welcome the much greater awareness of sustainable development issues among companies, and we have identified several measures that should be taken to reinforce such changes of attitude and approach, and ensure they become universal. There are challenges to business in spreading more generally the more far-sighted approaches of the best companies and especially in changing attitudes in smaller firms to enable them to capture the commercial and environmental advantages of better practices.

8.76 Alongside newer approaches, we believe that environmental standards (as the term is used in this report) will continue to provide an essential framework to guide action towards a more sustainable future. As targets, they can provide a structure within which non-regulatory approaches to environmental improvements can be applied; in the international arena they set goals for individual nations, whereas the details of implementation can be left to be developed within the social and legal framework of each contracting party. Standards backed by legal enforcement machinery are an appropriate way of dealing with some of the worst forms and sources of pollution; they can embody moral concerns; and, in circumstances in which non-statutory measures might otherwise be preferred, they can be held in reserve, for use if agreement is not forthcoming. The continued importance of direct regulation was acknowledged by representatives of major companies in their evidence to us.[12] They found a clear, consistently enforced structure of legal controls helpful in running their businesses. If reliance were placed solely on voluntary action to protect the environment, companies would be likely to suffer from a lack of credibility with the public. Pressure from an external source is required to maintain standards in all firms and to reassure the public that industry is not harming the environment.[13]

8.77 The procedures we have outlined in this chapter are designed to be flexible so that they can form the basis not only for the setting of numerical standards but also for developing new approaches to environmental policy and regulation, such as those referred to above.

8.78 Overcoming the new challenges will not involve a great extension in the role of government and government agencies. An increase in the bureaucracy of environmental regulation or the complexity of controls would not be acceptable to industry, commerce or the public. It would risk obscuring, not clarifying, the way policies should be developed. We do not believe that the kinds of uncertainty we have identified will be overcome by expanding the staff and resources of standard-setting and regulatory bodies so that they can devote greater effort to deploying more and more sophisticated transformations of highly uncertain data.

8.79 The analytical stage of the decision procedure and its several components are nevertheless crucial. Scientists must be more aware of public concerns and priorities and better informed about the needs of the policy process. They must work together more closely to ensure that dispassionate advice is readily available to inform policy. In the last decade, great efforts have been made to increase public understanding of science both through the media and through mechanisms such as public meetings and science fairs. Initiatives of this kind should be continued and extended, with the aim of reducing or eliminating distortions which enter into the environmental debate, especially about what science has to offer. There should be a long-term programme of public education, extending across all ages, about the true nature of our understanding of the environment and its management.

8.80 The need to integrate environmental considerations into other policy areas is now widely recognised. In the future, there must be a much greater coherence in policies for environmental protection, not a series of discrete measures aimed at particular sources of pollution.

8.81 This raises questions about how the particular aspects of the environment for which the Environment Agencies are responsible can be related to key local authority responsibilities such as land use and transport planning and air quality management. The government has stressed that the Environment Agency must work openly and in partnership with local stakeholders and engage in effective dialogue with local communities. There is a tension between on the one hand, responsiveness to local circumstances, and on the other, consistency in environmental protection, nationally or across the European Community. There may need to be further evolution in organisation in order to achieve a coherent portfolio of functions at a level at which procedures can be genuinely participatory and informed by people's values. Environmental and managerial arguments would point towards this strengthening being at regional level. Corresponding arguments would apply to the Scottish Environment Protection Agency.

8.82 Our original purpose in this study was to help establish a more consistent and robust basis for setting standards for environmental protection. Our conclusions about the overall procedure for standard setting, and its individual components, are brought together in the next chapter. We hope that this report will also serve a wider purpose in promoting a clearer understanding of the current and future significance of environmental standards, and of the social, political, and scientific contexts within which they will need to be set.

Chapter 9

CONCLUSIONS

Our aim has been to indicate the broad directions in which we believe protection of the environment should evolve, not to make specific recommendations. There are nevertheless a number of matters on which we have reached conclusions. These conclusions, which appeared in bold type in the appropriate contexts in previous chapters, are brought together in this chapter.

Significance of environmental standards

9.1   The nature of environmental concerns has changed significantly in terms of the objectives of policy, the time-scales considered, the geographical scales considered, and the kinds of environmental modification that are addressed. These changes have implications for the way environmental standards are used and set. They also have implications for the types of evidence, in particular the types of scientific evidence, required to support decisions on policies and standards (1.13).

9.2   Environmental standards take diverse forms (1.17 and box 1A). They include not only numerical and legally enforceable limits, but standards which are not mandatory but contained in guidelines, codes of practice or sets of criteria for deciding individual cases; and standards not set by governments which carry authority for other reasons, especially the scientific eminence or market power of those who set them (1.15).

9.3   Standards are a crucial element in the environmental policy process (1.22). Numerical standards have come to occupy a central position in a much expanded system of environmental regulation (1.23).

9.4   Other key changes in the policy process over the last 30 years have been:

a. environmental policies and standards that apply in the UK are now determined predominantly on a European scale (1.24);

b. there has also been a great growth in the number and importance of international conventions relating to the environment, at both global and regional scale (1.26);

c. formal techniques have been used increasingly to aid decision making (1.27).

d. the influence of environmental non-governmental organisations (NGOs) has grown (1.31).

Procedures for setting standards

9.5   Environmental issues reach the agenda by diverse routes. The stages of recognising and defining the problem, framing the questions that need to be answered and formulating policy aims are all important. They need to be informed, not only by evaluations of the effectiveness of existing policies, but by the articulation of people's values (figure 8-I and 8.33–8.39).

9.6   After a problem has been recognised and defined, and policy aims formulated, the stages in the policy process are:

rigorous and dispassionate investigation and analysis;

deliberation and synthesis, informed by people's values;

the decision whether to set a standard, and if so what type of standard;

specifying the content of the standard;

monitoring and evaluating its effectiveness (figure 8-I and 8.40–8.50).

9.7 Better ways need to be developed for articulating people's values and taking them into account from the earliest stage in what have been hitherto relatively technocratic procedures (8.37).

9.8 The analytical stage of the policy process has several complementary and closely inter-related components:

scientific assessment;

analysis of technological options;

assessment of risk and uncertainty;

economic appraisal; and

analysis of implementation issues, including the geographical scope of standards.

Conceptually, this approach would apply to any kind of environmental policy or standard but the nature of a particular environmental problem will determine the resources which should be devoted to each type of analysis in practice (8.4).

9.9 The presentation to decision-makers of the results of the analyses referred to above should clearly state the assumptions and limitations of each analysis. It will usually be necessary to offer several options and their implications, so far as these can be gauged (8.11).

9.10 Any body involved in setting standards should, in all its pronouncements, draw an explicit distinction between scientific statements and recommendations it wishes to make after considering a scientific assessment in conjunction with other factors; and should identify clearly what those other factors are (8.57).

9.11 Bodies setting standards ought to take into account the entire range of considerations we have identified as being relevant to such decisions and this should be required by their terms of reference (8.61).

9.12 There should be an audit trail documenting all the considerations taken into account in reaching a decision and how they were taken into account (8.62).

9.13 All environmental standards should be reviewed at pre-set intervals or earlier if significant new evidence emerges or there is an unforeseen change in circumstances (8.62).

9.14 Bodies setting environmental standards must operate in an open and transparent way. By 'transparent' we mean that there must be full publicity for their existence, their terms of reference, the decisions they take and the reasons for them. By 'open' we mean that there must be adequate opportunities for those outside an institution, especially those with a particular interest in a given decision, to contribute fully to the decision-making procedure (8.63).

9.15 All the analyses should also be subject to peer review and scrutiny (8.63).

9.16 It is important that global scientific bodies work transparently, and that their scientific assessments are subject to peer review and published, with the affiliations of the scientists involved made explicit (8.67).

9.17 A body setting standards should be able to relate its decisions to decisions about other environmental risks within the geographic area it covers. A body setting standards should also have sufficient resources and continuity of existence to ensure that periodic reviews of standards are carried out, and that there is a fast reaction if new evidence emerges either about a new form of hazard or about the risks associated with a known hazard (8.68).

Scientific understanding

9.18 In setting an environmental standard, the starting-point must be scientific understanding of the cause of the problem or potential problem under consideration (2.68).

9.19 Despite the great difficulties involved, determining dose-effect relationships for the effects of substances on the natural environment is an essential exercise if appropriate environmental policies are to be adopted. When environmental policies or standards are adopted, it should always be made clear in an explicit statement whether they are designed to protect the natural environment, human health, or both, and the degree and nature of protection they are intended to afford (2.50).

9.20 Use of any model of pollutant-effect relationships should be dependent on careful consideration of the way it represents understanding of the development of the specific toxic effect being considered (2.25).

9.21 All exposure models (indeed, all mathematical models used within scientific assessments) should be regarded with caution until they are properly validated (2.56).

9.22 A clear dividing line should be drawn between analysis of scientific evidence and consideration of ethical and social issues which are outside the scope of a scientific assessment (2.69).

9.23 In a scientific assessment of an environmental issue there are bound to be limitations and uncertainties associated with the data at each stage. Standard setting and other decision-making procedures should recognise that (2.66). The requirement for sound science as the basis for environmental policy is not a requirement for absolute knowledge or certainty and should not be interpreted as such (2.73).

9.24 When considering the process of scientific assessment and its output, two separate issues need to be addressed. First, is the science well done, and are uncertainties and limitations in the data properly recognised? The answer to this question determines whether the assessment represents good science. Second, does the science provide a firm basis for policy decisions? The answer to this question determines how useful the assessment will be to the policy-maker, whether decisions will have to be taken in the face of uncertainty, and whether further studies (perhaps including experimental work) should be carried out (2.74).

9.25 Scientific assessments should indicate clearly where the boundaries of knowledge lie. To be helpful to policy-makers they should indicate clearly both what is known or considered to be indisputable and what is considered to be speculative (2.75).

9.26 Transparency should be the watchword in presenting assessments. It is essential that there should be a succinct narrative summary of the assessment covering the underlying scientific basis, uncertainties in the evidence and the rationale for any methods used to cope with variability and uncertainties (for example, any safety factors used) and the assumptions implicit in their use (2.76).

9.27 A scientific assessment should present the range of possible interpretations of the available evidence, or the range of scientific possibilities and options concerning a particular course of action, accompanied by acknowledgement of the assumptions and uncertainties implicit in the assessment. The output of a scientific assessment should not normally be presented as a single option or statement; an assessment yielding a single answer (especially a single number) may give a spurious impression of accuracy (2.80).

9.28 It is necessary to build review processes and the potential for revision into standard-setting procedures. Scientific knowledge can move rapidly and standards must be readily adjustable and regularly reviewed, so that new insights can be incorporated (2.83).

9.29 To prevent development of new understanding being restricted by established regulatory procedures, vested interests or small closed communities of experts, publicly funded programmes of environmental research should include provision for independent investigation and inquiry (2.86).

9.30 We welcome monitoring by the Office of Science and Technology (OST) of:

a. the extent to which Departments are modifying their procedures for using scientific advice in policy making in response to the principles produced by the Chief Scientific Adviser (2.77);

b. Departmental and agency procedures for early identification of issues for which scientific research or advice will be needed (2.87).

Technological options

9.31 While environmental regulation has broadened from considering emissions to a single environmental medium to considering emissions to all media from a process, analysis of environmental performance has been extended even further to cover the whole material and energy supply chains associated with a product or service (3.30).

9.32 Taking account of life cycle considerations is the preferable way of managing the overall environmental impact of particular processes or particular industrial sectors because it directs attention to the points at which intervention to protect the environment will be most effective and efficient (3.31).

9.33 Policy guidance is needed on where the boundaries of life cycle assessments should be drawn (3.47).

9.34 To ensure that the full ranges of options and repercussions are considered, assessments of technological options carried out as inputs to decisions on environmental policies or standards should be on a life cycle basis (3.46).

9.35 The aim of assessments of technological options should be seen as widening the range of options considered, including those that involve technology forcing or commercialisation forcing (3.50).

9.36 Particular options should not be excluded from life cycle assessments on the ground that action required to implement them falls outside the responsibilities of the immediate regulator (3.48).

9.37 To the extent that regulation of industrial activities continues to use permits and forms of standard on lines similar to those used at present, their use should in future be informed by a life cycle perspective. If necessary, there should be changes in legislation so that the full potential for that can be realised (3.49).

9.38 Broadly based assessments of options on a life cycle basis must not be allowed to become an excuse for avoiding or delaying significant improvements available at particular stages in the cycle (3.53).

9.39 There should be scope for suppliers or users of improved technologies to stimulate tightening of standards (3.51).

9.40 The Environment Agencies must harness highly qualified staff (3.52).

9.41 The very slow progress made with assessment of existing chemical substances has demonstrated the need for an entirely fresh approach. The current reviews provide a timely opportunity (3.44).

9.42 We consider that the criterion of comparison with the risk presented by other available substances should be introduced into all regulatory procedures for the marketing and use of chemicals, including those covering reactants and intermediates (3.45).

Risk and uncertainty

9.43 We see the assessment of risk and uncertainty dealing with two important components:

> looking at broader uncertainties about the current issue which extend beyond the available scientific evidence and considering a wider range of possibilities;

> where sufficient data are available, quantifying and analysing the risks associated with the issue under consideration.

The relative importance of these two aspects will vary according to the circumstances, and in any given case one of them may predominate (4.49).

9.44 Risk assessments prepared in support of decisions on environmental policies or standards should start with information about the nature of the hazard which the policy or standard seeks to address and the extent and quality of the evidence available for assessing the risks it poses. This part of the analysis should indicate whether the hazard is of a relatively well-understood type; if it is unfamiliar, an attempt should be made to identify the most nearly analogous hazards and the aspects which are not understood (4.50).

9.45 The limitations and uncertainties in any estimates of risk must always be made clear in ways which are meaningful to people without particular specialist knowledge (4.52).

9.46 Risk assessments should identify the uncertainties which have the largest implications and the actions that would need to be taken to reduce or resolve them. However, it would be inappropriate and misleading to attempt to incorporate into risk assessments estimated probabilities for the correctness of particular scientific theories or interpretations (4.53).

9.47 Whatever action is taken in the name of precaution (from use of worst-case scenarios and safety factors in assessments through to application of the precautionary principle in decision making) should be transparent and subject to review in the light of development of understanding. Relevant data should be collected and reviewed on a continuous basis; and if a standard has been set, it should be revised up or down as necessary (4.48).

9.48 If there are sufficient data, and sufficient knowledge of the underlying processes, quantitative risk assessments should cover not only risk of human deaths but risks of other harmful outcomes. For each estimate the assumptions made should be explicit and clearly stated (4.54).

9.49 No satisfactory way has been devised of measuring risk to the natural environment, even in principle, let alone defining what scale of risk should be regarded as tolerable (4.26).

9.50 As well as distinguishing between different types of effect from a hazard, risk assessments should also:

> *a.* indicate the distribution of risks (whether they are especially high for people in certain localities, age groups or occupations, or people with certain medical conditions or genetic predispositions);

> *b.* characterise as far as possible the respective perceptions of the risks held by relevant groups, the meanings the risks will have for them, and their views about the tolerability of the risks.

Quantitative information on these points should be provided where it is available, otherwise qualitative assessments should be given (4.56).

9.51 For risks of the same general type, and where data are available and the processes sufficiently understood, direct comparison between options may be useful in informing decisions, for example:

> *a.* between the risks from the hazard being addressed and other risks of the same general type affecting the same group of people or compartment of the environment, so that estimates can be made of the total risk of that type to which these will be subject;

> *b.* between the risks from the hazard being addressed and the risks from different sources or pathways for the same pollutant or different pollutants from the same source, in order to identify any options for risk reduction that might obtain a larger benefit for a similar cost.

However, making comparisons between risks which the public does not perceive as comparable can undermine the credibility of regulators and governments (4.57).

Economic appraisal

9.52 Economic appraisal should be regarded as an aid to making decisions which also take other factors into account. Formal techniques such as multi-criteria analysis should likewise be regarded as aids to decision making (5.49).

9.53 An economic appraisal of an environmental policy or standard should identify the objectives of the policy or standard and the options to be considered; summarise and analyse all the consequences of the options; and indicate what that analysis implies for the decision that has to be made. It should cover consequences which cannot easily be valued in money terms, as well as those that can easily be valued in money terms. Where consequences are not valued in money terms, they should be represented either qualitatively or in terms of other quantities. It should indicate the timing of the costs and benefits (5.50).

9.54 When performing an economic appraisal it should be borne in mind that the *relative* values of the things under consideration may change over time (5.27).

9.55 The report of the appraisal should describe the major uncertainties. It should include a sensitivity analysis showing the effects of changing key assumptions (5.51).

9.56 The report of an appraisal should normally incorporate a description of the information that will need to be collected to enable a retrospective evaluation of the policy or standard to be undertaken at a later date (5.53).

Implementing environmental policies

9.57 We consider environmental standards should be set for the smallest area for which it is sensible and effective to do so (6.31).

9.58 We consider that, where a standard is set at European or international level, it should be set in a form that allows as much discretion about the methods of implementing it as is feasible without undermining its effectiveness (6.33).

9.59 Despite attempts to resolve the situation, there is still a need for an internationally agreed set of principles to deal with the potential difficulties caused by the overlap between the General Agreement on Tariffs and Trade (GATT) rules and trade provisions contained in multilateral environmental agreements (MEAs), and for ambiguities in the operation of the GATT to be clarified. Greater effort is needed by the international community to resolve the difficulties (6.12).

9.60 An essential condition for effective direct regulation is that there should be adequate inspection and adequate monitoring of compliance with limit values (6.37).

9.61 Numerical standards for concentrations of substances should always incorporate protocols for sampling and the analytical techniques or methods by which compliance is to be measured, and should require analyses to be carried out in laboratories which are participating in appropriate accreditation and proficiency testing schemes (6.38).

9.62 Every numerical standard should be specified in a way that takes full account of the nature of the substance to which it relates, the extent of statistical variation in the parameter to which it relates and (where it is legally enforceable) the requirements for verification. Many current environmental standards are defective in terms of these criteria, most often in not being verifiable. Where that is the case, it should be remedied by setting a supplementary standard for verification, with the aim that environmental standards should be, wherever possible, statistically verifiable ideal standards. Reviews of existing standards should pay particular attention to this aspect (6.44).

9.63 The drawbacks of direct regulation and the tensions to which it may give rise mean there are considerable attractions in complementary approaches which seek to internalise environmental considerations within the decision procedures of potential polluters, either in financial terms or in cultural terms (6.55).

9.64 While economic instruments are not a panacea, and administrative controls may be required as well, economic or financial incentives should be used wherever possible to reinforce the effect of direct regulation (6.59).

9.65 Well-designed economic instruments should be capable of achieving a better overall result for the environment, by providing incentives for the introduction of clean technology and other innovations, although improvements are likely to be differently distributed and the environmental outcome in some areas might be inferior to that which would have been brought about by direct regulation. Use of economic instruments should also limit the cost of environmental protection, both in resources used and in transaction costs. They are especially valuable in controlling pollution from diffuse sources. Use of economic instruments does not dispense with the need for legislation, monitoring and criminal sanctions because a legal framework is required for their operation (6.68).

9.66 Many actions that benefit the environment are taken primarily or exclusively because individuals, either on their own account or as company managers, place a high value on protecting the environment (6.72).

9.67 One form of action that many people take is to buy products which they believe to have been produced in ways that are environmentally sustainable or to be less damaging to the environment than competing products (6.76). Many environmental claims for products are made in very vague terms, and may have only a flimsy basis. To be effective, standards for making environmental claims will have to be established on a European or global scale (6.79).

9.68 There is a need to clarify the relationship between labelling schemes and the GATT rules. More needs to be done to ensure that ecolabelling schemes do not disadvantage developing countries (6.14).

9.69 Firms should be strongly encouraged to instal environmental management systems; in due course all firms above a certain size might be required to operate such systems, in a form which involves regular publication of information about their environmental performance (6.85).

9.70 Basic issues arise over how transparency and openness can be increased, and accountability maintained, in a system in which there is a substantial measure of self-regulation (6.91). New forms of standard, possibly in some cases with legal force, can help to make self-regulation function more effectively (6.95).

9.71 We believe that self-regulation and the use of economic instruments should be regarded, not as alternatives to direct regulation, but as complementary to it (6.93). In seeking to deploy the wide range of legal and quasi-legal instruments available in order to control pollution and enhance the environment, policy-makers should identify those strategies which will be most effective in influencing behaviour and the legal status that will best complement those strategies. To ensure transparency and openness, self-regulation and use of economic instruments should take place within the framework of clear published targets for environmental quality set by government after taking into account all relevant considerations and on the basis of wide participation of all relevant interests (6.97).

9.72 Use of a combination of approaches in setting and implementing environmental standards is the best way to further general adoption of clean technology, whilst not putting at risk compliance with numerical standards set to protect humans and the natural environment against specific hazards (6.100).

Articulating values

9.73 Consultation has an important role to play in publicising proposals, stimulating critical debate, and eliciting a broad range of comments on the practicability and desirability of proposals (7.13).

9.74 When environmental standards are set or other judgements made about environmental issues, decisions must be informed by an understanding of people's values. Traditional forms of consultation, while they have provided useful insights, are not an adequate method of articulating values (7.20).

9.75 Parliaments can have a significant influence on environmental standards by requiring Ministers and others to explain and justify their proposals on the basis of objective criteria, by independently seeking advice from experts, and in debate if proposals are laid before them. Parliaments are able to express public attitudes and values to some extent. Nevertheless, governments should use more direct methods to ensure that people's values, along with lay knowledge and understanding, are articulated and taken into account alongside technical and scientific considerations (7.17).

9.76 A more rigorous and wide-ranging exploration of people's values requires discussion and debate to allow a range of viewpoints and perspectives to be considered, and individual values developed (7.23).

9.77 Values should be articulated at the earliest stage possible in setting standards and developing policies. The public should be involved in the formulation of strategies, rather than merely being consulted on already drafted proposals (7.22).

9.78 The decision whether to use one of the new methods for eliciting people's values in any given context should depend on the nature of the issue under consideration (7.40).

9.79 In setting environmental standards, these new methods should be used primarily in connection with issues which are both complex or controversial and of broad scope. Rather than attempting to cover every proposed standard, efforts to elicit values should focus on general questions of principle or procedure (7.41).

9.80 No method for determining or articulating people's values, whether traditional or novel, provides a guaranteed solution. Novel approaches should be evaluated for their ability to elicit a full spectrum of values on the issue in question from representative participants, so that the procedures used can be refined in the light of experience and their full potential realised (7.42).

9.81 The cost of methods for articulating public values is significant: a judgement has to be made in each case as to whether gains in the quality and robustness of the decision are likely to outweigh the time and resources required (7.46).

9.82 Local authorities should review existing provision for public participation in relation to their environmental functions, and seek to extend this as appropriate. Greater use should be made of community fora to create consensus on local issues. The aim should also be to expand the local partnerships established through Local Agenda 21 initiatives to embrace consideration of policy issues (7.27).

9.83 The Environment Agencies should explore ways of stimulating public input into policies relating to all aspects of their work at the earliest stage possible. Local Environment Agency Plans are a welcome innovation. The Environment Agency should consider how procedures can be introduced which will be more effective in articulating the values of all sections of the relevant communities (7.28).

9.84 Improving the mechanisms for articulating values should be high on the agenda for the future development of European institutions (7.37).

9.85 The Department of the Environment, Transport and the Regions, in consultation with other government Departments, should:

> *a.* consider how the new methods should be incorporated into the procedures for considering environmental issues and setting environmental standards, including the framing of questions to be addressed in analysis and communicating the results of scientific assessments in a comprehensible form;

> *b.* collate the experience gained, and draw up a code of practice for use of the new methods, designed both to maximise their effectiveness and preserve their integrity.

Some bodies may require additional resources for this purpose (7.47).

ALL OF WHICH WE HUMBLY SUBMIT FOR YOUR MAJESTY'S GRACIOUS CONSIDERATION

John Houghton *Chairman*
Selborne
Geoffrey Allen
Tom Blundell
Martin Holdgate
Michael Banner
Geoffrey Boulton
Clair Chilvers
Roland Clift
Peter Doyle
John Flemming
Richard Macrory
Michael Marmot
J. Gareth Morris
Penelope Rowlatt

David Lewis   *Secretary*

David Aspinwall }
Peter Douben   }   *Assistant Secretaries*

REFERENCES

Chapter 1

1. For example, evidence from the Environment Agency, January 1996.

2. Evidence from: Chemical Industries Association, January 1996; Confederation of British Industry, January 1996.

3. Joint evidence from the Water Services Association and the Water Companies Association, January 1996.

4. North, R.D. (1995). *Life on a Modern Planet: A manifesto for progress.* Manchester University Press; Wildavsky, A. (1995). *But Is It True? A citizen's guide to environmental health and safety issues.* Harvard University Press, Cambridge (Massachusetts);
    Bate, R. (Ed.) (1997). *What Risk? Science, politics and public health.* Butterworth-Heinemann, Oxford.

5. Estimate by United Nations Development Programme of spending on purchase of goods and services; reported in: *Financial Times*, 8 April 1997.

6. The commitment to pursue sustainable development was made at the United Nations Conference on Environment and Development held in Rio de Janeiro in June 1992. The conclusions of this conference were adopted by the United Nations General Assembly in November 1992.

7. The concept of sustainable development was first elaborated in: International Union for Conservation of Nature and Natural Resources (IUCN) (1980). *World Conservation Strategy.* IUCN, Gland. The definition quoted here is taken from: World Commission on Environment and Development (1987). *Our Common Future.* Oxford University Press (the Brundtland Report).

8. United Kingdom (1994). *Sustainable Development. The UK Strategy.* Cm 2426. HMSO. January 1994. See summary, paragraph 1, page 6. This uses the definition of sustainable development quoted at paragraph 1.8 in this chapter.

9. Department of the Environment, Transport and the Regions (DETR) (1998). *Opportunities for Change: Consultation paper on a revised UK strategy for sustainable development.* This consultation paper was also made widely available as a leaflet.

10. Burhenne, W. and Irwin, W. (1986). *The World Charter for Nature.* Erich Schmidt Verlag, Berlin. The World Charter for Nature was adopted by the United Nations General Assembly in 1982.

11. The Convention originated at the United Nations Conference on Environment and Development held in Rio de Janeiro in June 1992. The Convention was signed by over a hundred states.

12. See, for example, the distinction between 'standards' and 'objectives' drawn by the Commission in its Fifth Report (paragraph 180).

13. The typology used here is broadly similar (though with some differences) to those set out in: Holdgate, M.W. (1979). *A Perspective of Environmental Pollution.* Cambridge University Press. See chapter 6; Haigh, N. (1989). *EEC Environmental Policy and Britain.* Second Edition. Longman, Harlow. See chapter 3 (drawing on Holdgate (1979)).

14. Fifth Report, paragraph 172.

15. Goldblatt, D. (1996). *Social Theory and the Environment.* Polity Press, Cambridge.

16. Gummer, J. (1994). *Europe, what next? Environmental Policy and the Community.* A speech to the ERM Environmental Forum organised by the Green Alliance and hosted by the Royal Society of Arts; quoted in: Lowe, P. and Ward, S. (Eds.) (1998). *British Environmental Policy and Europe.* Routledge.

17. Article 130r(1)–(2).

18. United Kingdom (1990). *This Common Inheritance. Britain's Environmental Strategy.* Cm 1200. HMSO. September 1990.

19. Department of Trade and Industry (1990). *Guide to Compliance Cost Assessment: Releasing enterprise, counting the cost to business.* HMSO. A further guide to compliance cost assessment, *Checking the Cost of Regulation*, was published by the Cabinet Office Deregulation Unit in 1996.

20. Department of the Environment (DOE) (1991). *Policy Appraisal and the Environment: A guide for government departments.* HMSO;
DOE (1994). *Environmental Appraisal in Government Departments.* HMSO.
21. DOE (1995). *A Guide to Risk Assessment and Risk Management for Environmental Protection.* HMSO.
22. Treasury (1991). *Economic Appraisal in Central Government: A Technical Guide for Government Departments.* HMSO.
23. DETR (1998). *Policy Appraisal and the Environment: Policy guidance.*
24. These views were expressed at a workshop held by DETR in November 1997 as part of the revision of the guidance on risk assessment and risk management.
25. Treasury (1997). *Appraisal and Evaluation in Central Government: Treasury Guidance ('The Green Book').* The Stationery Office.
26. ERM Economics (1996). *The Role of Cost-Benefit Analysis in Environmental Standards.* T. Denne and J. Fisher. Report prepared for the Royal Commission on Environmental Pollution. September 1996.
27. United Kingdom (1994), paragraph 3.2. This is part of a general shift in developed countries which political scientists have identified as 'ecological modernisation'; see, for example: Weale, A. (1992). *The New Politics of Pollution.* Manchester University Press.
28. Ashby, E. (1978). *Reconciling Man with the Environment.* Oxford University Press.

Chapter 2

1. The procedure for the assessment of new substances was published in 1993 (Commission Directive 93/67/EEC of 20 July 1993. *Official Journal of the European Communities*, **L227**, 8.9.93) and that for existing substances in 1994 (Commission Regulation (EC) No. 1488/94 of 28 June 1994. *Official Journal of the European Communities*, **L161**, 29.6.94).
Information for this section is from the following sources, unless otherwise stated: *Risk Assessment of Existing Substances.* Guidance produced by a UK Government/Industry Working Group. Department of the Environment (DOE). July 1993; cited as DOE (1993);
Technical Guidance Document in support of Commission Directive 93/67/EEC on Risk Assessment for New Notified Substances, and Commission Regulation (EC) No. 1488/94 on Risk Assessment for Existing Substances. Part I. Report No. CR-48-96-001-EN-C. European Commission, Brussels. 1996;
Technical Guidance Document in support of Commission Directive 93/67/EEC on Risk Assessment for New Notified Substances, and Commission Regulation (EC) No. 1488/94 on Risk Assessment for Existing Substances. Part II. Report No. CR-48-96-002-EN-C. European Commission, Brussels. 1996; cited as EC Technical Guidance Part II (1996).
2. The source for box 2A is: Duffus, J.H. and Worth, H.G.J. (Eds.) (1996). *Fundamental Toxicology for Chemists.* Royal Society of Chemistry, Cambridge. See appendix 2. The definitions are derived from a glossary prepared by one of the editors for IUPAC (the International Union of Pure and Applied Chemistry) in 1993.
3. For a comprehensive treatment of the derivation of guidance values for health-based exposure limits, see: International Programme on Chemical Safety (IPCS) (1994). *Assessing Human Health Risks of Chemicals: Derivation of Guidance Values for Health-based Exposure Limits.* Environmental Health Criteria Document EHC 170. World Health Organization (WHO), Geneva.
4. Technical guidance states that to ensure that predicted environmental concentrations are realistic, 'the best and most realistic information should be given preference'. But guidance also states that 'it may often be useful to initially conduct an exposure assessment based on worst-case assumptions, and using default values when model calculations are applied. Such an approach can also be used in the absence of sufficiently detailed data'; see EC Technical Guidance Part II (1996).
5. An 'existing' substance is any substance listed on EINECS (the European Inventory of Existing Commercial Chemical Substances) published in 1990. EINECS lists over 100,000 substances which were on the European Community (EC) market at some time between 1 January 1971 and 18 September 1981. A 'new' substance is one which does not appear on EINECS, that is, one which has been placed on the EC market since 18 September 1981.
6. Information supplied by Dr Norman King, July 1998.

7. Seventeenth Report, paragraphs 6.11–6.15.

8. A description of several different types of such models is included in: Barnett, V. and O'Hagan, A. (1997). *Setting Environmental Standards. The statistical approach to handling uncertainty and variation. A report to the Royal Commission on Environmental Pollution.* Chapman and Hall. See section 3.2.

9. For further information see: Pershagen, G. (1997). Interpretation of epidemiological studies with modestly elevated relative risks. In: Bate, R. (Ed.) (1997). *What Risk? Science, politics and public health.* Butterworth-Heinemann, Oxford. Pages 191–200.

10. The source for box 2C is: Bradford Hill, A. (1971). *Principles of Medical Statistics.* Ninth Edition. Oxford University Press.

11. Barnett and O'Hagan (1997), section 1.4.1.

12. The source for figure 2-II is: Duffus and Worth (1996), section 2.3.

13. WHO (1993). *Guidelines for Drinking-Water Quality. Volume 1: Recommendations.* Second Edition. WHO, Geneva. See also: IPCS (1994).

14. Wilson, J.D. (1997). Thresholds for carcinogens: A review of the relevant science and its implications for regulatory policy. In: Bate (1997), pages 3–36.

15. The source for box 2D is: DOE (1994). *Benzene.* Expert Panel on Air Quality Standards. HMSO. February 1994.

16. Brown, D. (1998). Environmental risk assessment and management of chemicals. In: Hester, R.E. and Harrison, R.M. (Eds.) (1998). *Risk Assessment and Risk Management.* Issues in Environmental Science and Technology No. 9. Royal Society of Chemistry, Cambridge. Pages 91–111.

17. Oral evidence from Dr Stuart Dobson, Institute of Terrestrial Ecology, December 1996.

18. DOE (1993), section 4.1.2.

19. EC Technical Guidance Part II (1996).

20. Oral evidence from: Dr Stuart Dobson, Institute of Terrestrial Ecology, December 1996; Dr Steve Hopkin, University of Reading, December 1996; Professor Nico van Straalen, Free University of Amsterdam, December 1996.

21. DOE (1993), appendix 3.

22. A review of the use of fate and exposure models in estimating environmental concentrations is contained in: ECETOC (1992). *Estimating Environmental Concentrations of Chemicals Using Fate and Exposure Models.* Technical Report No. 50. European Centre for Ecotoxicology and Toxicology of Chemicals (ECETOC), Brussels.

23. See for example: Stone, M. (1974). Cross-validatory choice and assessment of statistical predictions. *J. Roy. Statist. Soc. B,* **36**, 111–147; Copas, J.B. (1983). Regression, prediction and shrinkage. *J. Roy. Statist. Soc.* B, **45**, 311–354.

24. Barnett and O'Hagan (1997), section 3.2.7.

25. Holdgate, M.W. (1979). *A Perspective of Environmental Pollution.* Cambridge University Press. See page 17.

26. Tenth Report, paragraph 1.11. The meaning the Commission itself attached to 'contamination' in the Tenth Report was 'the introduction or presence in the environment of alien substances or energy [without passing] judgment on whether they cause, or are liable to cause, damage or harm'. In contrast to these usages, the phrase 'contaminated land' has been used of land which at least 'represents an actual or potential hazard' (Eleventh Report, paragraph 2.50; Nineteenth Report, paragraphs 2.33 and, referring to the definition in the Environment Act 1995, 8.3).

27. Atlas, R.M. (1996). Slick solutions. *Chemistry in Britain,* No. 32, 42–45.

28. A critical load is defined as 'the quantitative estimate of an exposure to one or more pollutants below which significant harmful effects on specified sensitive elements of the environment do not occur according to present knowledge'. In: Nilsson, J. and Grennfelt, P. (Eds.) (1988). *Critical Loads for Sulphur and Nitrogen.* Report of a workshop held in Skokloster, Sweden, 19–24 March 1988. Nordic Council of Ministers, Copenhagen.

29. Sixteenth Report, paragraph 6.16 and box 6.6.

30. DOE (1972). *The Human Environment. The British View.* Basic paper contributed by the United Kingdom to the United Nations Conference on the Human Environment, Stockholm, 1972.

31. This was the third principle of policy in the First Community Environmental Action Programme; see: *Manual of Environmental Policy: The EC and Britain.* Ed. N. Haigh. Institute for European Environmental Policy, London. See chapter 2, pages 2.4–2.5.

32. Natural Environment Research Council (NERC) (1996). *Scientific Group on Decommissioning Offshore Structures. First Report.* A Report by NERC for the Department of Trade and Industry (DTI). April 1996.

33. United Kingdom (1990). *This Common Inheritance. Britain's Environmental Strategy.* Cm 1200. HMSO. September 1990. See paragraphs 1.15–1.17.

34. DOE, Ministry of Agriculture, Fisheries and Food and The Welsh Office (1996). *The Environment Agency and Sustainable Development. Statutory Guidance to the Environment Agency.* November 1996; The Scottish Office (1996). *The Scottish Environment Protection Agency and Sustainable Development. Statutory Guidance to the Scottish Environment Protection Agency.* November 1996.

35. Fisk, D. (1997). Sound science and the environment. *Science and Public Affairs,* Spring 1997, 46–49.

36. DOE (1977). *Environmental Standards. A description of United Kingdom Practice.* The Report of an Inter-Departmental Working Party. Pollution Paper No. 11. HMSO. See paragraphs 13 and 19.

37. Fisk (1997). Dr Fisk, Chief Scientist of the then DOE, was writing in a personal capacity; the views expressed are the author's alone, and do not necessarily represent those of the former DOE or the Department of the Environment, Transport and the Regions.

38. Office of Science and Technology (1997). *The Use of Scientific Advice in Policy Making.* DTI. March 1997.

39. The source for table 2.1 is: Funtowicz, S.O. and Ravetz, J.R. (1990). *Uncertainty and Quality in Science for Policy.* Theory and Decision Library: Series A: Philosophy and Methodology of the Social Sciences. Volume 15. Kluwer Academic Publishers, Dordrecht.

40. Rothstein, H. and Irwin, A. (1998). *Regulatory Science, Europeanisation and the Control of Agrochemicals.* Paper presented at 'Europeanisation and the Regulation of Risk Workshop', London School of Economics, 27 March 1998.

41. The source for box 2F is: Houghton, J.T., Jenkins, G.J. and Ephraums, J.J. (Eds.) (1990). *Climate Change. The IPCC Scientific Assessment.* Report prepared for IPCC by Working Group 1. Published for the Intergovernmental Panel on Climate Change by Cambridge University Press. See the Policymakers Summary, pages *xi–xii.*

42. Information obtained during Commission visits to Washington D.C. and to Research Triangle Park, North Carolina, October 1996.

43. Evidence from the Association of Directors and River Inspectors in Scotland (ADRIS), January 1996.

44. Office of Science and Technology (1997), paragraph 10.

45. Office of Science and Technology (1997), paragraphs 3–4.

Chapter 3

1. Seventeenth Report, paragraph 4.41; the standards are summarised in tables 2.1–2.3 on pages 11–13.

2. The actual requirement on the operator in an authorisation is to *use techniques which ensure* that emissions are always within the specified limits (*emphasis added*).

3. Environmental Protection Act 1990, section 7(4).

4. Environmental Protection Act 1990, section 7(7).

5. Framework Directive on combatting air pollution from industrial plants (84/360/EEC). *Official Journal of the European Communities,* **L188**, 16.7.84.

6. The source for box 3A is: Department of the Environment (DOE)/The Welsh Office (1997). *Integrated Pollution Control: A practical guide.* New Edition. See paragraphs 7.3–7.6 and 7.17.

7. DOE/The Welsh Office (1997), paragraph 7.17.

8. Information supplied by the Department of the Environment, Transport and the Regions (DETR), June 1998.

9. DOE/The Welsh Office (1997), paragraphs 6.9 and 7.14.

10. See for example: Environment Agency (1996). *Processes subject to Integrated Pollution Control: Waste Incineration.* Integrated Pollution Control Guidance Note S2 5.01. The Stationery Office. See section 1.1.

11. As an example, and for a statement of the Agency's approach, see: Environment Agency (1996), sections 5.1–5.3.

12. DOE/The Welsh Office (1997), paragraphs 7.9–7.11.

13. Information obtained during Commission visit to the Institute for Prospective Technological Studies, Seville, January 1998.

14. Council Directive 96/61/EC concerning integrated pollution prevention and control. *Official Journal of the European Communities,* **L257**, 10.10.96.

15. Emmott, N. and Haigh, N. (1996). Integrated Pollution Prevention and Control: UK and EC approaches and possible next steps. *Journal of Environmental Law,* **8**(2), 301–312;
Agency plays for high stakes in brave new world of IPPC. *ENDS Report,* No. 273, October 1997, 21–24;
Integrated Pollution Prevention and Control. *Clean Air and Environmental Protection,* **27**(6), November/December 1997, page 155.

16. Article 2(11).

17. DOE/The Welsh Office (1997), paragraph 7.8.

18. Information obtained during Commission visit to the Institute for Prospective Technological Studies, Seville, January 1998.

19. Van den Berg, N.W., Dutilh, C.E. and Huppes, G. (1995). *Beginning LCA: A guide into environmental life cycle assessment.* Centre of Environmental Science, University of Leiden.

20. The source for figure 3-I is: Allen, G. (1997). Financial investment and environmental performance. *Philosophical Transactions of the Royal Society, Series A,* **355**, 1467–1473; after: Clift, R. and Longley, A.J. (1994). Introduction to Clean Technology. In: *Clean Technology and the Environment.* Eds. R.C. Kirkwood and A.J. Longley. Blackie Academic and Professional, Glasgow. Pages 174–198.

21. The source for box 3B is: International Organization for Standardization (ISO) (1997). *Environmental management – Life cycle assessment – Principles and framework.* EN ISO 14040.

22. Sources for box 3C are: Macintosh, R. (1997). Pilkington's strategy for glass furnace pollution in France and Italy. In: *Proceedings of the Institution of Chemical Engineers Conference on Controlling Industrial Emissions.* 3–4 November 1997;
Nicholas, M.J., Clift, R., Walker, F.C., Azapagic, A. and Porter, D.E. (1997). Atmospheric Pollution Control in the Glass Industry: The Need for a Life Cycle Approach. In: *Proceedings of the Annual Conference of the Surrey/Brunel Engineering Doctorate Programme in Environmental Technology.* Eds. C. Ashton and M.J. Nicholas. Pages 29/1–29/12;
Nicholas, M.J. (1998). Legislation's going holistic. *The Chemical Engineer,* 30 April 1998, 33–34.

23. Lindfors, L.-G. (1995). *Nordic Guidelines on Life-Cycle Assessment.* Nordic Council of Ministers, Copenhagen;
Van den Berg *et al.* (1995).

24. Finnveden, G. and Ekvall, T. (1997). On the usefulness of LCA in decision-making – The case of recycling vs. incineration of paper. In: *Fifth LCA Case Studies Symposium.* SETAC-Europe, Brussels. Pages 9–17.

25. Wright, M., Allen, D., Clift, R. and Sas, H. (1997). Measuring corporate environmental performance: The ICI Environmental Burden System. *Journal of Industrial Ecology,* **1**(4), 117–127.

26. Unilever (1998). *Environment Report 1998. Making Progress.* Unilever Environment Group, London and Rotterdam.

27. Sources for box 3D are: Taylor, A.P. and Postlethwaite, D. (1996). Overall Business Impact Assessment (OBIA). In: *Fourth LCA Case Studies Symposium.* SETAC-Europe, Brussels. Pages 181–187;
Jackson, T. and Clift, R. (1998). Where's the profit in industrial ecology? *Journal of Industrial Ecology,* **2**(1), 3–5.

28. Douben, P. E.T. and Serageldin, M.A. (1998). The basis for industrial process regulation. In: Douben, P.E.T. (Ed.) (1998). *Pollution Risk Assessment and Management.* John Wiley and Sons, Chichester. Pages 49–92.

29. Clift and Longley (1994).

30. Baas, L., Hoffman, H., Huisingh, J., Koppert, P. and Newman, F. (1990). *Protection of the North Sea: Time for Clean Production*. Erasmus Centre for Environmental Studies, Erasmus University, Rotterdam.

31. Yorkshire firms to demonstrate waste reduction benefits. *ENDS Report*, No. 206, March 1992, page 12.

32. Yorkshire and Mersey projects show the way on waste minimisation. *ENDS Report*, No. 221, June 1993, 15–18.

33. Centre for the Exploitation of Science and Technology (1997). *Dee Catchment Waste Minimisation Project*.

34. Definition implicit in the Clean Technology Research Programme of the Engineering and Physical Science Research Council and given in: Clift and Longley (1994);
Clift, R. (1995). Clean Technology – An Introduction. *J. Chem. Tech. Biotechnol.*, **62**, 321–326.

35. The source for box 3E is: Garland, J. and Tomashefsky, S. (1996). *Electric Vehicle and Power Plant Emissions Update South Coast Air Basin*. California Energy Commission, Energy Forecasting and Resource Assessment Division, Electricity Resource Office; see also information available at website http://www.arb.ca.gov

36. Clift and Longley (1994).

37. Clift, R. (1997). Clean Technology – The Idea and the Practice. *J. Chem. Tech. Biotechnol.*, **68**, 347–350.

38. The tight standard for dioxin emissions from chemical incinerators in Germany was cited as an example of a technology-forcing standard; information obtained during Commission visit to Bayer, Leverkusen, October 1997.

39. The source for box 3F is: Wallace, D. (1995). *Environmental Policy and Industrial Innovation – Strategies in Europe, the US and Japan*. The Royal Institute of International Affairs, Energy and Environment Programme. Earthscan Publications Ltd.

40. Wallace (1995).

41. DETR (1998). *Sustainable Production and Use of Chemicals. Consultation paper on chemicals in the environment*. July 1998.

42. Chemical legislation across Europe to be reviewed – Meacher. *Department of the Environment, Transport and the Regions Press Notice*, No. 317, 25 April 1998.

43. Early disputes over new review of EC chemicals policy. *ENDS Report*, No. 279, April 1998, 39–40.

44. Sources for box 3G are: *Towards a Sustainable Chemicals Policy*. English Summary. Government Official Reports. 1997:84. Ministry of the Environment, Stockholm;
Sweden sets the agenda for tomorrow's chemicals policy. *ENDS Report*, No. 269, June 1997, 21–25.

45. Information obtained during Commission visit to the Institute for Prospective Technological Studies, Seville, January 1998.

46. Environment Agency (1997). *Best Practicable Environmental Option Assessments for Integrated Pollution Control. Volume I: Principles and Methodology. Volume II: Technical Data (for consultation)*. Technical Guidance Note (Environmental) E1. The Stationery Office.

Chapter 4

1. It has been suggested that what they have in common is a distinction between reality and possibility: Renn, O. (1998). Three decades of risk research: Accomplishments and new challenges. *Journal of Risk Research*, **1**(1), 49–71.

2. Chambers (1983). *Chambers 20th Century Dictionary*. New Edition 1983. Chambers, Edinburgh.

3. Treasury (1997). *Appraisal and Evaluation in Central Government: Treasury Guidance ('The Green Book')*. The Stationery Office. See annex B, paragraph 1.

4. Treasury (1997), paragraph 4.44.

5. For the engineering definition of 'risk' see: British Standards Institution (1991). *Quality vocabulary*. BS 4778; quoted in: Royal Society (1992). *Risk: Analysis, perception and management. Report of a Royal Society Study Group*.

6. Department of the Environment (DOE) (1995a). *A Guide to Risk Assessment and Risk Management for Environmental Protection.* HMSO. See paragraph 1.8.

7. This is deliberately a simplified example. A more sophisticated calculation would take into account losses or injuries short of death and distinguish between people who do or do not travel by train and do or do not cross railway lines regularly.

8. DOE (1991). *Policy Appraisal and the Environment: A guide for government Departments.* HMSO. See paragraphs 4.31–4.37.

9. United Kingdom (1994). *Sustainable Development: The UK Strategy.* Cm 2426. HMSO. January 1994. See summary, paragraph 15.

10. DOE (1995a).

11. The explanatory document accompanying the statutory guidance says (paragraph 5.6) 'When assessing the likely costs and benefits in the circumstances of the case, the Agency may consider it appropriate to consider the following: (i) principles, procedures and techniques–in particular, *risk assessment*, and economic and policy appraisal – for giving proper consideration to non-market impacts including those on the environment ...' (*emphasis added*).

12. Environment Agency (1997). *An Environmental Strategy for the Millennium and Beyond.* See page 20; Environment Agency, National Centre for Risk Analysis and Options Appraisal (1998). *A Guide to Risk Appraisal.* In 1997 the Centre published *Risk Profile No. 1: Road Transport and the Environment.*

13. In the USA this stage in the procedure is usually called 'risk assessment'. In the UK risk assessment often includes, as well as risk estimation, risk evaluation, i.e. determining the significance of the estimated risks for those affected.

14. Evidence from British Nuclear Fuels plc, January 1996.

15. Jasanoff, S. (1991). Acceptable evidence in a Pluralistic Society. In: Mayo, D.G. and Hollander, R.G. (Eds.) (1991). *Acceptable Evidence: Science and Values in Risk Management.* Oxford University Press, New York. Pages 29–47.

16. Royal Society (1983). *Risk Assessment. A Study Group Report.*

17. Royal Society (1992).

18. Fifth Report, paragraphs 175–177 and diagram on page 49. The distinction between limit values and guide values in European Community (EC) air quality legislation (see this report, appendix C, C.16) is not analogous because guide values defined levels of air quality which it was regarded as desirable to reach in the longer term.

19. International Commission on Radiological Protection (ICRP) (1977). *Recommendations of the ICRP.* ICRP Publication No. 26. Pergamon Press, Oxford.

20. A risk of 1 in 1,000 was the highest level of risk found to be ordinarily accepted by substantial groups of workers in any industry in the UK; it is exceeded only by fishermen and relatively small groups such as helicopter pilots, divers and demolition workers.

21. Health and Safety Executive (HSE) (1992). *The Tolerability of Risk from Nuclear Power Stations.* Revised 1992. HMSO.

22. Interdepartmental Liaison Group on Risk Assessment (ILGRA) (1996). *Use of Risk Assessment Within Government Departments.* HSE.

23. Treasury (1996). *The Setting of Safety Standards.* A report by an interdepartmental group and external advisers.

24. DOE (1995b). *The Review of Radioactive Waste Management Policy.* Cm 2919. HMSO.

25. Radwaste policy in tatters as Gummer blocks Nirex dump. *ENDS Report,* No. 266, March 1997, 13–14.

26. Wynne, B. (1992). Uncertainty and environmental learning: Reconceiving science and policy in the preventive paradigm. *Global Environmental Change,* June 1992, 111–127.

27. Seventeenth Report, paragraph 6.36.

28. Lash, S., Szerszynski, B. and Wynne, B. (1996). *Risk, Environment and Modernity: Towards a New Ecology.* Sage.

29. Hynes, M. and Vanmarcke, E. (1976). Reliability of embankment performance prediction. In: *Proceedings of the ASCE Engineering Mechanics Division Speciality Conference.* University of Waterloo Press, Waterloo, Ontario;

Henrion, M. and Fischhoff, B. (1986). Assessing uncertainty in physical constants. *Am. J. Phys.*, **54**, 791–798; quoted in Royal Society (1992).

30. For a description of how risks to human health from proposed incineration plants have been analysed quantitatively, see: Seventeenth Report, paragraphs 6.33–6.35.

31. Stern, P.C. and Fineberg, H.V. (Eds.) (1996). *Understanding Risk. Informing Decisions in a Democratic Society*. National Research Council. National Academy Press, Washington D.C.

32. National Research Council (1995). *Technical Bases for Yucca Mountain Standards*. National Academy Press, Washington D.C.; quoted in Stern and Fineberg (1996).

33. Stern and Fineberg (1996).

34. HSE (1992), paragraph 175.

35. Sapolsky, R. (1997). *Junk Food Monkeys and Other Essays on the Biology of the Human Predicament*. Headline. The outcome of psychological experiments by Tversky and Kahneman is summarised on pages 48–49.

36. Silverstone, R. (1985). *Framing Science. The making of a BBC documentary*. British Film Institute.

37. Slovic, P. (1987). Perception of risk. *Science*, **236**, 280–285.

38. Royal Society (1992).

39. United Kingdom (1990). *This Common Inheritance. Britain's Environmental Strategy*. Cm 1200. HMSO. September 1990. See paragraph 1.18.

40. Hey, E. (1992). The precautionary concept in environmental policy and law: Institutionalising caution. *Georgetown International Environmental Law Review*, **4**, 303–318; quoted in evidence from Owen McIntyre and Thomas Mosedale, Faculty of Law, University of Manchester, April 1996.

41. Joint evidence from the Countryside Council for Wales, English Nature, Scottish Natural Heritage and the Joint Nature Conservation Committee, January 1996.

42. Freestone, D. (1994). The Road from Rio: International Environmental Law after the Earth Summit. *Journal of Environmental Law*, **6**(2), 191–218.

43. Douglas, M. (1982). *Risk and Blame*. Routledge; quoted in Royal Society (1992).

44. Adams, J. (1996). *Risk*. UCL Press Ltd.

45. Twelfth Report, paragraph 2.32, information box on page 12 and appendix 3.

46. Renn (1998).

47. Stirling, A. (1998). Risk at a turning point. *Journal of Risk Research*, **1**(2), April 1998, 97–109.

Chapter 5

1. The source for box 5A is: Treasury (1997). *Appraisal and Evaluation in Central Government: Treasury Guidance ('The Green Book')*. The Stationery Office. See the glossary on pages 96–100.

2. See: Treasury (1997), paragraph 4.4;
    Department of the Environment (DOE) (1991). *Policy Appraisal and the Environment. A guide for government departments*. HMSO. See paragraph 4.2.

3. Treasury (1997), paragraph 2.1.

4. DOE (1991), paragraph 1.8.

5. Sources for box 5B are: *Economic evaluation of air quality targets for sulphur dioxide, nitrogen dioxide, fine and suspended particulate matter and lead. Final Report*. Institute for Environmental Studies (IVM), Amsterdam, the Netherlands; Norwegian Institute for Air Research (NILU), Kjeller, Norway; International Institute for Applied Systems Analysis (IIASA), Laxenburg, Austria. Contract No. B4-3040/96/00217/MAR/B1. October 1997;
    Proposal for a Council Directive relating to limit values for sulphur dioxide, oxides of nitrogen, particulate matter and lead in ambient air. *COM(97)500 Final*. Commission of the European Communities, Brussels, 8.10.97.

6. DOE (1991), paragraph 2.4.

7. DOE (1991), paragraphs 2.7 and 2.14.

8. Treasury (1997), paragraphs 2.14 and 4.12–4.13 and glossary (page 98).

9. The source for box 5C is: Eighteenth Report, appendix C. For advice on box 5C, the Commission is grateful to Professor Michael Jones-Lee, Centre for the Analysis of Safety Policy and Attitudes to Risk, University of Newcastle upon Tyne, August 1998.

10. DOE (1991), paragraph 4.25;
    Treasury (1997), paragraph 4.18.

11. DOE (1991), paragraph 4.15.

12. Treasury (1997), annex C, paragraph 13.

13. DOE (1991), paragraph 4.11;
    Treasury (1997), paragraphs 4.27–4.28.

14. A cost-effectiveness study for this purpose formed part of the European Auto/Oil Programme, and is summarised in the Twentieth Report (appendix D, paragraphs D.10–D.15).

15. DOE (1991), glossary and paragraphs 4.27–4.30.

16. Treasury (1997), annex C, paragraphs 13–15.

17. Stewart, T.J. (1992). A critical survey on the status of multiple-criteria decision making theory and practice. *OMEGA International Journal of Management Science*, **20**(5/6), 569–586.

18. DOE (1991), paragraph 4.29;
    Stern, P.C. and Fineberg, H.V. (Eds.) (1996). *Understanding Risk: Informing Decisions in a Democratic Society*. National Research Council. National Academy Press, Washington D.C. See pages 188–193.

19. Saaty, T.L. (1980). *The Analytic Hierarchy Process*. McGraw-Hill, New York.

20. Treasury (1997), annex C, paragraph 1.

21. Treasury (1997), annex C, paragraph 2; see also paragraph 2.20.

22. Information supplied by HM Treasury, August 1998.

23. Information supplied by HM Treasury, August 1998.

24. The Deregulation Initiative (1996). *Checking the Cost of Regulation. A Guide to Compliance Cost Assessment*. Cabinet Office Deregulation Unit. HMSO.

25. Environment Act 1995, section 39.

26. Environment Agency (1996). *Taking Account of Costs and Benefits*. Sustainable Development Publication SD3. See paragraphs 4.4 and 5.1–5.2 and figure 1.

27. Health and Safety Executive (HSE) (1992). *The Tolerability of Risk from Nuclear Power Stations*. Revised 1992. HMSO. See paragraph 36.

28. HSE (1992), paragraphs 36–37.

29. Article 130r.3 of the Treaty of Rome as amended.

30. Smith, T. and Macrory, R. (1998). Legal and political considerations. In: Douben, P.E.T. (Ed.) (1998). *Pollution Risk Assessment and Management*. John Wiley and Sons, Chichester. See pages 422–423.

31. Information supplied by HM Treasury, August 1998.

32. Regina vs. Secretary of State for the Environment. *Ex parte* Royal Society for the Protection of Birds; the Port of Sheerness Ltd intervening. Case C44/95. *The Times*, 2 August 1996, page 28.

33. Robbins, L. (1984). *An Essay on the Nature and Significance of Economic Science*. Third Edition. Macmillan Press, Hong Kong. See page 16.

34. Treasury (1997), annex C, paragraph 11.

35. Twentieth Report, table 1.1 (page 10).

36. Stirling, A. (1997). Limits to the value of external costs. *Energy Policy*, **25**(5), 517–540. See figure 1, page 530.

37. Sources for box 5D are: Inquiry decision questions value of River Kennet. *Environment Agency Press Release*, No. 21/98, 23 February 1998;
    Water abstraction decision deals savage blow to cost-benefit analysis. *ENDS Report*, No. 278, March 1998, 16–18;
    Axford inquiry prompts call for clarity on costs and benefits. *Environment Agency Press Release*, No. 62/98, 5 May 1998.

38. The source for box 5E is: Blow for incineration as recycling triumphs in EC cost-benefit study. *ENDS Report*, No. 267, April 1997, 23–26.

39. Arrow, K.J. *et al.* (1996). *Benefit-Cost Analysis in Environmental, Health, and Safety Regulation: A statement of principles*. American Enterprise Institute for Public Policy Research, Washington D.C.

40. DOE (1991), paragraph 23.

41. This point was acknowledged in the Eighteenth Report, paragraph 7.30.

42. Sagoff, M. (1988). *The Economy of the Earth*. Cambridge University Press. See page 93. See also:

Beckerman, W. and Pasek, J. (1997). Plural values and environmental valuation. *Environmental Values,* **6**, page 69.

43. Treasury (1997), paragraphs 2.36–2.37.

Chapter 6

1. As calculated by the Secretariat of the World Trade Organization (WTO).

2. As identified by the WTO Secretariat. They are listed on page 18 of: House of Commons Select Committee on the Environment. *World Trade and the Environment. Volume II: Minutes of Evidence and Appendices.* Fourth Report, 1995/96 Session. House of Commons Paper 149-II. HMSO.

3. Article 1 of the General Agreement on Tariffs and Trade (GATT).

4. Articles XX(b) and (g) of the GATT.

5. This discussion of the European Community (EC) draws on *The European Dimension of Standard Setting*, a report prepared for this Commission in August 1996 by the Institute for European Environmental Policy, London; and this is the source for information about the EC in this chapter for which no other source is given.

6. Paris et Bonn plaident pour une Europe plus décentralisée. *Le Monde,* 10 June 1998; interview with the Foreign and Commonwealth Secretary in: *New Statesman,* 14 August 1998.

7. Resolution A3-0380/92. *Official Journal of the European Communities,* **C42/40**, paragraph 8. 1993.

8. Lowe, P. and Ward, S. (Eds.) (1998). *British Environmental Policy and Europe.* Routledge.

9. Directive 91/414/EEC concerning the placing of plant protection products on the market. *Official Journal of the European Communities,* **L230**, 19.8.91; Directive 98/8/EC of the European Parliament and the Council concerning the placing of biocidal products on the market. *Official Journal of the European Communities,* **L123**, 24.4.98.

10. The Sixth Amendment Directive (Council Directive 79/831/EEC. *Official Journal of the European Communities,* **L259**, 15.10.79) to the 1967 EC Dangerous Substances Directive (Council Directive 67/548/EEC of 27 June 1967. *Official Journal of the European Communities,* **L196**, 16.8.67).

11. Ninth Amendment to Directive 76/769/EEC relating to restrictions on the marketing and use of certain dangerous substances and preparations. Directive 91/173/EEC. *Official Journal of the European Communities,* **L85**, 5.4.91.

12. Sustainable development becomes Treaty goal for EC. *ENDS Report,* No. 269, June 1997, 44–45; "Environmental guarantee" that never was. *ENDS Report,* No. 269, June 1997, 22–23.

13. Haigh, N. (1986). Devolved responsibility and centralization: Effects of EEC environmental policy. *Public Administration,* **64**(2), 197–207.

14. Buller, H. (1998). Reflections across the Channel. In: Lowe and Ward (1998).

15. Morphet, J. (1998). Local authorities. In: Lowe and Ward (1998).

16. Department of the Environment, Transport and the Regions (DETR) (1998). *A New Deal for Transport: Better for Everyone. The Government's White Paper on the Future of Transport.* Cm 3950. The Stationery Office. July 1998.

17. Baldwin, R. (1997). Regulation: After 'command and control'. In: Hawkins, K. (Ed.) (1997). *The Human Face of Law.* Clarendon Press, Oxford.

18. For example, in evidence from: the former National Rivers Authority, February 1996; Natural Environment Research Council, January 1996; Royal Statistical Society, January 1996.

19. Barnett, V. and O'Hagan, A. (1997). *Setting Environmental Standards. The statistical approach to handling uncertainty and variation. A report to the Royal Commission on Environmental Pollution.* Chapman and Hall.

20. Hutter, B.M. and Lloyd-Bostock, S. (1997). Law's relationship with social science: The interdependence of theory, empirical work, and social relevance in socio-legal studies. In: Hawkins (1997).

21. Smith, R.A. (1878). *Annual Report of the Proceedings of the Alkali Inspectorate for 1875 and 1876;* quoted in: Ashby, E. and Anderson, M. (1981). *The Politics of Clean Air.* Clarendon Press, Oxford.

22. Hawkins, K. (1984). *Environment and Enforcement. Regulation and the social definition of pollution.* Clarendon Press, Oxford. See page 4.

23. Hawkins (1984).

24. Environment Agency (1998). *Enforcement and Prosecution Policy. Draft for public consultation.* March 1998.

25. Fifth Report, paragraph 121.

26. Ayres, I. and Braithwaite, J. (1992). *Responsive Regulation: Transcending the Deregulation Debate.* Oxford University Press.

27. That was also the conclusion reached in the Sixteenth Report (paragraph 8.4).

28. A taxing issue. *The Economist,* 27 June 1998.

29. Anderson, M.S. (1994). *Governance by Green Taxes.* Manchester University Press.

30. *Self-regulation: A Common Statement.* Draft statement by the European Environmental Advisory Councils, formulated following the Fifth Conference of European Environmental Advisory Bodies, October 1997.

31. Environics International Ltd (1998). *Global Public Opinion on Climate Change and the Environment. The 1998 International Environmental Monitor Survey.* Toronto.

32. The source for box 6A is: DETR website, June 1998.

33. Twentieth Report, paragraph 2.48.

34. Information about Local Agenda 21 was obtained during a visit by the Commission Secretariat to Reading Borough Council in March 1998 to discuss a project operated by World Wide Fund for Nature (UK).

35. From the top. *The Guardian,* 5 April 1997; see also Nineteenth Report, paragraphs 5.108–120 and figure 5-I.

36. The source for box 6B is: Overcoming growing pains. *Financial Times,* 8 December 1997.

37. Government sticks to voluntary approach on green claims. *ENDS Report,* No. 265, February 1997, 27–28.

38. Launch of the 'Green Claims Code' described in: Meacher gives business a year to clean up 'Green Claims'. *Department of the Environment, Transport and the Regions News Release,* No. 103, 17 February 1998.

39. International Standards Organization (ISO) (1998). *ISO 14021: Environmental labels and declarations – Self-declared environmental claims.*

40. Roderick Paul, chairman of the Confederation of British Industry's Environmental Affairs Committee, in an interview with the Environment Agency in: *Environment Action,* **12**, February–March 1998.

41. Rover becomes first BS7750 holder to be fined for pollution. *ENDS Report,* No. 256, February 1997, 43–44;
Akzo becomes second BS7750 firm to be fined for pollution. *ENDS Report,* No. 267, April 1997, page 44.

42. Agency resists "light touch" for sites with ISO14001, EMAS. *ENDS Report,* No. 266, March 1997, page 3.

43. Organisation for Economic Co-operation and Development (OECD) (1997). *Reforming Regulation in OECD Countries.* OECD, Paris.

44. The source for box 6C is: Douben, P. E.T. and Serageldin, M.A. (1998). The basis for industrial process regulation. In: Douben, P. E.T. (Ed.) (1998). *Pollution Risk Assessment and Management.* John Wiley and Sons, Chichester. Pages 49–92.

45. Wallace, D. (1995). *Environmental Policy and Industrial Innovation.* Earthscan Publications Ltd; additional information supplied by Rae Tsutsumi, June 1998.

46. COM(96)561 Final.

47. Commission Recommendation of 9 December 1996 concerning environmental agreements implementing Community Directives. *Official Journal of the European Communities,* **L333**, 21.12.96.

48. Macrory, R. (1997). *The Concept of Self-Regulation.* Paper given at the Fifth Conference of European Environmental Advisory Bodies, Vinkeveen, the Netherlands, October 1997. Proceedings to be published.

49. Baldwin, R. (1995). *Rules and Government.* Clarendon Press, Oxford. See chapter 5, pages 125–141.

50. Work injuries not being investigated. *The Independent,* 13 November 1997.

51. DETR (1998). *Annual Report 1998. The Government's Expenditure Plans 1998–99.* Cm 3906. The Stationery Office. See figure 17a, page 133.

52. Baldwin (1997).

53. Lewis, D. (1984). Improving implementation. In: Lewis, D. and Wallace, H. (Eds.) (1984). *Policies into Practice: National and international case studies in implementation.* Heinemann.

Chapter 7

1. The Convention on Access to Information, Public Participation in Decision-making and Access to Justice in Environmental Matters, prepared by the United Nations Economic Commission for Europe (UNECE), was signed in June 1998 at the Fourth Pan-European Conference of Environment Ministers held at Aarhus, Denmark.

2. Broughton, D. (1995). *Public Opinion Polling and Politics in Britain.* Englewood Cliffs.

3. Information supplied by Market and Opinion Research International (MORI), December 1996.

4. House of Commons Select Committee on the Environment. *The Environmental Impact of Cement Manufacture.* Third Report, 1996/97 Session. See paragraphs 44–52.

5. House of Lords Select Committee on Science and Technology. *Decommissioning of Oil and Gas Installations.* Third Report, 1995/96 Session. House of Lords Paper 46.

6. House of Lords Select Committee on the European Communities. *Bathing Water.* First Report, 1994/95 Session. House of Lords Paper 6.

7. Department of the Environment, Transport and the Regions (DETR) and Local Government Management Board (LGMB) (1997). *Sustainable Communities for the 21st Century.*

8. The Local Agenda 21 Case Study Project funded by DETR and LGMB.

9. See: Local Sustainability: The European Good Practice Information Service, at website http://cities21.com/europractice/index.htm

10. Evidence from Dr Judith Petts, Loughborough University of Technology, February 1996.

11. Information provided by Dr Judith Petts, Loughborough University of Technology, July 1998.

12. Environment Agency (1998). *Local Environment Agency Plan. New Forest Consultation Report.* April 1998.

13. Morrison, I. (1997). People's Panel. In: *Report of the Public Consultation Meeting.* The Wellcome Trust. Pages 8–9.

14. Sources for box 7A are: Stewart, J., Kendall, E. and Coote, A. (Eds.) (1994). *Citizens' Juries.* Institute for Public Policy Research (IPPR);
    Coote, A. and Cooke, V. (1997). Citizens' juries. In: *Report of the Public Consultation Meeting.* The Wellcome Trust. Pages 7–8;
    Fishkin, J. and Jowell, R. (1997). Deliberative polls. In: *Report of the Public Consultation Meeting.* The Wellcome Trust. Pages 3–5;
    Grove-White, R., Macnaghten, P., Mayer, S. and Wynne, B. (1997). *Uncertain World: Genetically Modified Organisms, Food and Public Attitudes in Britain.* Centre for the Study of Environmental Change, University of Lancaster.

15. Sources for box 7B are: Joss, S. (1995a). Introduction. In: Joss, S. *et al.* (Eds.) (1995). *Public Participation in Science: The role of consensus conferences in Europe.* Science Museum. Anthony Rowe, UK;
    Joss, S. (1995b). Evaluating consensus conferences: Necessity or luxury? In: Joss *et al.* (1995);
    Durant, J. (1997). Consensus conferences. In: *Report of the Public Consultation Meeting.* The Wellcome Trust. Pages 5–6.

16. The source for box 7C is: Welsh Institute for Health and Social Care (1997). *Citizens' Jury on Genetic Testing for Common Disorders: A description of the process.*

17. Stewart *et al.* (1994).

18. Ministry of Agriculture, Fisheries and Food (1998). *The Food Standards Agency. A Force for Change.* CM 3830. The Stationery Office. January 1998. See appendix 2.

19. Commission for the European Communities (1996). *General Guidelines for Legislative Policy.* January 1996;
    House of Lords Select Committee on the European Communities. *Community Environment Law: Making it work.* Second Report, 1997/98 Session. House of Lords Paper 12. July 1997. See appendix 9, pages 84–88.

20. European Commission, Directorate-General for Environment, Nuclear Safety and Civil Protection

(1996). *Implementing Community Environmental Law: Communication to the Council of the European Union and the European Parliament.* Office for Official Publications of the European Communities, Luxembourg. October 1996.

21. European Commission, Directorate-General for Environment, Nuclear Safety and Civil Protection (1997). *Options for a Sustainable Europe: Policy recommendations from the General Consultative Forum on the Environment. Introduction.* Office for Official Publications of the European Communities, Luxembourg.

22. Nentwich, M. (forthcoming). Opportunity structures for citizens' participation: The case of the European Union. In: Nentwich, M. and Weale, A. (Eds.) (forthcoming). *Political Theory and the European Union: Legitimacy, Constitutional Choice and Citizenship.* Routledge.

23. These suggestions are contained in guidelines for citizens' juries drawn up by the Institute for Public Policy Research; see: Lenaghan, J. (1997). Citizens' juries: Towards best practice. *British Journal of Health Care Management,* **3**(1), 20–22.

24. The figure for a consensus conference is from Durant (1997) and the figure for a citizens' jury from Coote and Cooke (1997). The other cost information was supplied by the Office of Public Service, Cabinet Office, in July 1998 and represents the cost of services provided by MORI using the People's Panel (7.29).

Chapter 8

1. Grove-White, R., Macnaghten, P., Mayer, S. and Wynne, B. (1997). *Uncertain World: Genetically Modified Organisms, Food and Public Attitudes in Britain.* Centre for the Study of Environmental Change, University of Lancaster.

2. Grove-White *et al.* (1997).

3. Market and Opinion Research International (MORI) (1997). *Business and the Environment 1997. Attitudes and behaviour of the general public.* August 1997. The question was 'How much confidence would you have in what each of the following have to say about environmental issues?' The proportion expressing 'a great deal' or 'a fair amount' of confidence in scientists working for the government was 44%, an increase on 38% in 1995 and 32% in 1996. The corresponding figures were 47% for scientists working in industry and 83% for scientists working for environmental groups.

4. Porter, T. (1995). *Trust in Numbers: The pursuit of objectivity in science and public life.* Princeton University Press, Princeton.

5. Jasanoff, S. (1986). *Risk Management and Political Culture.* Russell Sage Foundation, New York.

6. Jasanoff (1986).

7. Osborn, F.A. (1997). Some reflections on UK environment policy, 1970–1995. *Journal of Environmental Law,* **9**(1), 3–22.

8. Office of Science and Technology (1997). *The Use of Scientific Advice in Policy Making.* Department of Trade and Industry. March 1997.

9. Houghton, J. (1997). *Global Warming: The complete briefing.* Second Edition. Cambridge University Press.

10. The nature of interorganisational policy making is described and analysed in: Hanf, K. and Scharpf, F. (Eds.) (1978). *Interorganizational Policy Making.* Sage.

11. Tenth Report, paragraphs 2.33–2.78.

12. Oral evidence from the Chemical Industries Association, February 1996.

13. Oral evidence from the Confederation of British Industry, June 1996.

Appendix A

INVITATION TO SUBMIT EVIDENCE

On 26 September 1995 the Commission issued a news release in the following terms:

ROYAL COMMISSION SEEKS VIEWS ON BASIS FOR ENVIRONMENTAL STANDARDS

The Royal Commission on Environmental Pollution is inviting views for its new study on whether a more consistent and robust basis can be found for environmental standards.

The past twenty years have seen a considerable expansion of environmental legislation and policies. Increasing use has been made of numerical standards concerned with emissions, exposures, intakes, and concentrations of substances in the environment. Such standards have been set using various approaches by many different bodies – global, European and national – with the aim of protecting both human health and the natural environment.

It has recently been argued that some standards now being set are so stringent that the costs imposed on society will be out of proportion to the benefits obtained. Others argue that some forms of pollution (for example, prolonged exposure to very low concentrations of certain substances, especially in combination) are not being taken seriously enough.

The creation of new Environment Agencies responsible for regulating most forms of pollution makes it timely to try to establish a consistent and sustainable basis for standards. The recent transfer of responsibility for the Health and Safety Commission and Executive to the Department of the Environment has highlighted the relationship between pollution control and standards for occupational health.

The Royal Commission's study will compare the methods and procedures adopted in arriving at standards for all types of pollution and for all aspects of the environment. The term 'standards' means standards contained in law (for example, emission limits or environmental quality standards) and also non-statutory protocols, guidelines and targets, and criteria used in deciding individual cases. The study will examine what happens at European level, in other major countries, and in international organisations, as well as in the United Kingdom. It will also cover related issues about the approval of chemicals and the regulation of contaminants in food. The Royal Commission will focus in particular on different types of scientific evidence, the ways in which these are utilised, and the potential for resolving present uncertainties through further research.

As part of the study, views are now being sought on a number of issues. The Royal Commission wants to obtain input from all types of organisation and from the general public, based on the widest possible range of situations. Those submitting evidence are asked to describe the experience on which they are drawing. There may be legitimate differences in the approach to standard-setting according to the context.

The list of key issues identified by the Royal Commission (which is not necessarily exhaustive) is as follows:

The general approach to environmental standards
1. What should be the purpose of setting standards? How successfully do present standards achieve that purpose?

2. Is the level at which standards are set at present (global, European, national or local, or by individual regulators) appropriate?

3. What should be done to make the standard-setting process more explicit and transparent? What role should scientific experts have, and how should they be chosen? At national level, what role should Ministers and government Departments have? Ought there to be a greater role for the courts, or new forms of quasi-judicial regulatory hearing?

4. What role should quantification of costs and benefits play in setting and revising standards?

5. How adequate is present scientific understanding of toxicity, ecological tolerance and environmental processes as a basis for setting numerical standards?

6. Where scientific opinion and public perception are in conflict, what weight should each carry in setting standards and in determining the best practicable environmental option? Should attempts be made to modify public perceptions through education and information? Should the scientific community take more account of social preferences and sensitivities?

7. What is the best way of making allowance for uncertainties? When, and how, should the precautionary principle be applied?

8. What relationship should be sought between risks from pollution and levels of risk in other contexts? How should priorities be determined within pollution control?

Specific factors in standard-setting

9. How should standard-setting make allowance for natural variations in exposure to the same hazards?

10. In setting standards, what significance should be attached to particular vulnerability or susceptibility on the part of certain individuals, groups or species?

11. How valid is the concept of 'critical loads' and where can it be applied?

12. What should be the relationship between standards for exposure of the general public and standards for occupational exposure?

13. In what ways can standards best be set to encourage innovation, particularly investment in cleaner technologies?

Implementation and review of standards

14. What are the advantages and disadvantages of standards which are not legally binding?

15. In what circumstances could economic instruments (such as levies and tradeable permits) or voluntary measures provide a satisfactory replacement for government-defined standards?

16. How far do limitations on the detail or precision with which measurements can be made constrain the effectiveness of pollution control? What are the prospects for overcoming such constraints?

17. What should be the relationship between numerical standards for particular substances and what is overall the best practicable environmental option (as defined in the Royal Commission's Twelfth Report)?

18. What is the most effective way of linking standards for environmental quality, or critical loads, to standards for emissions or products?

19. What further provision is needed for keeping standards up to date?

Appendix B

CONDUCT OF THE STUDY

In order to carry out this study Commission Members sought written and oral evidence, commissioned studies and advice on specific topics and made a number of visits. For the preliminary work, they split into two groups, one chaired by Professor Clair Chilvers which investigated medical and scientific aspects of environmental standards, the other chaired by Professor Richard Macrory which investigated policy and legal aspects.

Evidence

In parallel with the news release inviting evidence, which is reproduced in appendix A, and advertisements placed in the *London, Edinburgh* and *Belfast Gazettes,* the Secretariat wrote direct to a large number of organisations.

The organisations and individuals listed below either submitted evidence or provided information on request for the purposes of the study or otherwise gave assistance. In some cases, indicated by an asterisk, meetings were held with Commission Members or the Secretariat so that oral evidence could be given or particular issues discussed.

Government Departments

> Department of the Environment*
> Department of the Environment (Northern Ireland)*
> Department of Health*
> Drinking Water Inspectorate
> Ministry of Agriculture, Fisheries and Food
> Office of Science and Technology*
> Office of Water Services*
> Pesticides Safety Directorate*
> Scottish Office Agriculture, Environment and Fisheries Department*
> Treasury*
> UK Ecolabelling Board*
> Veterinary Medicines Directorate*
> Welsh Office

European and international bodies

> European Centre for Ecotoxicology and Toxicology of Chemicals (ECETOC)
> European Commission, Directorate-General XI, Environment, Nuclear Safety and Civil Protection
> Food and Agriculture Organization of the United Nations

Other organisations

> Advisory Committee on Business and the Environment, Managing Environmental Issues Working Group
> Advisory Committee on Hazardous Substances
> Air Quality Consultants
> Aquatic Environmental Consultants
> Arjo Wiggins
> Associate Energy Projects

Association of the British Pharmaceutical Industry
Association of Directors and River Inspectors in Scotland
Association of Public Analysts
Aviation Environment Federation
Biffa Waste Services Ltd
Biotec Engineering Ltd
Biotechnology and Biological Sciences Research Council
Birch Assessment Services for Information on Chemicals (BASIC)
British Cement Association
British Ecological Society
British Gas
British Geological Survey
British Medical Association
British Nuclear Fuels plc
British Occupational Hygiene Society
British Standards Institution*
Building Research Establishment
Chemical Industries Association*
Confederation of British Industry*
Country Landowners Association
County Surveyors Society, Environment Group
Dames and Moore
Economic and Social Research Council, Global Environmental Change Programme
Energy from Waste Association
Energy Technology Support Unit (ETSU)
Engineering and Physical Sciences Research Council
Environment Agency*
Environment Council
Environmental Industries Commission
Environmental Services Association
European Sealing Association
Farthing Consultancy
Friends of the Earth*
Greenpeace*
Health and Safety Commission (joint with Health and Safety Executive*)
Her Majesty's Inspectorate of Pollution*
Her Majesty's Industrial Pollution Inspectorate
Institute for European Environmental Policy, London
Institute of Arable Crops Research, Rothamsted, Soil Science Department
Institute of Biology
Institute of Occupational Hygienists
Institute of Professional Soil Scientists
Institution of Environmental Sciences
Laboratory of the Government Chemist
Law Society, Environmental Law Sub-Committee
LEAF (Linking Environment And Farming)
Leeds City Council, Environment Department
London Borough of Hounslow, Environmental Services Department
London Planning Advisory Committee
London Underground Ltd, Engineering Directorate
London Waste Regulation Authority
Loss Prevention Council (joint with Association of British Insurers)
Macaulay Land Use Research Institute

Malt Distillers Association of Scotland
Medical Research Council (MRC)
National Farmers' Union
National Institute of Economic and Social Research
National Power
National Radiological Protection Board*
National Rivers Authority*
National Society for Clean Air and Environmental Protection (NSCA)
Natural Environment Research Council
Nuclear Electric plc
Peter Fisk Associates
PowerGen plc
Procter and Gamble plc
Radioactive Waste Management Advisory Committee
Reading Borough Council, Agenda 21 Team*
Royal Academy of Engineering
Royal College of General Practitioners
Royal College of Physicians, Society of Occupational Medicine and Faculty of Occupational
     Medicine
Royal Horticultural Society
Royal Institute of Public Health and Hygiene
Royal Society
Royal Society of Chemistry
Royal Society of Edinburgh
Royal Statistical Society
Royal Town Planning Institute
Scottish Association of Directors of Water and Sewerage Services
Scottish Environment Protection Agency*
Scottish Natural Heritage (joint with Countryside Council for Wales, English Nature and
     Joint Nature Conservation Committee)*
Scottish Nuclear Limited
Shanks and McEwan Limited
Shell UK Ltd
Silsoe Research Institute
Society of Public Health
Society of Public Teachers of Law, Environmental Law Group
Surfers Against Sewage
Transport and General Workers Union
UK Environmental Law Association
UK Nirex Ltd
UK Petroleum Industry Association Ltd
Waste Management International plc
Water Services Association (joint with Water Companies' Association)
Women's Environmental Network Trust
Women's National Commission
World Wide Fund for Nature (UK)
WRc*
Zeneca, Brixham Environmental Laboratory and Central Toxicology Laboratory

Individuals

Mr R. Angel, Agenda 21 Co-ordinator, Reading Borough Council
Dr Helen ApSimon, Centre for Environmental Technology, Imperial College of Science,
     Technology and Medicine

Professor Robin Attfield, University of Wales, Cardiff*

Dr H. Aubrey, University of Bath

Dr D.J. Ball and Mr H. Rakel, Centre for Environmental and Risk Management, University of East Anglia

Dr A.K. Barbour

Dr Brendan Barker, National Institute of Science and Technology Policy, Japan

Mr M.J. Beckett

Professor Peter Calow, University of Sheffield

Dr David Carruthers, Cambridge Environmental Research Consultants*

Professor Stephen Clark, University of Liverpool*

Dr D. Coggan, MRC Environmental Epidemiology Unit (University of Southampton)

Ms M. Corrado, Market and Opinion Research International (MORI)*

Dr C. Davison*

Dr Stuart Dobson, Institute of Terrestrial Ecology*

Dr Sally Eden, School of Geography and Environmental Management, University of Middlesex

Dr Stan Ellis

Dr Tim Evans, Terra Ecosystems

Dr R. Fairman, King's College, University of London

Mr John Fawell, WRc*

Professor S. Fineman, University of Bath

Ms Elizabeth C. Fisher, University of Oxford

Dr Peter Freer-Smith, Forestry Commission*

Professor Robin Grove-White, Centre for the Study of Environmental Change, University of Lancaster

Mr Nigel Haigh*

Dr Paul Harrison, Institute for Environment and Health

Mr Nick Hartley, OXERA Environmental Ltd

Dr K. Hawkins, University of Oxford*

Professor Christopher Hood*

Dr S.P. Hopkin, University of Reading*

Mr Tom Horlick-Jones, Centre for Environmental Strategy, University of Surrey

Dr C.V. Howard, University of Liverpool

Robert C. and Margaret Hunt

Mr A. Ingham, University of Southampton

Ms Rachel Iredale, Welsh Institute for Health and Social Care, University of Glamorgan

Professor Sheila Jasanoff*

Professor Michael Jones-Lee, Centre for the Analysis of Safety Policy and Attitudes to Risk, University of Newcastle upon Tyne

Dr Norman King

Dr Ludwig Krämer, European Commission, Directorate-General XI*

Professor Terry Mansfield, University of Lancaster*

Professor Anil Markandya, Department of Economics and International Development, University of Bath

Dr A. McDonald

Mr Owen McIntyre and Mr Thomas Mosedale, Faculty of Law, University of Manchester

Professor Konrad von Moltke, Environment Studies Program, Dartmouth College, USA, and the Institute for Environmental Studies, Free University of Amsterdam*

Mr Joseph Murphy, School of Geography and Earth Resources, University of Hull

Dr K. Neal, University of Nottingham

Mr P. L. O'Brien

Dr Onora O'Neill, University of Cambridge*

Mr Derek Osborn, Chairman of the Board of the European Environment Agency*

Dr Susan Owens, Department of Geography, University of Cambridge

Dr Martin Parkes, SAC (Scottish Agricultural College)

Dr Judith Petts, Centre for Hazard and Risk Management, Loughborough University of Technology*

Mrs Anita Pollack, MEP*

Professor Andrew Porteous, Open University

Mr Tom Radice

Mr Robert Rogers

Professor Anthony Seaton, Aberdeen University, Chairman of the Expert Panel on Air Quality Standards*

Dr Elizabeth Shove, Centre for the Study of Environmental Change, University of Lancaster

Dr Ellen Silbergeld, Environmental Defense Fund

Mr Eric Silvester

Professor Jim Skea, Science Policy Research Unit, University of Sussex

Dr David Slater, Managing Director, OXERA Environmental Ltd

Professor Lewis Smith, Institute for Environment and Health*

Mr Turner T. Smith Jr., Hunton and Williams, Washington D.C.*

Sir Richard Southwood*

Dr Clive Spash, Department of Land Economy, University of Cambridge

Professor N.M. van Straalen, Free University of Amsterdam*

Mr Joseph Tanega, Kingston Business School, University of Kingston

Dr H.F. Thomas, MRC Epidemiology Unit (South Wales)

Mr Stephen Tindale*

Dr Steve Trudgill and Professor Keith Richards, Department of Geography, University of Cambridge

Dr Steven Vertovek, University of Oxford*

Mr David Wallace*

Professor Christopher Wathes, Silsoe Research Institute*

Mr Mark Watts, MEP*

Professor Albert Weale, University of Essex

Mr E.H. Wiggins

Professor Bernard Williams, University of Oxford*

Professor Robert Worcester, Market and Opinion Research International (MORI)*

Professor Brian Wynne, Centre for the Study of Environmental Change, University of Lancaster*

Commissioned studies

The following studies were commissioned in the course of the study:

The European Dimension of Standard Setting. David Wilkinson, Sally Mullard, Neil Emmott, Claire Coffey and Nigel Haigh. Institute for European Environmental Policy, London. August 1996.

The Role of Cost-Benefit Analysis in Environmental Standards. Tim Denne and Jonathan Fisher. ERM Economics. September 1996.

Setting Environmental Standards: The Statistical Approach to Handling Uncertainty and Variation. Professor Vic Barnett and Professor Tony O'Hagan, University of Nottingham. January 1997.

A draft version of this last report was discussed at a workshop, Uncertainty and Variability in Standards, held in Edinburgh on 2–3 December 1996 and sponsored jointly by the Commission and the International Centre for Mathematical Sciences, Edinburgh. The report was updated and published as a book:

Barnett, V. and O'Hagan, A. (1997). *Setting Environmental Standards. The statistical approach to handling uncertainty and variation. A report to the Royal Commission on Environmental Pollution.* Chapman and Hall.

Visits

In the course of its work on environmental standards, Members of the Commission and its Secretariat made the following visits; the Secretariat is indebted to the British Embassies in Washington D.C., Stockholm, Copenhagen, Bonn and Paris, the UK Delegation to the Organisation for Economic Co-operation and Development in Paris, and the Consulate in Seville for the assistance received in organising the relevant itineraries:

2 February 1996 – National Environmental Technology Centre (NETCEN), Harwell
Presentations from staff of NETCEN and the Energy Technology Support Unit (ETSU), AEA Technology

10–11 October 1996 – Washington D.C.
During a two-day visit, Members had discussions with representatives from the following organisations:

> American Petroleum Institute; Centre for Strategic and International Studies; Chamber of Commerce; Chemical Manufacturers Association; Council on Environmental Quality; US Environmental Protection Agency; Forum on Science and Technology to Support Society's Environmental Goals; General Electric Company; Hunton and Williams; National Association of Manufacturers; National Environmental Policy Institute; National Research Council; Natural Resources Defense Council; Occupational Safety and Health Administration; Resources for the Future; Sierra Club; Union of Concerned Scientists; World Resources Institute

9–11 October 1996 – Research Triangle Park, North Carolina, and Washington D.C.
During this series of visits Members consulted widely with staff of the US Environmental Protection Agency and National Institute of Health at Research Triangle Park. Members joined in with the visits in Washington D.C. and also met with representatives of the Food and Drug Administration

21–24 October 1996 – Stockholm and Copenhagen
Discussions with staff from: KEMI, Swedish National Chemicals Inspectorate (Stockholm); European Environment Agency (Copenhagen); World Health Organization, Regional Office for Europe (Copenhagen); Dansk Industri (Copenhagen)

14–15 November 1996 – European Commission, Brussels
Discussions with staff from: Directorate-General XI – Environment, Nuclear Safety and Civil Protection; Directorate-General III – Industry; Commissioner Bjerregard's Cabinet

3–4 April 1997 – Environment Agency, Bristol
Discussions with Environment Agency staff and visits to and discussions with staff at Zeneca Pharmaceuticals, Avonmouth, and Britannia Zinc Ltd, Avonmouth

1–2 May 1997 – Scottish Environment Protection Agency, Edinburgh
Discussions with Scottish Environment Protection Agency staff and visits to and discussions with staff at Zeneca Pharmaceuticals, Grangemouth, and CSC Forest Products Ltd, Cowie

3 October 1997 – Belfast
Discussions with staff from the Environment and Heritage Service

15 October 1997 – University of Lancaster
Discussions with staff of the Centre for the Study of Environmental Change and the Department of Philosophy: Dr E. Darier, Mr J. Foster, Professor R. Grove-White, Dr A. Holland, Mr J. O'Neill, Dr B. Szerszynski and Professor B. Wynne

29–31 October 1997 – Germany
Discussions with staff from the Federal Environment Agency and the German Council of Environmental Advisors in Berlin; the Bavarian Ministry of the Environment and the Federal Environment Ministry in Bonn; the North Rhine Westphalia Ministry for the Environment, Planning and Agriculture in Düsseldorf; and Bayer AG in Leverkusen

21–22 January 1998 – Paris
Discussions with staff of the Organisation for Economic Co-operation and Development; the United Nations Environment Programme, Industry and Environment Section; the French Environment Ministry

27 January 1998 – Seville
Discussions with staff of the Institute for Prospective Technological Studies and the Andalucian Regional Environment Agency

Secretariat

Other Members of the Secretariat who made a significant contribution to the content of the report at various stages were Cathy Garretty, Claire Moran, Hülya Mustafa, Ilga Nielsen and Julia Penton.

Appendix C

OVERVIEW OF PRESENT ENVIRONMENTAL STANDARDS

C.1 This appendix provides an indication of the many different forms that environmental standards can take. The emphasis is on the main features of the current situation and on standards which relate directly or indirectly to the introduction of a substance, or energy, into the environment. The main forms such standards now take are listed in box 1A in the report, and this appendix deals with each of these forms in turn. The description is confined to those standards that apply in the UK, although they may have been set globally or by European bodies, as well as nationally or more locally; the final section of the appendix (C.81–C.113) looks at the geographical scope of standard setting.

C.2 Environmental standards are far from homogeneous. They may differ in their stringency (are they easily achievable or will technological advances be necessary to achieve them?), in their force (are they mandatory or do they provide guidance only?), or in their stability (are they subject to continual change or are they relatively fixed?).

C.3 In this overview we have attempted to provide a characterisation of the main forms that environmental standards may take. It is not, therefore, intended to be an exhaustive account, or to provide a comprehensive history of the subject. In compiling this appendix, we have drawn both on the *Manual of Environmental Policy: The EC and Britain*, published by the Institute of European Environmental Policy (IEEP), London, and a paper on the European dimension of standard setting commissioned from IEEP.[1]

Standards applying directly to the pathway

Biological standards

C.4 To the extent that environmental standards are intended to protect human health, the most direct form of judgement about the acceptability of modifications produced by human activity is a standard for modifications within the human body. As it may be difficult to measure the modifications that are ultimately of concern (for example, the effect of lead on intelligence), and as a given substance may have several different effects, biological standards usually take the form of a maximum allowable concentration of a substance in blood, or other readily accessible tissue, for example, hair, urine, fat, etc. Such measurements are essentially biomarkers of exposure not effect.

C.5 Biological standards do not in themselves provide a satisfactory basis for legally binding measures. Exceedance of a biological standard shows that a certain exposure has occurred, but it is too late by then to prevent that exposure, or the effect that may have ensued. Moreover, observation of such an exceedance does not in itself indicate what action is required to prevent further exceedances, as exposure may have been by a number of routes. A mandatory biological standard for lead was contained in a draft Directive proposed by the European Commission in 1975, but removed prior to its adoption.[2] A different situation exists in the field of occupational health, in that a worker who is found to have exceeded a biological standard can be removed from work which brings him into contact with the substance concerned.[3] There are therefore some legally binding biological standards for occupational exposure, including one for lead in blood.

Exposure standards

C.6 Exposure standards define acceptable exposures or doses at the point of entry to an organism.

163

Exposure of a person to a substance, or to energy, may occur through various routes: the main ones are absorption through the skin, inhalation, and ingestion of food or water.

C.7 Standards for external radiation relate to exposure to radiation at the body surface; standards for intakes of radioactive substances are based on the potential damage to internal organs. Primary recommendations for radiological standards are made by the International Commission on Radiological Protection (ICRP). This is a private and self-appointed body, and its authority and influence derive from the scientific standing of its members and the quality of its recommendations.[4] The recently established International Commission on Non-Ionising Radiation Protection is modelled on ICRP.

C.8 Protection from the effects of ionising radiation are based on three principles set out by ICRP:[5]

justification – no practice involving exposure to radiation should be adopted unless it produces sufficient benefit to the exposed individuals or to society to offset the radiation detriment it causes;

optimisation – radiation doses and risks should be kept as low as reasonably achievable, economic and social factors bïeing taken into account;

limits – the exposure of individuals should be subject to dose or risk limits above which the radiation risk would be unacceptable.

C.9 ICRP recommendations provide the basis for the dose limits set by European Directives which are legally binding in the UK. The *Ionising Radiations Regulations 1985*[6] provide protection for the work-force from ionising radiations and specify that radiation must be kept as low as reasonably practicable; they also set out the annual dose limits that should not be exceeded for both occupational exposure and exposure of the general public, as prescribed in a 1980 Euratom Directive.[7] As a result of recommendations from ICRP in 1990,[8] a Directive amending these dose limits was adopted by the Council of Ministers in May 1996 for formal implementation in May 2000.[9] The UK Regulations will need to be amended in the light of this latest Directive.

C.10 In the UK, the National Radiological Protection Board (NRPB) carries out scientific research on radiation hazards and advises the government on whether or not recommendations made by bodies such as the ICRP should be applied in the UK;[10] it also provides information and advice about radiation protection to government Departments and other interested parties.

C.11 For chemical substances, recommendations for exposure standards normally take the form of *tolerable* or *acceptable daily intakes* (TDIs or ADIs). These standards represent the amount of substance which can be consumed every day for an individual's entire lifetime in the practical expectation, on the basis of all known facts, that no harm will result, and may be expressed as a daily intake either for an individual, based on assumed average body weights (for example, 60 kg for an adult, 10 kg for a child and 5 kg for an infant), or per kg of body weight. TDIs and ADIs may cover either intake by all routes or intake by one specified route (normally, ingestion of food and drink); in the latter case, assumptions must be made about the amounts of the relevant substance entering the body by the different routes. Recommendations for TDIs are made by the International Programme on Chemical Safety (IPCS), set up in 1980 by three United Nations bodies, the United Nations Environment Programme (UNEP), the International Labour Organization and the World Health Organization (WHO), and contained in comprehensive evaluations of individual substances published by WHO in its *Environmental Health Criteria Series* (some forms of non-ionising radiation are also covered in this series). It is emphasised within these evaluations that each volume in the series represents the collective views of an international group of experts convened for the purpose, and 'does not necessarily represent the decisions or the stated policy' of any of the three sponsoring bodies. For many substances IPCS evaluations do not result in a recommended standard because there is too little evidence; in that case the conclusion may take the form that an intake of *x* mg/kg body weight a day 'will probably not cause adverse effects in humans by any route of exposure'[11] or even that a given substance 'appears ... relatively safe'.[12]

C.12 The main internationally recognised health-based standards (ADIs) for agricultural pesticides are produced by joint Food and Agriculture Organization (FAO)/WHO committees and meetings on pesticides.[13] Similar FAO/WHO committees and processes produce ADIs for veterinary medicines and are also active in deriving maximum residue levels (MRLs) (product standards) for a wide range of contaminants in foods and animal feedstuffs (C.49–C.51).

C.13 As well as protection of human health, IPCS evaluations also cover protection of the natural environment. They do not set exposure standards in that context, but they may make recommendations for other forms of environmental standard discussed below. The critical loads set by the United Nations Economic Commission for Europe (UNECE), to provide a basis for agreement on reducing emissions of pollutants to air (C.21), are a form of exposure standard for the natural environment. A *critical load* is a quantitative estimate of the exposure to one or more specified pollutants below which significant harmful effects on a sensitive element of the environment (such as a species, a type of species or a type of habitat) do not occur according to present knowledge.[14]

Quality standards for air

C.14 Perhaps the most obvious form of environmental standard is one applying to the quality of an environmental medium (sometimes called an ambient standard).

C.15 WHO prepares and publishes guideline values for concentrations of pollutants in air, averaged over specified periods, in order to provide 'a basis for protecting public health from adverse effects of air pollution and for eliminating, or reducing to a minimum, those contaminants of air that are known or likely to be hazardous to human health and wellbeing': this task is undertaken by the WHO Regional Office for Europe. Toxicologically-based guideline values were recommended in 1987 for 19 organic and inorganic air pollutants.[15] A revised set of air quality guideline values agreed in 1996 has not been published at the time of writing.

C.16 Despite the considerations mentioned above, the European Community (EC) set legally binding limit values for concentrations in air of suspended particulates and sulphur dioxide, lead and nitrogen dioxide in Directives adopted between 1980 and 1985.[16] It also set more stringent guide values for nitrogen dioxide, sulphur dioxide and suspended particulates as the basis for Member States to develop longer-term policies for improving air quality. UK legislation implementing these Directives places a duty on the Secretary of State to take 'any appropriate measures' to ensure that the limit values are not exceeded and to establish monitoring sites to check concentrations.[17]

C.17 In 1996 the Framework Directive on Ambient Air Quality Assessment and Management was adopted.[18] This provides for 'daughter legislation' to set legally binding limit values, target values and/or alert thresholds as appropriate for the pollutants covered in earlier legislation (particulate matter, nitrogen dioxide, sulphur dioxide, lead and ozone[19]), and also for a further seven pollutants or pollutant groups.[20] The 1996 revision of the WHO air quality guidelines, conducted in collaboration with the European Commission and IPCS, will provide the basis for these Daughter Directives. The European Commission's proposal for the first Daughter Directive – covering sulphur dioxide, nitrogen oxides, particulate matter and lead – includes, where appropriate, limit values at the levels recommended by WHO; the exception is particulate matter, for which WHO did not recommend a guideline value.[21]

C.18 In 1991 the Department of the Environment (DOE) established the Expert Panel on Air Quality Standards (EPAQS) to advise the government on air quality standards. Subsequently, the Environment Act 1995 (the 1995 Act) for the first time placed a duty on the Secretary of State to prepare a national strategy containing standards for air quality.[22] The advice of EPAQS has taken the form of recommended standards for the eight pollutants which DOE identified as priorities for its National Air Quality Strategy – benzene, 1,3-butadiene, carbon monoxide, lead, nitrogen dioxide, ozone, fine particles and sulphur dioxide. Seven of these standards, and in the remaining case, the WHO guideline value for lead, form the basis for the air quality objectives which define the air quality to be achieved by 2005, incorporated in the Strategy and accompanying regulations.[23] In May 1998, that is, after publication of the Air Quality Strategy in March 1997, EPAQS proposed a standard for lead lower than that recommended by WHO; this standard will be considered in the first review of the National Air Quality Strategy announced in February 1998.[24]

C.19 The National Air Quality Strategy defines 'standards' as benchmarks or reference points for air quality set purely with regard to medical or scientific evidence about the effects of a particular pollutant on public health. The first EC Daughter Directive proposes standards which are the same as, or less stringent than, the National Air Quality Strategy standards for sulphur dioxide, nitrogen oxides, particulate matter and lead. If the Daughter Directives finally adopted within the Community specify standards and objectives which are more stringent than those contained in the National Air Quality Strategy, the Community legislation will prevail.

C.20 The present EC and UK legislation does not assign air quality standards the role of directly controlling emissions. This is achieved through other forms of environmental standard. The 1995 Act requires the Environment Agencies and local authorities to have regard to the Strategy in discharging their pollution control functions; and requires a local authority to review and assess air quality and prepare an action plan for any part of its area in which a prescribed air quality standard or objective is not being achieved or is not likely to be achieved within a prescribed period.[25]

C.21 Whereas the UK National Strategy is at present confined to protection of human health, the EC Framework Directive provides for air quality standards to protect the 'environment as a whole'. The first draft Daughter Directive proposes more stringent limit values to apply outside urban areas for nitrogen dioxide and sulphur dioxide in order to protect ecosystems. These are based on separate air quality guidelines produced by WHO for the protection of the natural environment from effects of air pollutants. In carrying out the 1996 revision of its air quality guidelines,[26] WHO co-operated with the Working Group on Effects under the UNECE Convention on Long-Range Transboundary Air Pollution (LRTAP) in order to capitalise on the scientific work undertaken since 1988 to formulate criteria for the assessment of the effects of air pollutants on the natural environment (i.e. the development of critical levels and loads).

C.22 The Department of the Environment, Transport and the Regions (DETR) provides information on air pollution levels through its public information system,[27] intended to alert people whose health is sensitive to air pollution and to encourage people to act to reduce pollution. Information is provided on key air pollutants – sulphur dioxide, ozone, nitrogen dioxide, airborne particles (PM_{10}) and carbon monoxide – on the basis of four health-based bands, representing 'low', 'moderate', 'high' and 'very high' levels of pollution. (Hourly information on benzene and 1,3-butadiene levels is also provided but not included within the banding system.) The banding system provides a broad guide to likely pollutant effects on health and is consistent with the National Air Quality Strategy and advice from the Department of Health's (DH's) Committee on the Medical Effects of Air Pollutants (COMEAP). For example, at pollutant levels falling within the low band, effects are unlikely to be noticed even by individuals who know they are sensitive to air pollutants; within the high band, significant effects may be noticed by sensitive individuals and action to reduce these effects may be needed. The low band covers levels of pollutants up to the air quality standard contained in the Air Quality Strategy. The breakpoints between the moderate, high and very high bands – respectively the 'standard threshold', the 'information threshold' and the 'alert threshold' – were recommended by COMEAP. In reality, there are no sudden steps in effects as levels pass from one band to the next; rather there is a gradually increasing risk of effects as concentrations of pollutants rise.

C.23 For ozone, EC legislation does not set a limit value but requires that information and guidance should be provided to the general public if certain threshold levels are exceeded. The information threshold and alert threshold in the UK public information system correspond to the population information threshold and the population warning threshold respectively, as specified in the 1992 EC Ozone Directive.[28] The Directive incorporates as threshold levels WHO's 1987 guideline values for the protection of vegetation from the effects of ozone.

Quality standards for natural waters

C.24 The vast majority of the earth's surface water is contained within the oceans, including estuarine and coastal waters. Fresh surface water is normally confined in rivers, streams and lakes. The earliest standard for water quality was an implied standard established by property rights. Owners of land adjoining a river had a right to take fish from that river, and therefore a right to take legal action under common law against anyone polluting the river to such an extent that it could no longer support fish. Many such actions were successfully mounted, often with the assistance of the Anglers' Co-operative Association. When discharges to inland waters became subject to statutory regulation, the conditions attached to consents to discharge took account of the state and uses of a river, but there was no formal framework for doing so.

C.25 Water quality standards have been designed predominantly to benefit the natural environment, especially species of fish; standards for water supporting freshwater fish were established by EC legislation in 1978,[29] and for coastal waters used for production of shellfish in 1979.[30] Setting quality standards for groundwater would be a much more complex exercise and has not so far been attempted. Some quality standards, such as those in the EC Directive on bathing waters,[31] are intended to protect human health. The EC requirements concerning the quality of water abstracted for use as drinking water,[32] and quality objectives for 'dangerous substances' (under the framework of the 1976 Dangerous Substances in Water Directive,[33] discussed alongside emission standards for the same substances in C.39–C.40) are a less significant form of health protection because water is treated after abstraction, before being put into supply. The proposed EC Framework Directive on water resources would set a broad general standard for water quality throughout the European Union (EU) by requiring Member States to protect waters already in good condition and bring other waters to 'a good ecological state' by 2010.[34]

C.26 There is sometimes a lack of clarity about the purposes which environmental standards are meant to serve (see chapter 2, 2.50). One example of the kind of confusion which can arise is to be found in the EC Directives on limit values and quality objectives for mercury discharged by the chloralkali industry.[35] The purpose of the Directive as set out in its preamble is 'to protect the aquatic environment of the Community against pollution by certain dangerous substances'. It sets emission limits and (because of the UK) quality objectives. One of the quality objectives is a biological standard for fish (the concentration of mercury is not to exceed 0.3 mg/kg of fish flesh) but this is set as an indicator to protect human consumers, not the fish or the environment, being derived from a study carried out by the UK on levels of mercury which did not pose a threat to human health.

C.27 A system of water quality objectives has been developed in England and Wales to provide the basis for deciding the terms of consents and planning investments in relation to those aspects of water quality which are not subject to EC requirements. In 1977 a system of river quality objectives was established administratively by the National Water Council (the umbrella body for the regional water authorities in England and Wales). In 1994 regulations established a river ecosystem classification scheme to provide a more consistent basis for setting river quality objectives. It consists of five classes defined in terms of eight chemical parameters selected to represent the quality requirements for particular communities of fish, plants and animals. A separate classification system, based on water chemistry, river biology and aesthetic value exists for Scottish rivers and coastal waters.

Appendix C

C.28 The Water Resources Act 1991 contains powers to establish statutory water quality objectives (SWQOs) for particular stretches of water; these are intended to provide a planning framework for regulatory bodies, dischargers, abstractors and river users. In 1995 eight river catchments in which the system would be piloted were selected; in October 1996 the Environment Agency submitted proposals for SWQOs in these catchments to the Secretary of State for approval. The proposed SWQOs were generally expressed in terms of achieving a given river ecosystem class within a five- to ten-year horizon of investment planning. In some cases an objective was less stringent than the previous existing river quality objective because of limitations on the investment likely to take place; in such cases, the river quality objective was reflected in a longer-term SWQO proposed for achievement within (provisionally) ten years. Further development of these and future SWQOs is still under consideration by the Environment Agency and DETR.

C.29 A non-statutory standard for classifying estuaries according to their quality was developed in time for use in the 1980 river quality survey. Points are allocated for various measures of biological quality (ability to allow the passage of migratory fish, to support an appropriate residential fish population and benthic community, and absence of elevated levels in the biota of persistent, toxic or tainting substances), aesthetic quality (essentially a judgement of the amount of pollution received and its effects), and dissolved oxygen. The points are summed and the area is placed in one of four classes ranging from good quality (class A) to bad quality (class D). The Environment Agency is now considering how the scheme might be developed for the future.

C.30 A corollary of relating environmental standards for water quality to the use or intended use of particular stretches of water is that the regulator has had substantial discretion about what use should be regarded as appropriate for a particular stretch, now or in the future. Key EC Directives left it to Member States to designate the stretches of water to which the requirements of each Directive should apply, although decisions by the European Court have shown that there are constraints on the exercise of that discretion. The setting of objectives has of course coincided with a general policy commitment to bring about improvements in water quality.

Quality standards for soil

C.31 Pollutants in soil are in general much less mobile than pollutants in air or water. The physical, chemical and biological properties of soil affect the downward passage of water and pollutants into groundwater; but in that context it has not been possible to do more than classify soils in broad bands according to their significance to the causation of groundwater pollution.[36] Even more than in the case of water, such quality standards as have been set for soil relate to particular uses.

C.32 In the case of agricultural land on which sewage sludge has been spread, an EC Directive specifies ranges within which Member States must set limit values for concentrations of heavy metals and certain other substances in soils.[37] There are wide variations in the limit values which have been set for the same substance in different countries, both inside and outside the EU.[38]

C.33 The major groups of standards for soil relate to the remediation of contaminated sites. Guidance on the remediation of contaminated sites and their subsequent use was published in 1987 by a government committee, the Interdepartmental Committee on the Redevelopment of Contaminated Land (ICRCL).[39] The general form of this guidance was to give two trigger concentrations for each combination of substance and future use of a site. If the relevant substance was present in the soil at a concentration below the 'threshold level', no further reduction in concentration was thought necessary before the site could be used for the specified purpose. If on the other hand the concentration was equal to or exceeded the 'action level', the site could not be used for that purpose unless it had first been remediated. If the concentration lay in what was usually a wide band (typically an order of magnitude) between the threshold level and the action level, ICRCL's guidance was that professional judgement must be used in deciding whether

168

remediation is necessary. The 'suitable for use' principle requires remedial action only where there are appropriate and cost-effective means available, taking into account the actual or intended use of the site.[40] ICRCL employed only a limited number of categories to describe future use, the main ones being hard cover (typically a car park), buildings, parks/playing fields/open spaces and domestic gardens/allotments. Other categories used in relation to certain contaminants are landscaped areas and 'anywhere plants are to be grown'.

C.34 ICRCL's guidance covered only 18 substances; an undertaking in 1990 to extend the guidance to cover 25 other substances[41] was not fulfilled. An initiative to produce new guide values, of broadly similar stringency but based on a new assessment model,[42] was expected to yield a first tranche of new guideline values in late 1998.[43] Although the NRPB has not found it practicable as yet to set standards for radionuclides on contaminated sites,[44] it has issued guidance on the application of existing radiological protection principles and standards to contaminated land situations.[45]

C.35 For substances on which no UK guidance is available, consultants working in the UK frequently apply soil standards set in other countries, although even these do not necessarily cover all the substances for which standards would be desirable.[46] The non-UK standards which have probably been applied most often in the UK are those published by the Dutch government in 1983 and revised in 1994. The 1994 revision produced standards in the form of an intervention level above which remediation was considered essential and a target level to be achieved after remediation. In broad terms, ICRCL threshold levels are at least one order of magnitude higher than the Dutch target values proposed in 1994 for the same substance.[47] In contrast to the ICRCL standards, the Dutch target levels were set on the principle of 'multifunctionality', in order 'to restore the functional properties of the ground for human beings, flora and fauna',[48] but this principle was abandoned in 1997.[49]

C.36 In drawing up its guidelines, ICRCL took into account human health effects related to direct ingestion of soil, inhalation of soil, consumption of contaminated plants and exposure of skin; toxicity to plants, but not, in general, other forms of damage to the natural environment; corrosion of building materials; and fire and explosion hazards. It is not clear that consistent methodologies were employed to analyse these hazards.[50]

Emission standards

C.37 As already noted, it is impracticable to use a quality standard as a direct control over emissions. In the 1970s there was heated debate within the European Community over whether it was preferable to regulate emissions site by site in the light of quality standards or control pollution by setting limit values at Community level for particular categories of fixed sources. The limit values approach left Member States free to set emission standards which were more stringent than the Community standards but not less stringent.

C.38 In the mid-1970s several international conventions were adopted in Europe with the aim of limiting discharges to the sea or to rivers which cross national frontiers. These include, for example, the Paris Convention, drawn up to protect the North Sea and north-east Atlantic from pollution from land-based sources, signed in 1974, and the Convention on the Protection of the Rhine against Chemical Pollution (the Rhine Convention, adopted in 1976). After the European Commission put forward proposals for co-ordinating implementation of these conventions (and the draft Strasbourg Convention for the Protection of International Watercourses against Pollution), a Framework Directive on discharges of dangerous substances to the aquatic environment was adopted in 1976[51] and has had wide significance.

C.39 The Directive sets a framework for eliminating or reducing pollution of inland, coastal and territorial waters by particularly dangerous substances. In 1983, the Council adopted a list (set out in a European Commission Communication of the previous year) of 129 substances considered to be so toxic, persistent or bioaccumulative in the environment that priority should be given to eliminating pollution by them. To date, Daughter Directives have been adopted for 17 of these priority substances, including mercury, cadmium, DDT, pentachlorophenol and chlorinated solvents such as carbon tetrachloride and chloroform. These have been given formal List I (or 'Black List') status as the most dangerous substances to the aquatic environment.

C.40 The Framework Directive contains alternative regimes for the control of List I substances:

> the preferred regime (adopted by all Member States except the UK) involves setting limit values for each substance in Daughter Directives, which emission standards set at national level are not to exceed;

> the alternative regime requires emission standards to be determined by reference to quality objectives contained in the Daughter Directives.

The second approach can be used only by a Member State which can prove to the European Commission, on the basis of a prescribed monitoring procedure, that the quality objectives are being met. For List II (or 'Grey List') substances, the less dangerous substances, all Member States use the second approach. The remaining substances on the priority list which have not been given formal List I status in Daughter Directives are treated as List II substances for regulatory purposes.

C.41 In 1979, a Directive on the protection of groundwater against pollution caused by dangerous substances was adopted for compliance in December 1981.[52] The Directive requires prevention of the discharge of List I substances to groundwater and investigation of List II substances prior to direct or indirect discharge. The Lists I and II referred to here are not identical to those in the Dangerous Substances in Water Directive; List I status in the Groundwater Directive is definitive and does not need confirmation in a Daughter Directive.

C.42 Further EC framework legislation[53] provides for Daughter Directives covering emissions to the atmosphere from particular industries or processes. Standards have subsequently been set for emissions of asbestos to air, for incineration plants and for new large combustion plant, and take the form of limits on concentrations of specified substances in the emissions.

C.43 Following past debates, there is now more common ground between Member States about the appropriate regulatory approach. For larger or more complex plants the dominant element in future is likely to be process standards based on the principle of 'best available techniques' (BAT) (see C.54–C.62). There may be circumstances where emissions standards or emission limits based on BAT may not provide sufficient protection for the environment, and more stringent limits will then have to be applied to emissions. This is recognised explicitly in the proposed EC Framework Directive on water resources, the EC Directive on air pollution from industrial plants (for particularly polluted areas or in areas which require special protection) and in the Directive on Integrated Pollution Prevention and Control.

C.44 In the case of emissions from mobile sources different considerations are involved. Limits on emissions from ships and aircraft are set globally. The MARPOL Convention aimed at preventing pollution from ships is administered by the International Maritime Organization (IMO) with scientific advice from the Joint Group of Experts on the Scientific Aspects of Marine Pollution (GESAMP), an advisory body set up in 1969 and at present sponsored by IMO, FAO, the United Nations Educational, Scientific and Cultural Organization, the World Meteorological Organization (WMO), WHO, the International Atomic Energy Agency, the United Nations and UNEP. Limit values for emissions from aircraft engines and for aircraft noise are set in technical annexes to the Chicago Convention on International Aviation administered by the International Civil Aviation Organization.

C.45 The EC Roadworthiness Directive sets limit values for emissions from road vehicles in use which are intended to deal with more grossly polluting vehicles.[54] Other EC Directives have set limits for emissions from new vehicles as manufactured.[55] The European Commission's proposals for more stringent limits to apply to vehicles sold after 2000 have been put forward as the most cost-effective approach to meeting WHO air quality guidelines by 2010, after studies which included modelling ozone levels across the EU and concentrations of other pollutants in seven European cities.[56] The European Parliament and Council reached agreement in June 1998 on more stringent emission limits for cars and light vans for 2000/01; a Directive is expected to be adopted towards the end of 1998. A Directive proposing more stringent emission limits for heavy duty diesel engines for 2000/01 is at an earlier stage of consideration. EC Directives have set limit values for noise from road vehicles.[57]

Total emissions standards

C.46 The type of emission standard discussed above relates to emissions from particular classes of source. In some cases it is more satisfactory to set a standard for total emissions of a pollutant from all sources, irrespective of their origin. This is often known as an emissions 'bubble'. This type of standard may apply nationally, across a wider area, such as the EC, or globally. The bubble approach was first used by the Community to control the production (and hence effectively the emission) of chlorofluorocarbons (CFCs), and subsequently in the Large Combustion Plant Directive to control emissions of sulphur dioxide and oxides of nitrogen. As in this case, it can be used to secure proportionally larger reductions from some countries than from others. The approach has achieved prominence again in the burden-sharing measures agreed to tackle climate change. The bubble approach allows considerable flexibility in controlling the emissions from individual sources: an increase from one is permitted, provided it is offset by an equivalent decrease from others so that the total emissions ceiling (the bubble) is not breached. It is thus the regulatory basis for the emissions trading in sulphur dioxide which has been introduced in the USA (see chapter 6, 6.61–6.64). It is most appropriate for controlling global pollutants such as greenhouse gases, which do not cause local damage when they are emitted.

Product standards

C.47 The presence of a substance in a marketed product may add to levels of the substance (or its breakdown products) in the environment as a result of the product's use or disposal and, in the case of food or drink, contributes directly to human exposure to the substance. In some cases, the most effective way of preventing harm from a substance is to set a standard for its concentration in a specified category of products. For example, an EC Directive sets limits on various substances in motor fuels, and also covers physical characteristics of the fuel which have environmental implications. Reducing concentrations of certain substances in motor fuels has indirect as well as direct benefits: the presence of sulphur in fuels increases emissions of particulates, and both sulphur and lead may render pollution control devices fitted to vehicle exhausts ineffective and interfere with the operation of less polluting types of engine.[58]

C.48 Some product standards have been set under EC legislation on the marketing and use of dangerous substances[59] (C.66); for example, an amendment to the original Marketing and Use Directive sets limits on the mercury content of alkaline manganese batteries.[60]

C.49 Guide values in the form of maximum residue levels (MRLs) for a wide range of inorganic and organic contaminants in food, beverages and animal feedstuffs are set by the Codex Alimentarius Commission, a joint body of FAO and WHO.[61] In particular it derives MRLs for concentrations of specified pesticides in various commodities.[62] ADIs for pesticides (C.12) provide the toxicological baseline to which residue levels are referred. While ADIs are defined as measures of safety, MRLs are derived from estimates of the maximum residues 'that might occur when pesticides are used according to good agricultural practices',[63] and are designed to ensure that pesticide residues are as low as practicable. Exposure to residues in excess of MRLs does not automatically imply a hazard to health. It may indicate, however, that label directions or use standards are not being adhered to and should act as a trigger for follow-up action. MRLs for agricultural pesticides are proposed by the Joint FAO/WHO Meetings on Pesticide Residues which also set the ADIs.

C.50 A 1990 Framework Directive[64] made the setting of MRLs mandatory rather than optional within the Community; the UK *Pesticides (Maximum Residue Levels in Crops, Food and Feedingstuffs) Regulations 1994* now implement not only the 1990 Framework Directive but subsequent Daughter Directives concerning pesticide residues. The 1994 Regulations lay down MRLs for 87 pesticides and apply to more than 150 foods, including meat, milk, eggs, tea and cereals, as well as a sizeable list of fruit and vegetables. Most of the MRLs are precisely those stipulated in the relevant EC Directives, which draw on proposals from the EC Standing Committee on Plant Health and the United Nations Codex Alimentarius Commission. National MRLs, relating to crops, food and feedstuffs which are not the subject of Directives, are also included in the Regulations.

C.51 An EC Framework Regulation[65] lays down Community procedures for contaminants in food and enables the European Commission to elaborate MRLs for particular chemical contaminants in food. Controls for contaminants in food for sale set at Community level and in the UK are, however, limited. They include a Directive to protect consumers of shellfish, which lays down bacteriological and chemical standards for bivalves.[66] Statutory limit values set by specific UK regulations apply for the following contaminants: arsenic, lead and tin in food, and tetrachloroethylene in olive oil.

C.52 WHO publishes guidelines for drinking water quality covering a large number of parameters with the primary aim of protecting human health. Prepared by its Regional Office for Europe, these guidelines are intended to be used as a basis for the development of national standards.[67] They cover both concentrations of chemical substances and some microbiological parameters. Successive sets of WHO guidelines provided the basis for a Directive on drinking water quality in 1980,[68] which set both limit values and guide values, and for its proposed revision presented by the European Commission in 1995.[69] The 1980 Drinking Water Directive has been implemented in the UK by regulations which set 11 additional standards for matters not covered by the Directive.

C.53 Following the Chernobyl accident, intervention levels for radioactive contamination of food were specified in a 1987 Regulation of the Council of the European Communities and are binding in the UK.[70] Since then ICRP and NRPB have continued to provide further recommendations and advice on appropriate intervention levels.[71] The Council Regulation does not specify intervention levels for radioactive contamination of drinking water supplies but the NRPB has suggested an action level for this purpose.[72]

Other forms of environmental standard

Process standards

C.54 Other forms of standard, which do not relate to the concentration of a substance at a particular point in a pathway, also have an important role in environmental protection. Process standards identify a set or sets of techniques for a specified industrial process in order to provide a criterion for deciding what emissions to the environment should be permitted from any given site. Process standards are contained in guidance notes issued by the regulatory authorities (C.58–C.59).

C.55 The Environmental Protection Act 1990 (the 1990 Act) provides the statutory basis for integrated pollution control (IPC), requiring the operator of any prescribed industrial process in England, Wales or Scotland to prevent the release into any environmental medium of substances prescribed for that medium or, where that is not practicable using 'the best available techniques not entailing excessive cost' (BATNEEC), to use such techniques to reduce releases of substances to a minimum and render them harmless.[73] (Regulations bringing Northern Ireland's industrial pollution control system broadly in line with that of the rest of Britain came into force in March 1998. The new system will be phased in for existing processes over a four-year period to December 2002.[74])

C.56 As a result of the 1995 Act the previous pollution control authorities were brought together in 1996 to create the Environment Agency in England and Wales and the Scottish Environment Protection Agency (SEPA). In most respects the Environment Agencies have continued to operate under the legislation which applied to the various forms of pollution prior to the 1995 Act. DETR is carrying out a review to identify respects in which the legislation needs to be amended to remove barriers which hinder their taking a holistic approach to safeguarding the environment.

C.57 The UK legislation on integrated pollution control will be superseded by the EC Directive on Integrated Pollution Prevention and Control,[75] adopted in 1996, which must be transposed into national legislation by October 1999. This will apply to a much larger number of processes than the system at present applying in England, Scotland and Wales and to more prescribed substances (see chapter 3).

C.58 BATNEEC can in itself be regarded as a qualitative process standard. A very general standard has the advantage of leaving scope for the regulator to exert pressure on the operator to innovate and improve performance in ways that would not be possible if the technology had been precisely specified. In practice, however, the requirement to use BATNEEC has been supplemented in several directions. First, more specific but non-binding process standards have been set in guidance about the techniques the regulator is likely to regard as satisfying the BATNEEC requirement in the case of a given industrial process. Under the 1990 Act, industrial processes were divided into two groups: Part A and Part B processes. The more technically difficult Part A processes are subject to IPC (covering releases to all environmental media) administered by the Environment Agency (in England and Wales) and SEPA. Guidance on Part A processes is provided by the Environment Agency in a series of Integrated Pollution Control Guidance Notes;[76] there are no comparable notes produced in Scotland and, in practice, SEPA uses the Environment Agency's guidance.

C.59 Under the 1990 Act, local authorities were given new powers to control air pollution from Part B processes (in Scotland, SEPA has responsibility for both Part A and Part B processes). Process Guidance Notes (PGNs) issued by the Secretary of State, and published on behalf of DETR, The Welsh Office and The Scottish Office, cover each of the Part B process sectors.[77] Part B processes tend to be more standardised than Part A processes and, as such, PGNs can be more prescriptive. PGNs are intended to assist enforcing authorities in drawing up authorisations and setting appropriate conditions of operation. They may also include general requirements for staff training, equipment operation and maintenance, and response to abnormal emissions. As distinct from Part A guidance, PGNs constitute statutory guidance[78] and, as such, local enforcing authorities are required to have regard to it.

C.60 Guidance will also be provided under the EC Directive on Integrated Pollution Prevention and Control; the Directive specifies that the European Commission must publish every three years BAT Reference Documents (BREFs) containing the results of information exchange it will have organised between Member States and industry about best available techniques and ongoing developments; the competent authorities in Member States must take these reference documents into account when determining what are the best available techniques at a particular plant and granting a permit for its operation.

C.61 The requirement to use BATNEEC (process standards) has also been supplemented by the inclusion in the guidance issued by the regulator of presumptive limits on emissions which represent the performance the specified techniques can be expected to achieve. There is therefore in this case some overlap between process and emission standards. Inspectors take these prescriptive limits into account in setting the limits on emissions from individual sites. They also have to take into account the requirements of international conventions and EC legislation.

C.62 Process standards may specify the conditions which must be maintained during the operation of a process. For example, in order to limit the formation and emission of dioxins, the EC Directive on emissions from incineration plants for municipal waste specifies the temperature which must be maintained during incineration and the proportion of oxygen that must be present. (In practice, dioxin formation also depends on other factors, such as the rate of cooling of combustion gases.) Operators are allowed to use other techniques for reducing emissions of dioxins if these are equally effective.

Life cycle-based standards

C.63 The attempt to achieve the 'best practicable environmental option' (BPEO) has focused on considering all the emissions from a particular industrial process, but a more comprehensive view of the environmental implications of industrial processes and products requires a life cycle assessment of the product or process, on lines discussed in chapter 3.

C.64 The entire life cycle of a product is likely to include many different stages, spanning processes at different sites, probably under the control of different companies, and possibly in different countries. Statutory product standards based on life cycle assessment are not permitted under the General Agreement on Tariffs and Trade (discussed in chapter 6), which prohibits national governments from discriminating against 'like products' (see chapter 6, 6.10). The only practicable form of standard based directly on life cycle assessment therefore is a label indicating that the life cycle of a product in question meets certain criteria.

C.65 In 1992 the EC adopted a voluntary scheme for the award of ecolabels based on life cycle assessment.[79] Up to the end of 1996, detailed criteria had been agreed for the award of ecolabels to 12 categories of product. In only a very few cases has the award of an ecolabel to an individual product been approved.

Use standards

C.66 'Use standards' constitute another form of environmental standard related to products. They differ from the product standards discussed above in that they relate, not to the concentration of a given substance in a product, but to whether it is acceptable to market or use the product at all, and if so, for what applications and subject to what precautions. The general framework for bans or restrictions on the marketing and use of dangerous substances was created in the 1976 Marketing and Use Directive.[80] Restrictions are set out in this and subsequent amending Directives.[81] As an example, the original Marketing and Use Directive specifies that polychlorinated biphenyls and terphenyls may be used only in closed system electrical equipment, large condensers and for certain other specified applications. In general, restrictions on dangerous substances usually arise first in one or more Member States and are subsequently developed on a Community-wide basis. National restrictions must be notified under EC law as they constitute barriers to trade and the Commission must then propose harmonisation legislation or prevent the original national action.

C.67 Restrictions on the marketing and use of chemical substances may arise through EC procedures for the authorisation of new substances and the review of existing ones. (The methodology for the assessment of new and existing substances is described in chapter 2). Under new substances legislation[82] any manufacturer or importer intending to place a substance on the EC market for the first time must notify, at least 60 days before marketing, the competent authority of one of the Member States of their intention to do so, and must also provide certain information on the substance, depending on the quantity being marketed. These two components together comprise a notification. Notification requirements are the same in all Member States and a notification accepted in one Member State is valid for all. Notification was originally intended to ensure that sufficient information about a new substance's properties was available to label and package it and enable its safe handling. The information submitted also alerted the notifier, potential users of the substances and governments in Member States to any properties that might pose a risk to man and the environment from the manufacture, use and disposal of the substance. The original Directive implied that the notifier should assess risk. The competent authority (in the UK, jointly DOE and the Health and Safety Executive) was responsible for evaluating the notification dossier and determining whether it complied with the legislation. When the legislation was revised in 1992, the notification scheme was extended to include risk assessment.

C.68 Existing substances (those which are recorded as having been marketed in the EC between 1971 and 1981) produced in or imported into the EC in quantities greater than 10 tonnes/year must be notified to the European Commission.[83] The legislation covers over 100,000 existing substances and has been in operation since 1993. These substances are being assessed in a long-term programme which could, in principle, result in the phasing-out of some substances or other measures to reduce risks. By the end of 1997, three lists covering over 100 substances for priority assessment had been prepared by the European Commission but not one risk assessment has yet reached a stage of agreed action.[84]

C.69 Some categories of substance, such as medicinal products, plant protection products and cosmetics, are exempt from the requirements of the new substances legislation because of separate assessment and authorisation legislation applying to them.

C.70 The well-established UK regime for agricultural pesticides under the Food and Environment Protection Act 1985 and the Control of Pesticides Regulations 1986 (as amended) will increasingly be superseded by the EC harmonised regime for plant protection products.[85] This establishes a two-tier system for the approval and authorisation of pesticides: an approved positive list of active ingredients will be established at Community level, whilst products containing those active ingredients will be approved by individual Member States. This system allows Member States to conduct risk assessments for products which take account of local factors such as climate. Risk assessments must be conducted according to a set of common standards (known as the 'Uniform Principles'). The objective of the Directive is to secure high common standards of human and environmental protection whilst achieving much greater harmonisation in the Community market for agricultural pesticides. A programme is underway for the gradual examination of the large number of products on the market before the Directive came into force in July 1992, which contain active ingredients not on the positive list.

C.71 Controls on the use of pesticides in non-agricultural applications are contained in separate legislation which will also be gradually replaced by a new harmonised authorisation procedure included in the EC Biocides Directive,[86] which introduces a similar two-tier approvals system. Provisions for 'mutual recognition' within the plant protection and biocidal products Directives allow for the approval of one country's authorisation decisions by others.

C.72 The authorisation process for marketing and use of veterinary medicines is also based on EC legislation, implemented in the UK by Regulations which came into force in 1995.[87] The Veterinary Medicines Directorate (an executive agency of the Ministry of Agriculture, Fisheries and Food (MAFF)) administers the process. The availability of veterinary medicines is controlled on the basis of assessment of three criteria: their safety to the patient being treated, to the persons making, handling or administering the medicines, to the consumer who needs safe food free of potentially harmful residues, and to the environment; their quality (aspects relating to the manufacturing process); and their efficacy. Data supporting all aspects of safety, quality and efficacy must be provided for authorisation.[88]

C.73 One category of substances which has been the subject of worldwide control measures covers those substances which deplete the stratospheric ozone layer, notably CFCs. The Vienna Convention for the Protection of the Ozone Layer provided the necessary legal framework and the subsequent agreements known as the Montreal Protocol on Substances that Deplete the Ozone Layer contained control measures.[89]

Management standards

C.74 Finally, there are standards which relate to the capability of a company to deal with the environmental effects of its operations. For example, the 1990 Act introduced a new test of whether an applicant for or holder of a waste management licence is a 'fit and proper person' to hold that licence. This has three components; the applicant must

> have no conviction for any relevant offence;
>
> be technically competent; and
>
> demonstrate financial provision adequate to discharge the obligations arising from a licence.

DOE provided guidance on determining fit and proper status.[90]

C.75 Another form of management standard relates to systems and procedures. A company may apply for certification that its systems and procedures meet a specified standard. The first such environmental standard in the world was British Standard (BS) 7750, published in 1992 and revised in 1994, which specified a management system aimed at delivering continuous improvement in environmental performance, in accordance with a publicly stated policy. It considerably influenced subsequent developments, and has been superseded by the corresponding standard produced by the International Organization for Standardization (ISO), ISO 14001. This commits certificated organisations to pollution prevention, but in other respects is less specific than BS 7750.

C.76 Concern by a group of business leaders, the World Business Council for Sustainable Development, that developing countries might lose markets because they would not be able to demonstrate convincingly that their products are produced in an environmentally sustainable way led them to prompt ISO to produce a family of 26 environmental management standards. As well as ISO 14001, the family will include standards on environmental management performance, environmental indicators, life cycle analysis, ecolabelling and assessment methods for contaminated land.

C.77 The EU Eco-Management and Audit Scheme (EMAS) is a voluntary European scheme for individual industrial sites that is designed to provide recognition for companies which have established a programme of positive action to protect the environment, and which seek continuous improvement in their performance in that respect. EMAS, established by European law in April 1995,[91] also requires the adoption of an environmental management system; those companies already operating an ISO 14001 system will be deemed to have met most of the requirements of EMAS. But EMAS additionally requires companies to report publicly on their environmental performance at least every three years and to have the report independently verified by an accredited verifier. Third-party independent verification of the environmental statement is intended to reassure stakeholders by providing an objective, credible assessment of whether a company is fulfilling its responsibilities under EMAS. This should be 'designed for the public and written in a concise, comprehensible form'. The European Commission has mandated CEN (the European standards body) to produce standards to supplement EMAS.

C.78 The UK has adapted EMAS to create a management standard for local authorities. The aim is to help local authorities manage their environmental impacts in a systematic and considered way. Unlike the industry scheme, Local Authority EMAS considers the environmental effects of service provision, as well as the direct effects of an organisation's own operations.[92]

C.79 Within the EU, take-up of EMAS has been variable, whereas ISO 14001 has proved more popular. ISO 14001 has also proved popular in Japan and other south-east Asian countries. There is a variety of reasons underlying the take-up of such environmental management systems. Certification to ISO 14001 has become a frequent condition of contracts with suppliers, and there is, therefore, a cascade through supply chains. The speed and direction of events reflect the globalisation of the economy and the growth of international trade.

C.80 While EMAS and ISO 14001 have concentrated on management systems to assure environmental performance, they have been criticised for insufficient attention to ensuring environmental improvements. This criticism has also been directed at the approaches to quality management, particularly BS 5750 and ISO 9001, on which they are based. While ISO 14001 can promote better environmental management along a supply chain, this is not necessarily the same as better environmental performance.

The geographical scope of standard setting

C.81 It will be apparent from the foregoing description that a high proportion of the standards which apply in the UK have originated in international or EC law. The following sections describe the main levels of activity. Chapter 6 discusses the question of subsidiarity.

International conventions

C.82 International conventions are agreements between national governments (sometimes including regional organisations such as the EC). They can be between two nations (bilateral) or several (multilateral); around 200 such multilateral environmental agreements (MEAs) have been set up. Multilateral conventions are normally classed as either regional or global depending on the range of states which it is hoped will accede. Multilateral conventions are sometimes promoted by international organisations (such as UNEP or UNECE) but some conventions themselves establish a secretariat or commission to service them (such as OSPAR, see C.89). Some secretariats (such as the OSPAR Commission) are quite pro-active, whilst others act only as facilitators, with all real influence resting with the conference of the parties.

C.83 International conventions covering various aspects of the environment have usually had one or more of the following justifications:

they were needed to deal with problems which are international in nature and require international action to counter them (for example, at a global level, depletion of the stratospheric ozone layer and global warming, or, at a regional level, acid rain);

they regulate activities which are international in nature (for example, pollution from ships and aircraft travelling between countries or movements of waste across national frontiers);

they protect aspects of the environment which have come to be regarded as of common concern to the human race (for example biological diversity, and in the light of the Stockholm Declaration of 1972,[93] the environment beyond the limits of national jurisdiction).

C.84 The obligations undertaken by a nation state in acceding to a convention are a matter for that state to implement. In general, conventions have no directly effective enforcement mechanism.[94] In order for a multilateral convention to come into force, it usually has to be ratified by a specified number of states. Ratification procedures vary from country to country. In the United Kingdom it has become customary for the government to lay conventions before Parliament before ratifying them. In the USA, for example, ratification of an international convention requires the approval of Congress. Once a convention has come into force, it is legally binding on any state which has ratified it. In the United Kingdom (but not in some other states) a ratified convention has to be transposed into national legislation (unless existing UK legislation already adequately covers the subject or it has already been given effect in directly applicable EC legislation) in order for its provisions to become legally binding on firms and individuals.

C.85 Prime examples of global conventions are those arising from the 1992 Rio Summit, that is, the Convention on Biological Diversity, and the Framework Convention on Climate Change. Others include the Basel Convention on the Control of Transboundary Movements of Hazardous Wastes and their Disposal, and the Convention on International Trade in Endangered Species of Wild Flora and Fauna (CITES). Global conventions may place different obligations on states which are at different stages of economic development, and require developed nations to assist less-developed nations through technology transfer and in other ways.

Guidance at global scale

C.86 There is much other work undertaken on a global scale to set environmental standards which, although it does not result in standards binding in international law, is nevertheless of great practical significance, particularly for the protection of human health. Examples are the recommendations of the Codex Alimentarius Commission (C.49–C.50) on concentrations of pesticides and other contaminants in food (as well as food additives), the recommendations of the IPCS (C.11, C.13), the private international commissions which set standards for radiation (C.7–C.9), and the WHO guidelines for air quality (C.15, C.21) and for drinking water (C.52).

C.87 *Global scientific co-operation* There is much scientific activity on environmental issues at the global level which can be differentiated from the work of the bodies described in C.86 as not having a direct regulatory purpose. Much of it is nevertheless closely linked to the work of regulatory bodies. For example, the United Nations Scientific Committee on the Effects of Atomic Radiation carries out regular reviews of the scientific evidence which provides the basis for the work of the ICRP; it does not itself make recommendations about acceptable levels of exposure or put forward guidelines. The work of the Intergovernmental Panel on Climate Change, established by WMO and UNEP, led to the Climate Change Convention, and its scientific assessments continue to provide a major input to implementation of the convention.

C.88 To a large extent the motivation for the growth of global scientific bodies, whether or not they become involved with regulation, has been to ensure that the most effective use is made of scarce expertise and all available information is utilised. It reflects the greater complexity and longer time-scale of the environmental issues now causing most concern, which have created needs to assess enormous amounts of data and carry out very large modelling studies, for example, those predicting global climate change.

Regional conventions

C.89 Many international conventions have been drawn up on a regional basis by the group of nations most affected by, or able to influence, the type of pollution in question. The Convention on Protection of the North Sea and North East Atlantic (the OSPAR Convention), signed in 1992, replaced the Oslo Convention on dumping from ships and aircraft, signed in 1972, and the Paris Convention on land-based sources of marine pollution, signed in 1974; it regulates those forms of marine pollution which are not covered by other global conventions. The Parties to the Convention are drawn from those states whose coasts border the area concerned, together with the EC, Switzerland and Luxembourg. Its main objective is the protection of the marine environment so as to safeguard human health through the elimination and prevention of pollution. Conservation and repair of the marine ecosystem are regarded as equally important objectives. Parties to the Convention are required to implement control programmes to reduce the amounts of a wide range of substances reaching the sea. The substances include pesticides, heavy metals, oil and hydrocarbons, and organohalogen compounds. Parties to the Convention are required to have regard to 'best environmental practice', a concept which covers both use of the best available techniques (see chapter 3, box 3A) and other elements such as information to the public, product labelling, and collection and disposal systems. One of the tasks of the OSPAR Commission responsible for implementing the Convention is to draw up documents specifying best available techniques for disposal, reduction and elimination of a range of substances from various industrial sectors.

C.90 Since 1984, the main impetus for reducing marine pollution has come from a series of North Sea Conferences, even though the agreements arising from them are not legally binding. The Third North Sea Conference in 1990 agreed a number of measures, including specified cuts in inputs to the North Sea of 39 hazardous substances from rivers and estuaries; a 50% cut in inputs of dangerous substances from the air; substantial reductions in the quantities of pesticides reaching the North Sea; the phasing-out and environmentally safe destruction of all identifiable polychlorinated biphenyls (PCBs); and secondary treatment of both municipal sewage discharges and industrial discharges. The Fourth North Sea Conference in 1995 called for the cessation of discharges and emissions of hazardous substances within 25 years.

C.91 UNECE covers both eastern and western European countries as well as Canada and the USA. Under its auspices the Convention on Long-Range Transboundary Air Pollution (LRTAP) was signed in 1979 and came into force in 1983. Protocols under the Convention require individual states, and in some cases the EC as a whole, to reduce total emissions of sulphur dioxide, nitrogen oxides and volatile organic compounds by specified percentages. In some cases the reductions differ for different states. LRTAP Protocols dealing with emissions of persistent organic pollutants and heavy metals have been negotiated and opened for signature; the UK signed both Protocols in June 1998. Preparatory work is taking place on a multi-pollutant, multi-effect Protocol.

European Community

C.92 European Community environmental standards now cover most aspects of water pollution, outdoor air quality, emissions to the atmosphere from motor vehicles and several types of industrial process, the assessment, marketing and export of chemicals, and the composition of some products. This is the most important source of legally binding environmental standards for the UK and other Member States. There are also voluntary EC ecolabelling and environmental management schemes, and process standards will in future be set at the Community level.

C.93 The extent of present-day EC environmental standards is remarkable considering the absence of any mention of the environment in the Treaty of Rome (1957). This did not prevent the adoption of measures concerning the environment in the late 1950s and 1960s but they were primarily intended to harmonise rules within the internal market (on the packaging and labelling of chemicals, for example) or to avoid technical barriers to trade (on vehicle noise, for example). The concern to protect human health from radiation is reflected in standards adopted under the Euratom Treaty during the same period.

C.94 During the 1960s environmental issues became more prominent and came to be seen more and more in an international context. This movement in a sense culminated in the Conference on the Human Environment organised by the United Nations in Stockholm in 1972. This succeeded in establishing the environment as a major subject for attention by international organisations.

C.95 Acknowledging this growing movement, the Heads of State and Government explicitly declared in 1972 that the Community should have an environmental policy. The declaration did not resolve the tension between what the Treaty of Rome called 'a harmonious development of economic activity' and the argument that in a finite world expansion cannot be continuous.[95] It did, however, mean that purely environmental measures could be developed quite legitimately. The test of completing the internal market was no longer required. The principles and objectives of a Community environment policy were approved in 1973 in the First Environmental Action Programme. This went on to spell out action that would be proposed to reduce and prevent pollution and nuisances, improve the natural and urban environments, tackle problems caused by

Appendix C

the depletion of certain natural resources, and promote environmental awareness.⁹⁶ Subsequent Action Programmes were approved in 1977, 1982, 1987 and 1993 and reports on progress were made in 1980, 1984 and 1996. Throughout the 1970s, and to an even greater extent throughout the 1980s and 1990s, a stream of policy measures has been adopted by the Community. The Fifth Environmental Action Programme in 1993 signalled a change in emphasis, moving away from the 'legislative factory approach' of the 1980s, towards a programme built around mixed policy instruments and shared responsibility.⁹⁷

C.96 From a legal point of view, the Single European Act in 1987 established a Treaty basis for the Community's environmental policy; and this was strengthened in 1993 by the Treaty on European Union (the Maastricht Treaty). The importance of the Single European Act was threefold. It provided a legal basis for wider-ranging environmental measures than hitherto, required environmental protection to be a component of the Community's other policies, and introduced qualified majority voting (QMV) for matters affecting the establishment of the internal market, and an associated co-operation procedure which increased the influence of the European Parliament. The Maastricht Treaty went on to set principles, such as the precautionary principle, into the formal basis of the Community's environmental policy. It also extended QMV to most environmental measures; extended the co-operation procedure; introduced a new co-decision procedure in a limited number of areas (thereby strengthening the European Parliament's ability to amend draft legislation); and gave legal force to the doctrine of subsidiarity. When the Treaty of Amsterdam comes into force it will make the co-decision procedure the norm for most environmental legislation, although some exceptions will remain. The Treaty of Amsterdam has also clarified the importance of sustainable development as a component of Community policy (see box C⁹⁸).

C.97 Within the European Commission, Directorate-General XI (Environment, Nuclear Safety and Civil Protection) is in the lead on most environmental issues but other Directorates-General have responsibilities which significantly and directly affect the environment (for example, DG III (Industry), DG VI (Agriculture), DG VII (Transport) and DG XVII (Energy)). When it comes to propose standards, the European Commission has access to several sources of advice. As well as national experts seconded to the Commission itself, these include advisory committees, the European Environment Agency, research activities funded by the Community, and independent sources of expertise, such as those within the United Nations system and individual nation states. The advisory committees to which the Commission has access include:

expert committees, composed of government officials and technical experts nominated by Member States to ensure that a wide range of viewpoints receives adequate consideration when proposals are being formulated; and

standing consultative committees, made up of representatives of sectoral interests appointed by the Commission.

Officially, consultation with these advisory committees is 'non-compulsory' but in practice this view has been contentious, with the European Court of Justice deciding that consultation with the Scientific Committee on Cosmetology (dealing with cosmetics) was intended to ensure that adopted measures were scientifically accurate and was therefore mandatory.

C.98 The second type of committee assists the European Commission in its executive role and includes nearly 300 advisory, management and regulatory committees. Formal procedures have been established to regulate the procedures of these committees. Consultation with them is compulsory. They are made up of government officials, technical and scientific experts, and sectoral representatives, and carry out specified functions under existing legislation. Many of them are established by specific items of legislation to monitor and review standards in that item of legislation, in line with technical and scientific progress. In addition to this role, these committees also now provide a primary political check on the delegated powers of the Commission.

180

BOX C	TREATY OF AMSTERDAM

The Treaty of Amsterdam amended both the Treaty on European Union and the Treaties establishing the European Communities.

As a result, the **Consolidated Treaty on European Union** now provides:

Article 2
The Union shall set itself the following objectives: to promote economic and social progress and a high level of employment and to achieve balanced and sustainable development …

The **Consolidated Treaty Establishing the European Community** now contains the following general principles with respect to environmental policies:

Article 2
The Community shall have as its task, by establishing a common market and an economic and monetary union and by implementing common policies or activities referred to in Articles 3 and 4, to promote throughout the Community a harmonious, balanced and sustainable development of economic activities … [and] a high level of protection and improvement of the quality of the environment …

Article 6
Environmental protection requirements must be integrated into the definition and implementation of the Community policies and activities referred to in Article 3, in particular with a view to promoting sustainable development.

(Note: Article 3 lists the 21 general policies and activities of the Community, which include matters such as the prohibition of customs duties and quantitative restrictions on the import and export of goods, the internal market, the approximation of the laws of Member States to the extent required for the functioning of the common market, and the various common policies (agriculture, fisheries, transport and the like).)

Article 174
1. Community policy on the environment shall contribute to pursuit of the following objectives:
    preserving, protecting and improving the quality of the environment;
    protecting human health;
    prudent and rational utilisation of natural resources;
    promoting measures at international level to deal with regional or worldwide environmental problems.

2. Community policy on the environment shall aim at a high level of protection taking into account the diversity of situations in the various regions of the Community. It shall be based on the precautionary principle and on the principles that preventive action should be taken, that environmental damage should as a priority be rectified at source and that the polluter should pay …

3. In preparing its policy on the environment, the Community shall take account of:
    available scientific and technical data;
    environmental conditions in the various regions of the Community;
    the potential benefits and costs of action or lack of action;
    the economic and social development of the Community as a whole and the balanced development of its regions.

C.99 Legislative proposals from the Commission are discussed in detail in working groups of the Council of Ministers. Representatives of those Member States which have a strong capability in environmental science will seek at that stage to remedy what they see as defects in the proposals, but that becomes more difficult once a proposal has been published.

C.100 The EC plays an active part in global and regional bodies, through the European Commission or the Presidency in areas of Community competence and otherwise through the concerted action of Member States. As one important area of Community competence is external trade, the Commission handles relations with the World Trade Organization. The Maastricht Treaty extended the objectives for Community action on the environment in article 130r to include promoting measures at international level to deal with regional or worldwide environmental problems.

C.101 The EC's participation in global and regional environmental bodies may restrict the freedom of manoeuvre in negotiations, although it can add weight to the debate when internal agreement exists. Some EC legislation implements measures agreed in wider fora, for example the EC Regulation controlling substances that deplete the ozone layer.[99] Sometimes, as here, the EC legislation goes beyond the terms of the international agreement. The adoption of an EC Regulation to implement an international agreement means that all Member States have a consistent policy, rapidly introduced.

C.102 Where proposals for environmental legislation put forward by the European Commission do not stem from the requirements of global or regional conventions, they may be based closely on guidance from global bodies. Examples are WHO's guidelines for air quality and drinking water; the European Commission contributed to the cost of WHO's revision of its 1987 air quality guidelines. By following global guidance, the Commission is able to remedy to some extent deficiencies in the scientific advice available to it. But it can on occasion depart from that guidance. And the legislation eventually agreed will in any case differ to a greater or lesser extent from the draft originally put forward by the Commission.

National scale

C.103 *Government Departments* DETR is the government Department responsible for environmental protection and pollution control in England. It takes the lead for the UK in negotiating most international and EC environmental measures and is responsible for their implementation in England and Wales. Its specific functions under UK legislation include setting standards for air quality and drinking water. In practice, the main influence exercised by DETR over water quality is that the Secretary of State certifies to the Director General of Water Services (the economic regulator for the water industry) the environmental improvements which should be taken into account when setting price limits for water companies (see appendix E).

C.104 UK standards often simply reproduce standards in EC legislation or in international conventions. Legally binding standards in the UK which result from Community legislation may differ in detail from those set at European level; this depends on the article of the EC Treaty under which a Directive is adopted and the extent to which the terms of the Directive themselves leave Member States with some discretion. EC standards can be implemented under the general powers contained in the European Communities Act 1972, but in this case must reproduce exactly the provisions of the relevant European legislation.[100] For this reason governments have often preferred to introduce primary legislation or to make regulations under other powers. These routes may enable them to extend the provisions of the Community legislation if they wish.

C.105 DETR part funds, oversees, and receives advice from, the Environment Agency for England and Wales, which is a non-departmental public body whose chairman and board are appointed by Ministers. The Agency has responsibility for delivering integrated environmental protection and enhancement through managing and regulating the water environment and controlling industrial pollution and wastes. The corresponding bodies for Scotland and Northern Ireland are SEPA and the Northern Ireland Environment and Heritage Service. The functions of the two Environment Agencies include setting process standards and emissions standards under integrated pollution control.

C.106 The 1990 Act gave DETR wide powers to set environmental standards and secure their implementation through the system of integrated pollution control (see C.55 and chapter 3). The Secretary of State may establish standards, objectives or requirements in relation to particular industrial processes or particular substances, including environmental quality standards to apply either generally or in specified areas.[101] The Secretary of State is also empowered to make plans for:[102]

   a. establishing limits for the amounts of any substance which may be released into the environment in the UK or any area within it;

   b. implementing such limits by allocating quotas for the release of the substance in question to persons carrying on processes which produce it;

   c. establishing standard limits for the release of any substance from prescribed processes, 'so as to progressively reduce pollution of the environment';

   d. progressive improvement in previously established quality objectives or quality standards.

In administering integrated pollution control, the regulator must attach appropriate conditions to authorisations to achieve compliance with any requirement specified by or under such a plan or otherwise prescribed and any directions given by the Secretary of State in order to implement European or international obligations.[103]

C.107 DETR also sponsors the Health and Safety Commission (HSC) and its executive body, the Health and Safety Executive (HSE), the statutory bodies whose overall purpose under the Health and Safety at Work etc. Act is to ensure that risks to people's health and safety from work activities are properly controlled. HSC and HSE are responsible for proposing regulations to DETR Ministers covering, among other things, occupational exposure to radiation and to toxic substances. HSE, in turn, receives advice on radiation exposure from DH, from the NRPB (which is funded and overseen by DH), and from the Committee on Medical Aspects of Radiation in the Environment; and from its own Advisory Committee on Toxic Substances (ACTS, to which DETR sends an observer). HSE also has environmental responsibilities under other national or EC legislation, for example, national legislation concerning non-agricultural pesticides and EC legislation on the contained use of genetically modified organisms.

C.108 DH does not have policy responsibility for setting environmental standards. DH and its expert committees advise other Departments on the health implications of their policies. DH and its committees may advise on a level at which for public health reasons it considers a standard might be set, but it is for others to consider that advice in a wider context. DH committees include the three Committees on Toxicity, Carcinogenicity, and Mutagenicity of Chemicals in Food, Consumer Products and the Environment (which report to the Chief Medical Officer) and COMEAP. DH is closely involved with the work of the advisory committees concerning policy on genetically modified organisms (the three Advisory Committees on Releases to the Environment, Genetic Modification, and Novel Foods and Processes).

C.109 MAFF takes the lead in defining standards for food safety, the welfare of livestock and controls on use for agrochemicals. While DETR leads on the protection of the marine environment generally, MAFF and Fisheries Departments have a key role in monitoring and advising on pollution of the sea and are responsible for controlling deposits in the sea either for disposal (dumping) or construction. MAFF is also involved with DETR in setting standards for the protection of water.

C.110 The role of MAFF regarding food safety is subject to change due to the proposed establishment of the Food Standards Agency. At present, MAFF takes the lead on issues concerning food standards, chemical safety of food, food labelling, food technology and meat and milk hygiene. DH takes the lead on issues of general food hygiene, microbiological safety and nutrition. The Scottish Office, Welsh Office and Northern Ireland Department of Health and Social Services have responsibility for food issues within their geographical areas. Lead Departments take primary responsibility for developing policy on issues within their remit and for preparing legislation. MAFF is served by a number of Executive Agencies (such as the Veterinary Medicines Directorate and the Pesticides Safety Directorate) in the execution of its policies. The Agriculture and Health Departments are supported in their work on food safety by a range of advisory committees whose role is to supply independent expert advice on particular areas of work. Committees may be statutory, such as the Advisory Committee on Pesticides and the Veterinary Products Committee, or non-statutory, such as the Food Advisory Committee, the Committee on Toxicity in Food, Consumer Products and the Environment, and the Advisory Committee on Novel Foods and Processes. Cross-membership of these advisory committees exists in many cases.

C.111 Proposals for the Foods Standards Agency were published in a government White Paper in January 1998.[104] They envisage an Agency with a clear focus on protecting public health, open and transparent in its workings, and with responsibility for formulating policy and advising government on the need for legislation on all aspects of food safety and standards and certain aspects of nutrition for the whole of the UK. Consultation on the White Paper yielded over 1,000 responses and draft legislation for further consultation is now in preparation.

Local scale

C.112 The Environment Agencies set one form of standard at a local level. These are the statutory water quality objectives for individual river catchments, which require the approval of the Secretary of State and cover those parameters not set by EC legislation and other national or international requirements. The Environment Agency is now seeking to replace catchment management plans which were drawn up by its predecessor, the National Rivers Authority, and specified water quality objectives by Local Environment Agency Plans covering all aspects of the environment within a given river catchment (see chapter 7 and appendix F).

C.113 Local authorities in Britain have not had any significant role in setting environmental standards (except, until recently, in waste management licences); although they have a regulatory function for air pollution from processes not subject to control by the Environment Agencies, the conditions they apply are derived from statutory guidance produced by the Secretary of State (C.59). Similarly, they have a role in enforcing health and safety matters in certain premises but not in setting standards. Local authorities have now become responsible for planning the management of air quality in their areas within the framework of standards set at national and European scale (C.17–C.20). The local authority is responsible for managing road traffic and discharging its other functions in the light of this and other policy objectives. There is a Memorandum of Understanding between local authorities and the Environment Agency to provide a national framework for transparency, information exchange, consultation and co-operation; and a protocol on air quality also relating to information exchange and consultation which recognises the statutory obligation on the Agency to contribute to the achievement of national air quality objectives. It is too early to say how effective these arrangements for co-ordination will be.

References

1. *Manual of Environmental Policy: The EC and Britain.* Ed. N. Haigh. Institute for European Environmental Policy (IEEP), London; cited as IEEP Manual of Environmental Policy;
    The European Dimension of Standard Setting. D. Wilkinson, S. Mullard, N. Emmott, C. Coffey and N. Haigh. A report prepared for the Royal Commission on Environmental Pollution. IEEP, London. August 1996.

2. Haigh, N. (1987). *EEC Environmental Policy and Britain.* Second Edition. Longman, Harlow. See pages 213–219.

3. Holdgate, M.W. (1979). *A Perspective of Environmental Pollution.* Cambridge University Press. See pages 144 and 146.

4. Harbison, S.A. (1994). UK and international standards for nuclear health and safety. *Journal of Radiological Protection,* **4**(4), 317–324; quoted in evidence from Dr R. Fairman, January 1996.

5. International Commission on Radiological Protection (ICRP) (1990). *1990 Recommendations of the International Commission on Radiological Protection.* ICRP Publication 60. Annals of the ICRP, Volume 21, Nos. 1–3. Pergamon Press.

6. *The Ionising Radiations Regulations 1985.* Statutory Instrument 1985 No. 1333.

7. Directive (80/836/Euratom) amending the Directives laying down the basic safety standards for the health protection of the general public and workers against the dangers of ionising radiation. *Official Journal of the European Communities,* **L246**, 17.9.80.

8. ICRP (1990).

9. Council Directive (96/29) laying down basic safety standards relating to ionising radiation. *Official Journal of the European Communities,* **L159**, 29.6.96.

10. National Radiological Protection Board (NRPB) (1993). *Board Statement on the 1990 Recommendations of ICRP.* Documents of the NRPB, Volume 4, No. 1.

11. International Programme on Chemical Safety (IPCS) (1996). *Methomyl.* Environmental Health Criteria Document EHC 178. World Health Organization (WHO), Geneva. See page 107.

12. IPCS (1993). *Methyl ethyl ketone.* Environmental Health Criteria Document EHC 143. WHO, Geneva. See page 121.

13. Food and Agriculture Organization (FAO)/WHO (1996a). *Pesticide Residues in Food – 1995. Evaluations 1995: Part I – Residues.* FAO Plant Production and Protection Paper No. 137. FAO, Rome. This was the outcome of one of the regular joint meetings of the FAO Panel of Experts on Pesticide Residues in Food and the Environment and the WHO Toxicological and Environmental Core Assessment Groups.

14. Defined in: Nilsson, J. and Grennfelt, P. (Eds.) (1988). *Critical Loads for Sulphur and Nitrogen.* Report of a workshop held in Skokloster, Sweden, 19–24 March 1988. Nordic Council of Ministers, Copenhagen.

15. WHO (1987). *Air Quality Guidelines for Europe.* WHO Regional Publications, European Series No. 23. WHO Regional Office for Europe, Copenhagen.

16. Directive on air quality limit values and guide values for sulphur dioxide and suspended particulates (80/779/EEC). *Official Journal of the European Communities,* **L229**, 30.8.80;
Directive on a limit value for lead in the air (82/884/EEC). *Official Journal of the European Communities,* **L378**, 31.12.82;
Directive on air quality standards for nitrogen dioxide (85/203/EEC). *Official Journal of the European Communities,* **L87**, 27.3.85.

17. *Air Quality Standards Regulations 1989* (Statutory Instrument 1989 No. 317) and *Air Quality Standards (Amendment) Regulations 1995* (Statutory Instrument 1995 No. 3146). These Regulations were made under the European Communities Act 1972 as there were no specific powers in UK legislation to set standards for air quality.

18. Council Directive 96/62/EC of 27 September 1996 on ambient air quality assessment and management. *Official Journal of the European Communities,* **L296**, 21.11.96. Its provisions are summarised in box 2A of the Twentieth Report (page 21).

19. Directive on air pollution by ozone (92/72/EEC). *Official Journal of the European Communities,* **L297**, 13.10.92.

20. Arsenic, benzene, cadmium, carbon monoxide, mercury, nickel and polycyclic aromatic hydrocarbons.

21. Proposal for a Council Directive relating to limit values for sulphur dioxide, oxides of nitrogen, particulate matter and lead in ambient air. *COM(97)500 Final.* Commission of the European Communities, Brussels, 8.10.97.

22. Environment Act 1995, section 80(1) and (5).

23. *The United Kingdom National Air Quality Strategy.* Department of the Environment (DOE), The Scottish Office and The Welsh Office. CM 3587. The Stationery Office. March 1997;
Air Quality Regulations 1997. Statutory Instrument 1997 No. 3043.

24. Department of the Environment, Transport and the Regions (DETR) (1998). *Lead.* Expert Panel on Air Quality Standards. The Stationery Office;
New air quality standard for lead recommended. *Department of the Environment, Transport and the Regions News Release,* No. 341, 11 May 1998.

25. Environment Act 1995, sections 81 and 82–85 respectively.

26. The previous set of air quality guideline values for protection of the environment date from 1987; see: WHO (1987), chapters 32–34.

27. Smog information made clear. Ministers announce a new system of public information on air pollution. *Department of the Environment, Transport and the Regions News Release,* No. 463, 19 November 1997.

28. Directive on air pollution by ozone (92/72/EEC). *Official Journal of the European Communities,* **L297**, 13.10.92.

29. Directive 78/659/EEC on the quality of fresh waters needing protection or improvement in order to support fish life. *Official Journal of the European Communities,* **L222**, 14.8.78.

30. Directive 79/923/EEC on the quality required for shellfish water. *Official Journal of the European Communities,* **L281**, 10.11.79.

31. Directive 76/160/EEC concerning the quality of bathing water. *Official Journal of the European Communities,* **L31**, 5.2.76.

32. Directive 75/440/EEC concerning the quality required of surface water intended for abstraction for drinking water. *Official Journal of the European Communities,* **L194**, 25.7.75.

33. Framework Directive on pollution caused by certain dangerous substances discharged into the aquatic environment of the Community (76/464/EEC). *Official Journal of the European Communities,* **L129**, 18.5.76.

34. Lengthy negotiations ahead for Directive on water resources. *ENDS Report,* No. 266, March 1997, 41–44.

35. Directive on limit values and quality objectives for mercury discharges by the chloralkali electrolysis industry (82/176/EEC). *Official Journal of the European Communities,* **L81**, 27.3.82.

36. Nineteenth Report, box 8G (page 142).

37. Council Directive of 12 June 1986 on the protection of the environment, and in particular of the soil, when sewage sludge is used in agriculture. Directive 86/278/EEC. *Official Journal of the European Communities,* **L181**, 4.7.86.

38. Ministry of Agriculture, Fisheries and Food (MAFF)/Welsh Office Agriculture Department (1993). *Code of Good Agricultural Practice for the Protection of Soil.* MAFF Publications;
Nineteenth Report, paragraph 6.32.

39. DOE (1987). *Guidance on the Assessment and Redevelopment of Contaminated Land.* Second Edition. Interdepartmental Committee on the Redevelopment of Contaminated Land (ICRCL) Guidance Note 59/83.

40. DOE/The Welsh Office (1994). *Framework for Contaminated Land. Outcome of the government's policy review and conclusions from the consultation paper 'Paying for Our Past'.* See paragraph 2.4.

41. DOE (1990). *The Government's Response to the First Report from the House of Commons Select Committee on the Environment: Contaminated Land.* Cm 1161. HMSO.

42. Nineteenth Report, paragraph 8.48. The Contaminated Land Exposure Assessment (CLEA) model was described in box 8D (page 133).

43. Information supplied by DETR, June 1998.

44. Nineteenth Report, paragraph 8.46.

45. NRPB (1998). *Radiological Protection Objectives of Land Contaminated with Radionuclides.* Documents of the NRPB, Volume 9, No. 2.

46. Nineteenth Report, paragraph 8.40.

47. Nineteenth Report, paragraph 8.44 and table 8.3.

48. Dutch Memorandum of 9 May 1994 on 'Intervention values for soil clean-up'.

49. Dutch policy retreat on contaminated land. *ENDS Report,* No. 269, June 1997, page 46.

50. Visser, W.J.F. (1994). *Contaminated Land Policies in Some Industrialised Countries.* Technical Soil Protection Committee. The Hague.

51. Framework Directive on pollution caused by certain dangerous substances discharged into the aquatic environment of the Community (76/464/EEC). *Official Journal of the European Communities*, **L129**, 18.5.76.

52. Directive 80/68/EEC on the protection of groundwater against pollution caused by dangerous substances. *Official Journal of the European Communities*, **L20**, 26.1.80.

53. Framework Directive on combatting air pollution from industrial plants (84/360/EEC). *Official Journal of the European Communities*, **L188**, 16.7.84.

54. The European Community (EC) Roadworthiness Directive 77/143/EEC (and amendments) lays down the requirements for roadworthiness testing for goods vehicles. Subsequent Directives have covered private cars (Directive 91/328/EEC) and tightened the requirements for all vehicles (Directive 92/55/EEC).

55. A series of EC Directives covers emissions from new vehicles in three classes: passenger cars (Directive 70/220/EEC and amendments); commercial vehicles (Directive 88/77/EEC and amendments); two- or three-wheel motor vehicles (Directive 97/24/EEC).

56. The Auto/Oil Programme, described in the Twentieth Report, appendix D.

57. Twentieth Report, paragraph 3.6.

58. Twentieth Report, paragraphs 2.29–2.30.

59. Directive 76/769/EEC relating to restrictions on the marketing and use of certain dangerous substances and preparations. *Official Journal of the European Communities*, **L262**, 27.9.76.

60. Directive 91/157/EEC on batteries and accumulators containing certain dangerous substances. *Official Journal of the European Communities*, **L78**, 26.3.91.

61. FAO/WHO (1996b). *Codex Alimentarius. Volume 1A: General Requirements*. Second Edition. FAO, Rome.

62. FAO/WHO (1993). *Codex Alimentarius. Volume 2: Pesticide Residues in Food*. FAO, Rome.

63. FAO/WHO (1996a).

64. Council Directive of 27 November 1990 on the fixing of maximum levels of pesticide residues in or on certain products of plant origin, including fruit and vegetables. *Official Journal of the European Communities*, **L350**, 14.12.90.

65. Council Regulation (EEC) No. 315/93 of 8 February 1993 laying down Community procedures for contaminants in food. *Official Journal of the European Communities*, **L37**, 13.2.93.

66. Directive 91/492/EEC on the protection of consumers of shellfish. *Official Journal of the European Communities*, **L268**, 24.9.91.

67. WHO (1993). *Guidelines for Drinking-Water Quality. Volume 1: Recommendations*. Second Edition. WHO, Geneva. See section 1.1.

68. Council Directive of 15 July 1980 relating to the quality of water intended for human consumption (80/778/EEC). *Official Journal of the European Communities*, **L229**, 30.8.80.

69. Proposal for a Council Directive (COM(94)612) concerning the quality of water intended for human consumption. *Official Journal of the European Communities*, **C131**, 30.5.95. A common position on this Directive was reached by Ministers in October 1997 but a Directive has not been adopted at the time of writing.

70. Regulation 87/8954/Euratom laying down maximum permitted radioactivity levels for foodstuffs in the event of a nuclear accident. *Official Journal of the European Communities*, **L371**, 30.12.87.

71. ICRP (1993). *Principles for Intervention for Protection of the Public in a Radiological Emergency*. ICRP Publication 63. Annals of the ICRP, Volume 22, No. 4. Pergamon Press;
NRPB (1994). *Guidance on Restrictions on Food and Water Following a Radiological Accident*. Documents of the NRPB, Volume 5, No. 1.

72. NRPB (1994).

73. Environmental Protection Act 1990, section 7(4).

74. New industrial pollution control rules for Northern Ireland. *ENDS Report*, No. 277, February 1998, page 40.

75. Council Directive 96/61/EC concerning integrated pollution prevention and control. *Official Journal of the European Communities*, **L257**, 10.10.96.

76. Integrated Pollution Control Guidance Notes are available from The Stationery Office. Examples include notes on: Petrochemical processes (IPR 4/1); Ferrous foundry processes (IPR 2/2); Pharmaceutical processes (IPR 4/9); etc.

77. Process Guidance Notes are available from The Stationery Office. Examples include notes on: Hot dip galvanising processes (PG 2/2); Asbestos processes (PG 3/13); Hide and skin processes (PG 6/21); etc.
78. Environmental Protection Act 1990, section 7(11).
79. Regulation 880/92 on a Community ecolabel award scheme. *Official Journal of the European Communities,* **L99**, 11.4.92.
80. Directive 76/769/EEC relating to restrictions on the marketing and use of certain dangerous substances and preparations. *Official Journal of the European Communities,* **L262**, 27.9.76.
81. For a list of amendments to Directive 76/769/EEC, see: IEEP Manual of Environmental Policy, section 7.5.
82. The present EC legislation on new substances is contained in the Seventh Amendment (Council Directive 92/32/EEC of 30 April 1992. *Official Journal of the European Communities,* **L154**, 5.6.92) to the 1967 EC Dangerous Substances Directive (Council Directive 67/548/EEC of 27 June 1967. *Official Journal of the European Communities,* **L196**, 16.8.67), and is implemented in the UK by the *Notification of New Substances Regulations 1993* (Statutory Instrument 1993 No. 3050).
83. EC legislation on existing substances is contained in a 1993 EC Regulation (Council Regulation (EEC) No. 793/93 of 23 March 1993. *Official Journal of the European Communities,* **L84**, 5.4.93) and implemented in the UK by the *Notification of Existing Substances Regulations 1994* (Statutory Instrument 1994 No. 1806).
84. Early disputes over new review of EC chemicals policy. *ENDS Report,* No. 279, April 1998, 39–40.
85. Directive 91/414/EEC concerning the placing of plant protection products on the market. *Official Journal of the European Communities,* **L230**, 19.8.91.
86. Directive 98/8/EC of the European Parliament and the Council concerning the placing of biocidal products on the market. *Official Journal of the European Communities,* **L123**, 24.4.98.
87. *The Marketing Authorisations for Veterinary Medicinal Products Regulations 1994.* Statutory Instrument 1994 No. 3142.
88. *Legislation for the Control of Chemicals.* A report prepared for DOE by IEEP, London. June 1995. See chapter 7;
information provided by the Veterinary Medicines Directorate, December 1995.
89. The Vienna Convention, signed in 1985, is a Framework Convention which covers such matters as co-operation on monitoring and research to assess the threat to the stratospheric ozone layer posed by chlorofluorocarbons (CFCs) and other ozone-depleting chemicals (notably the halons). It does not in itself place any obligation on the Parties to take any specific measures to protect the ozone layer. These were to be laid down in separate protocols of which the 1987 Montreal Protocol on Substances that Deplete the Ozone Layer is an example. The Montreal Protocol was reviewed and updated in 1990 and 1992; it has been strengthened and revised since then in the light of scientific evidence at regular meetings of the Parties to the Protocol. It is implemented in the UK by EC Regulation 3093/94 (*Official Journal of the European Communities,* **L333**, 22.12.94).
90. DOE (1994). *Licensing of Waste Management Facilities. Guidance on the drafting, supervision and surrender of Waste Management Licences.* Waste Management Paper No. 4. Third Edition. HMSO.
91. Regulation (1836/93) allowing voluntary participation by companies in the industrial sector in a Community eco-management and audit scheme. *Official Journal of the European Communities,* **L168**, 10.7.93.
92. DOE/The Welsh Office (1995). *The Voluntary Eco-management and Audit Scheme (EMAS) for Local Government.* DOE Circular 2/95. 21 February 1995. HMSO;
Bond, R. (1996). Managing our environment. *Surveyor,* 22 February 1996, pages 14 and 19;
Cockrean, B. (1996). Local Authority EMAS – how Sutton succeeded. *Environmental Assessment,* **4**(1), December 1996, 138–139.
93. The Declaration adopted by the United Nations Conference on the Human Environment at Stockholm in 1972 recognised a duty on states to refrain from actions that would cause damage to the environment beyond the limits of national jurisdiction.
94. IEEP Manual of Environmental Policy, chapter 13.
95. The declaration asserted that '... economic expansion is not an end in itself: its first aim should be to enable disparities in living conditions to be reduced ... It should result in an improvement in the quality of life as well as in standards of living. As befits the genius of Europe, particular attention will be given to intangible values and to protecting the environment so that progress may really be put at

the service of mankind.' See: Haigh, N. (1984). *EEC Environmental Policy and Britain. An essay and a handbook.* Environmental Data Services Ltd. Page 6.

96. IEEP Manual of Environmental Policy, chapter 2.

97. Lowe, P. and Ward, S. (Eds.) (1998). *British Environmental Policy and Europe.* Routledge.

98. *Treaty of Amsterdam.* European Communities No. 14 (1997). Cm 3780. The Stationery Office. October 1997.

99. Regulation 3093/94 on substances that deplete the ozone layer. *Official Journal of the European Communities,* **L333**, 22.12.94.

100. For example, in the environmental field the *Town and Country Planning (Assessment of Environmental Effects) Regulations* (Statutory Instrument 1988 No. 1199) implemented the relevant EC legislation but went no further, although there was pressure to do so. The government was prevented from going beyond the EC legislation since it was implemented in the UK as secondary legislation under the European Communities Act 1972. If the government had wished to include other aspects, primary legislation would have been necessary unless other existing UK legislation allowed it to do so. The government subsequently took powers in the Planning and Compensation Act 1991 to require assessments for projects not listed in the Directive.

101. Environmental Protection Act 1990, section 3(1)–(4).

102. Environmental Protection Act 1990, section 3(5).

103. Environmental Protection Act 1990, section 7(2)(b)–(d).

104. Ministry of Agriculture, Fisheries and Food (1998). *The Food Standards Agency. A Force for Change.* CM 3830. The Stationery Office. January 1998.

Appendix D

PARLIAMENTARY INVOLVEMENT IN SETTING STANDARDS

D.1 A significant way of exposing legislative proposals to public values and opinions, of ensuring that relevant interests have been properly considered, and that legislation is generally workable is through Parliamentary scrutiny. Policy developments are always matters for Parliamentary attention but many individual standards are highly technical and are set without the need for scrutiny or approval by any Parliamentary process. When standards are contained in European legislation, however, Parliaments are able to take a close interest even in this type of standard. This appendix describes the development of the European Parliament's powers to influence environmental legislation and the role played by the UK Parliament in scrutinising European Community (EC) proposals.

The European Parliament

D.2 The European Commission, the European Parliament and the Council of Ministers have responsibility for initiating, scrutinising and finally adopting Community legislation.[1] The European Parliament is the only directly-elected supra-national assembly of its kind, but its legislative powers contain a significant gap in comparison with many national Parliaments, since the only body which may formally table a proposal for legislation is the Commission. If the Parliament or the Council wishes to see new legislation, they are restricted to presenting the Commission with ideas or asking it to propose legislation.

D.3 Nevertheless, the Parliament's powers in forming legislation have increased considerably since its early days. Before the Maastricht Treaty came into force in 1993, much decision making on environmental proposals required the unanimous agreement of the Council. The exception concerned measures relating to the establishment of the internal market which used the procedure set out in Article 100a, involving qualified majority voting. The Parliament was required to produce its opinion on the proposal but the Council was not obliged to follow it. This procedure still applies to certain environmental measures. These are 'provisions primarily of a fiscal nature; measures concerning town and country planning, land use with the exception of waste management and measures of a general nature, and management of water resources; measures significantly affecting a Member State's choice between different energy sources and the general structure of its energy supply.'[2]

D.4 The Maastricht Treaty extended the use of the 'co-operation procedure' to most policy areas, including the environment. This increased the influence of the Parliament by allowing it to propose amendments at the first reading on the Commission's proposal and at the second reading on the Council's common position. At this stage four courses are open to the Parliament. It can take no decision; approve the common position; propose amendments to the common position; or reject the common position. In the first two cases the Council can adopt the proposal by qualified majority. If Parliament rejects the common position, the Council may adopt the proposal but only by unanimity. Otherwise the proposal fails. If Parliament amends the proposal, the Commission re-examines it and gives its opinion. If the Commission's opinion is unfavourable, the Parliament's amendments can be approved only if unanimity is reached in the Council. If the Commission agrees with the Parliament, a decision can be reached by qualified majority.

D.5 A new 'co-decision procedure' was introduced by the Maastricht Treaty.[3] It provided for joint legislative power between the Parliament and the Council in 14 policy areas. This procedure requires increased practical and political co-operation between the Commission, Council and Parliament, particularly as a conciliation committee is convened if there are continuing differences between the Parliament and the Council. At the end of the procedure, the European Parliament has the right to reject the proposal, a power which it lacks under the co-operation procedure. The Maastricht Treaty applied the co-decision procedure to action programmes on the environment and to measures adopted under Article 100a (to establish the internal market). These could have important implications for the environment. When the Amsterdam Treaty comes into force it will extend the co-decision procedure to most environmental proposals (with the exception of the measures referred to in D.3 above).

D.6 The Maastricht Treaty gave the Parliament formal powers in two other respects. First, it provided that the Parliament 'may, acting by a majority of its Members, request the Commission to submit any appropriate proposal on matters on which it considers that a Community act is required' in order to implement the Treaty.[4] There is no corresponding formal requirement on the Commission to respond to such a request. Second, it empowered the Parliament, at the request of a quarter of its Members, to 'set up a temporary Committee of Inquiry to investigate ... alleged contraventions or maladministration in the implementation of Community law.'[5] The Parliament established a temporary Committee on fraud in the transit procedure, and another to monitor action taken on recommendations made concerning bovine spongiform encephalopathy (BSE). Before these amendments were made, the Parliament had relied on provisions contained within its own Rules of Procedure and therefore on the co-operation of the other institutions without having any legal recourse. The Parliament is now also involved in the process of agreeing the Commission's annual legislative programme.

The Parliament's Committees

D.7 At the time of writing, the Parliament has 20 standing committees whose most important function is that of considering all legislative proposals and other legislative documents before they can be presented to plenary sessions. Environmental legislation is scrutinised by the Committee on Environment, Public Health and Consumer Protection. The President of the Parliament may ask for opinions from other relevant committees which are then forwarded to the lead committee (in the case of environmental standards the Environment Committee). The committee nominates one of its members as rapporteur to prepare a report on the proposal which will set out a proposed opinion including amendments. Usually the rapporteurs have specialist subjects but they may also ask for outside expert advice and assistance in preparing the report. They may also organise open meetings to improve understanding of proposals by all present, and of the interests affected by them.

D.8 The lead committee votes on the amendments that are to be tabled in plenary; and the final report goes to the plenary for the vote. An opinion is then agreed which is forwarded to the Council and the Commission.

D.9 The Parliament has begun to use public hearings on an *ad hoc* basis as a way of trying to influence the policy debate. There is no formalised programme and Members are not in a position to interrogate officials, but these are a useful way of bringing together experts to discuss issues.

The UK Parliament

D.10 The scrutiny by Parliament of government policy can take several forms. First, both policies and specific provisions (such as limit values) can be questioned and amendments sought during the passage of primary or secondary legislation. Second, Parliamentary questions may be tabled to extract detailed information from government and this can be used for research and debate outside as well as within Parliament. Third, there are the reports of investigatory Parliamentary committees, informed by expert and lay opinion, which enable Parliament to influence government policy and the conduct of EC and international negotiations.

D.11 The House of Commons has a series of Select Committees, each of which oversees the activities of a particular government Department. The Environment Sub-Committee of the Select

Committee on the Environment, Transport and the Regions takes the lead on environmental matters but other committees are often also faced with environmental issues. In recognition of the horizontal nature of environmental policy, the House has established the new Select Committee on Environmental Audit. All of these committees have the power to enquire into areas of policy of their choosing, to call for oral and written evidence from Ministers and their officials, from outside experts, and from the general public. Evidence is published in full with the committees' reports. Similarly the House of Lords Select Committee on Science and Technology investigates and reports on important aspects of public policy, and there is a tradition of *ad hoc* House of Lords Select Committees (for example, one on Sustainable Development, which reported in 1995[6]).

D.12 As described above, under the co-decision procedure which will apply to most Community environmental legislation, the European Parliament has a significant role as co-legislator with the Council of Ministers. The national Parliaments of the Member States also influence to varying degrees the positions taken by their governments in negotiating Community-wide environmental standards and policies. The United Kingdom Parliament has a well-developed system for scrutinising proposals by the European Commission for new legislation or policy initiatives, through the House of Commons European Legislation Committee and the House of Lords European Communities Committee. The task of these Committees is to consider the roughly 900 documents produced annually by the European Union institutions. Many are considered several times in the light of further developments. A Resolution of the House of Commons constrains UK Ministers from agreeing (except in special circumstances) to any EC legislative proposal which has not cleared the scrutiny process. Successive governments have undertaken to observe similar constraints in respect of the House of Lords.

D.13 In clearing the documents, the Committees operate in a complementary fashion. The key functions of the House of Commons Committee are to decide on the legal and political importance of a proposal, decide whether it should be debated, pursue with the government areas of doubt or controversy, police the government's discharge of its obligations and monitor institutional developments in the European Union. The Committee finds about 400 documents a year to be of legal or political significance and it includes analysis of them in its weekly reports to the House. It may decide to give scrutiny clearance on its own authority (allowing Ministers to agree to proposals in the Council); but in the case of the 50 or so documents it recommends each year for debate, a debate in European Standing Committee or on the Floor of the House must be followed by a Resolution of the House to clear a document. The European Legislation Committee co-operates with the 19 investigative Select Committees in the Commons; and although it rarely undertakes conventional inquiries, it takes oral evidence from Ministers on particular documents. It has also introduced a system for 'pre- and post-Council Scrutiny' in which Departments produce annotated agendas for each Council meeting and Ministers may be examined on their approach to a particular Council and its outcome.

D.14 The House of Lords European Communities Committee, through its six subject-based Sub-Committees, has a fully investigatory role and may consider not only documents deposited in Parliament but also existing Community policies or legislation. This is possible because each Sub-Committee selects only a few proposals (or areas of policy) – usually between four and six each year – on which to conduct a substantial inquiry and make a report. These are selected by the Sub-Committees following a preliminary sifting of the deposited documents by the Chairman of the Select Committee. About two-thirds of the documents are cleared by the Chairman without reference to the Sub-Committee.

D.15 To a large extent the value of the Select Committees' work lies in distilling a mass of information for Parliament and for the wider public, and in forcing the Executive and other persons in authority to defend their positions in the face of public examination before people with experience in the subject matter and in related fields. In this way they are able to put pressure on Ministers to demonstrate that they have taken the public interest properly and fairly into account and that they have consulted satisfactorily with experts, interest groups and citizens.

References

1. Except where otherwise indicated, the section of this appendix dealing with the European Parliament draws heavily on the following report prepared for the Royal Commission: *The European Dimension of Standard Setting.* D. Wilkinson, S. Mullard, N. Emmott, C. Coffey and N. Haigh. Institute for European Environmental Policy, London. August 1996.

2. Article 175 of the Treaty of European Union as amended by the Treaty of Amsterdam (formerly Article 130s). The Amsterdam Treaty is not in force at the time of writing. See: *Treaty of Amsterdam.* European Communities No. 14 (1997). Cm 3780. The Stationery Office. October 1997.

3. Article 189(b). This has become Article 251 in the post-Amsterdam consolidated Treaty.

4. Article 138b.

5. Article 138c.

6. House of Lords. *Report from the Select Committee on Sustainable Development.* 1994/95 Session. House of Lords Paper 72. 1995.

Appendix E

DECISION MAKING ON WATER QUALITY IMPROVEMENTS

E.1   The duties of the Director General of Water Services are to ensure that water undertakers carry out their functions properly and that the appointed companies are able to finance their authorised activities. Additional duties include protecting consumer interests with respect to charges and the quality of services, and to promote efficiency and economy within the appointed companies. He also has nature conservation and other environmental duties. The Director General is responsible for carrying out the periodic review of water company price limits. The price limits agreed under the review largely determine the level of investment in environmental improvements in the future, and the extent to which advances in quality can be pursued.

E.2   One of the key aims of the review is to set limits on the amount the water companies in England and Wales can charge their customers. To do this it needs a reasonably clear idea of the obligations which may be placed on companies, including obligations agreed within the European Community (EC), and those which may be imposed nationally by UK Ministers, particularly those proposed by the Environment Agency. In order to establish the range of possible quality obligations and the costs of the different measures, for the period 2000–2005, the Office of Water Services (Ofwat) has participated in multi-party discussions with the government, water companies and the quality regulators (the Environment Agency and the Drinking Water Inspectorate). It has also consulted its Customer Service Committees. The main concern is that by setting out the expectation that prices will come down in real terms, Ofwat may constrain environmental improvements. Any refusal to permit costs to increase 'for desirable and necessary environmental improvements, over and above those met from efficiency savings, in order to deliver price cuts may directly conflict with the objectives of sustainability and of the environmental and nature conservation regulators'.[1]

E.3   In *Setting the Quality Framework,* an open letter to the Secretary of State for the Environment, Transport and the Regions and the Secretary of State for Wales,[2] the estimated costs involved in meeting a number of different quality obligations and their implications for customers' bills are set out by the Director General. The estimated costs supplied by water companies for capital expenditure programmes to achieve environmental improvements have been challenged by Ofwat in some cases. A technical paper produced by Ofwat[3] sets out the initial assessment of the scope for future improvements in water company efficiency. In this paper, Ofwat suggests that efficiency savings could enable substantial investment for quality as well as service improvements or security of supply within real price stability from 2001 onwards. This would allow Ofwat to limit increases in customer costs and meet one of its key aims for the 1999 price review.

E.4   The Environment Agency is responsible for advising the government on the 'National Environment Programme', the programme of environmental improvements that should be carried out by each water company. This programme includes measures to improve the quality of water around the coasts as well as in rivers and lakes. Like Ofwat, the Environment Agency believes that as a result of efficiency savings and reduced costs, there is scope for a substantial programme of environmental improvements without bills rising in real terms. In *A Price Worth Paying* the Environment Agency sets out its proposals for the National Environment Programme, with a plan of action to meet legal obligations, new threats and higher expectations.[4]

E.5   The Environment Agency consulted widely before putting forward the action plan and believes that it received a strong message that people do not want price cuts at the expense of a better environment. In October 1997, the Agency commissioned market research into households' views on water bills. A survey of approximately 2,500 bill-payers across England and Wales was undertaken. The results of the survey suggested that a large one-off cut in water bills was unnecessary because 95% of customers surveyed said they would prefer their bill to remain at its present level and see some environmental improvements, rather than see a reduction in their bills and no improvements. A significant proportion also expressed a willingness to pay more on their bills in order to safeguard the environment.[5]

E.6 In addition to the householder survey, a formal consultation exercise was conducted. The consultation paper entitled *Outlook for the Environment* set out priorities for investment by water companies. The views of over 200 organisations were sought. The Environment Agency believes that the responses confirm the results of the customer surveys; that people do not want to see a reduction in their bills at the expense of the environment. The consultation also invited people to comment on the issues that were of most importance to them. Of least importance to those who responded were keeping bills to a minimum and improvements to the quality of drinking water at the tap. On the basis of the survey and consultation results, the Environment Agency concluded that there is widespread support for a programme of action by water companies to improve the water environment.

E.7 Other surveys are being carried out, and many companies have begun to consult their customers using qualitative methods such as focus groups. Ofwat agreed on the need to take the views of customers into consideration, but disputed the Environment Agency's interpretation of the survey data and consultation exercise. It argued that survey data results should be treated with greater caution and with an understanding of the way in which views have been sought. Ofwat believes that customers are generally poorly informed about water and sewerage services and that it can be difficult to express issues in terms which customers   can relate to. Customer views are not uniform and regional variations in response may occur which reflect local issues.

E.8 Ofwat provided a different interpretation of the results, arguing that in answer to a different question, over 70% of respondents expressed a preference for price cuts, and 79% favoured spreading the costs of improvements over a prolonged period to enable future generations to contribute to clean-up costs.[6] Ofwat claims that 'generally, customers would object to overall increases in their bills, but may be prepared to see investment in improvements in the context of stable or falling prices. This is, however, crucially dependent on seeing tangible outputs from that investment, which appears not to have been the case so far for many customers'.[7] Ofwat has little evidence to suggest that customers would be willing to see their money used to meet all the potential obligations discussed in the open letter.

E.9 The dispute surrounding the use of market research methods illustrates the difficulties involved in evaluating survey results and the potential for manipulation of survey data suggested in chapter 7.

E.10 The UK Round Table on Sustainable Development has voiced concerns over the role and responsibilities of the economic regulators, and in particular with respect to the environmental and social impacts of their decisions.[8] There is a need to achieve a balance between investment to deliver desirable environmental and quality improvements and the level of water bills. Determining this balance requires taking economic, social and environmental considerations into account. Under present arrangements, the government takes into account the information provided by the Director General, the Environment Agency and the industry, and issues non-statutory guidance to the Director General as to the companies' environmental obligations for the period under review. The government has stated that, subject in due course to Parliamentary approval of the necessary powers, it intends to issue statutory guidance to all utility regulators on social and environmental issues. The government considers that the existing arrangements for the water industry are helpful to all parties and should continue alongside the new statutory guidance proposed above.

References

1. UK Round Table on Sustainable Development (1998). *Economic Regulation.* January 1998.

2. Office of Water Services (1998a). *Setting the Quality Framework: An open letter to the Secretary of State for the Environment, Transport and the Regions and the Secretary of State for Wales.* April 1998.

3. Office of Water Services (1998b). *Assessing the Scope for Future Improvements in Water Company Efficiency: A technical paper.* April 1998.

4. Environment Agency (1998). *A Price Worth Paying: The Environment Agency's proposals for the National Environment Programme for Water Companies 2000–2005.*

5. Environment Agency (1998).

6. 'Green projects favoured' over water bill cuts. *Financial Times,* 17 December 1997; Agency challenges water bill cuts. *The Independent,* 5 December 1997.

7. Office of Water Services (1998a).

8. UK Round Table on Sustainable Development (1998).

Appendix F

METHODS OF ARTICULATING VALUES ON A LOCAL SCALE

F.1   This appendix provides three examples which illustrate how values might be articulated at a local level:

the Bradford on Avon open forum, which was developed as a Local Agenda 21 initiative;

the use of community advisory fora to address waste management in Hampshire; and

the development of Local Environment Agency Plans, which provide a way of entering into a dialogue with local people.

Bradford on Avon open forum: Transport, Traffic and You

F.2   The case study of the Bradford on Avon open forum illustrates how community fora can be used to bring together a wide range of people to debate issues of importance to that community. The aim of the Bradford on Avon scheme was to enable local people to participate in decisions about traffic issues in the town, and to achieve, by consensus, a co-ordinated plan to help reduce traffic problems. The initiative stemmed from the activities of a local pressure group which had been campaigning against a proposal for a by-pass around Bradford on Avon. The pressure group suggested that an open meeting be organised to explore the issues, and a steering group was formed to organise the meeting. The project was managed by an umbrella group drawn from each of the issue groups, and town, district and county councillors. Every local organisation was invited to attend the forum, although people were asked to attend as individuals and not representatives of their own organisation. The forum was also advertised in the local media.

F.3   The first forum was attended by over 200 people from the town's population of 8,815 and was organised on the basis of small group discussions of no more than 15 people. The consultancy Urbanologists MPT assisted in the development of the participatory process and trained local people to facilitate group discussions. The forum was initially used to identify the main traffic problems facing the town. Discussions were then held to see how the town might address them. It was agreed that issue groups should be established to investigate further the main issues identified and that they should report back to a second open forum meeting. The second forum took the form of an open market with stalls displaying the ideas that specific issue groups had researched.

F.4   The ongoing work of the issue groups has influenced major development programmes in the centre of town, and has led to the development of a range of Wiltshire 'Travelwise' initiatives and greater acceptance of the benefits of a participatory approach by Councillors. The forum discussions identified community environmental objectives, such as the need to reduce car dependency.[1]

Community involvement and consensus-building in Hampshire: Waste management strategy development

F.5   Community involvement in the waste management strategy began in the context of the failed application to build a new energy-from-waste incinerator at Portsmouth. The building of such an incinerator was identified as a more acceptable proposal than either landfill or incineration without energy recovery, according to best practicable environmental option (BPEO) criteria, and a traditional style consultation process had been conducted. The proposal encountered well-organised opposition from local pressure groups and Portsmouth City Council. Although some public meetings and exhibitions had been arranged, neither the developer nor the County Council had made a full effort to listen to people's views and to take them on board during the development of the proposal. The County Council failed to get approval for its plans and faced an urgent waste disposal problem. It was also under pressure to replace the County's existing four incinerators, and to treat increased quantities of waste whilst upholding its commitment to handle all waste within Hampshire.

F.6   In 1993 a voluntary public involvement programme was launched, with the aim of examining the different options for waste management in order to establish a broad base of support for an integrated strategy which could be implemented on a long-term basis. The programme ran for two years, and began with the County Council drafting an outline strategy. The public was involved through the establishment of three community advisory fora, one in each waste management area, which were representative of a range of community interests (environmental, business, health, voluntary organisations, etc.). Each had an independent chairman, and monthly meetings were held for six months, with additional site visits and seminars. Independent consultants were hired to develop, manage and facilitate the programme of public involvement. The first function of the process was to bring people to a level of knowledge sufficient for them to start discussion. The key objectives of the community advisory fora were to provide an independent perspective on the development of an integrated waste management strategy; to identify issues and areas of concern; to provide feedback to the County Council; and to comment on communication with the wider public. The community advisory fora reached a consensus on the need for an integrated waste management strategy and the role of energy-from-waste incineration within that, with only a small minority opposed. A more traditional public information programme complemented the community advisory fora.[2]

F.7   The public outreach programme included a public information campaign involving exhibition displays, media campaigns, a telephone 'hot line', an information booklet and a newsletter. The County Council also ran 12 focus groups, whose participants were randomly selected members of the public. These were used as a means of broadening the debate and discussing the issues with different socio-economic groups. The outreach programme also included a number of seminars and meetings and open days were held at local sites. It was run in parallel with the community advisory fora and, with the subsequent core forum that was formed, was seen as a component of the same debate. The information booklet and newsletter were distributed widely throughout the county with up to 2,000 people asking to receive the newsletter. The County Council also conducted a questionnaire survey of people across Hampshire (580 respondents).

F.8   In the summer of 1994, a single core forum was formed from the members of the three community advisory fora, and was given a brief to continue discussing key issues with the County Council. The core issues raised by this forum were taken into consideration by the Council in considering tenders for the waste disposal service. By the spring of 1995 the County Council had awarded the contract for the waste disposal service. A new strategy document was produced and the County Council organised general consultation using focus groups and interviews to elicit people's views on the proposals. The Council adopted a detailed strategy for waste management in January 1996.

The Environment Agency and Local Environment Agency Plans

F.9   The Environment Agency has been developing local participation in environmental planning with the development of Local Environment Agency Plans (LEAPs), and their associated consultation procedures. LEAPs developed from the catchment management plans which had been used by the National Rivers Authority (NRA) and they are now intended as a management tool for all the Agency's functions and as a means of promoting partnerships with other organisations. The NRA and subsequently the Environment Agency have shown how wider public concerns can be used to inform the setting of environmental quality objectives.

F.10 Catchment management plans were used by the NRA as a way of focusing attention on the water environment, to enable river basins to be managed in a sustainable manner and to allow the Authority to take account of all the uses made of the river system in question. The process of developing a catchment management plan began with the production of a catchment report, which described the characteristics of the catchment, the uses made of it, desirable environmental quality targets, and issues and actions to be undertaken. This was followed by widespread consultation of a traditional kind, accompanied by public meetings, media reports, library displays and other means of public involvement. After a period of consultation, an action plan was produced, which detailed the areas of work and investment proposed and incorporated comments received during consultation. Progress made with fulfilling the requirements of these action plans was monitored during an annual review, and the plans renewed every five years.

F.11 The Environment Agency has extended the idea of local environmental planning contained in catchment management plans through the introduction of LEAPs. The Agency aims to replace all existing catchment management plans with LEAP consultation reports by the end of December 1999. LEAPS will deal with the subjects included in catchment management plans and with new topics to cover the full range of the Agency's responsibilities (which additionally include integrated pollution control, waste regulation and radioactive substances regulation).

F.12 The development of LEAPs follows a set procedure, similar to that of the catchment management plans they are intended to replace. A consultation report is published which gives a broad view of the plan area and identifies issues to be tackled and ways of addressing them. The aim of the consultation process is to establish a common vision for environmental objectives, and a consensus view on the strategy needed for future action. After each period of consultation a statement of the consultation is published summarising the contributions received. The results are taken into consideration by the Agency when it develops an action plan for the area. The action plan firms up the issues and describes the actions that the Agency believes should be undertaken in the next five years. An annual review reports on the progress of the actions.[3]

F.13 The government consultation paper, *Local Democracy and Community Leadership*, proposes that local authorities should be given a new duty to promote the economic, social and environmental well-being of their area. It also puts forward the idea of a local public forum, which would be convened by the local authority, at which important issues can be raised and organisations can give an account of actions which might affect local communities. The government has made it clear to the Environment Agency that local people and communities can legitimately expect to engage in dialogue with the Agency before it reaches decisions on controversial cases affecting their areas. The Agency should be willing to explain how, why, and by whom, such decisions are made. The Environment Agency has launched a series of pilot studies and is considering implementing a full system of public consultation on controversial decisions next year.

References

1. *Bradford on Avon Open Forum: Transport, Traffic and You.* Obtained from: Local Sustainability: The European Good Practice Information Service, at website: http://cities21.com/europractice/index.htm

2. Petts, J. (1995). Waste management strategy development: A case study of community involvement and consensus-building in Hampshire. *Journal of Environmental Planning and Management,* **38**(4), 519–536;
   evidence from Dr Judith Petts, Loughborough University of Technology, February 1996;
   Petts, J. (1997). The public-expert interface in local waste management decisions: Expertise, credibility and process. *Public Understanding of Science,* **6**, 359–381.

3. See for example: Environment Agency (1998). *Local Environment Agency Plan New Forest Consultation Report.* April 1998.

Appendix G

MEMBERS OF THE ROYAL COMMISSION

CHAIRMAN TO JUNE 1998

SIR JOHN HOUGHTON CBE FRS#

Member of the Government Panel on Sustainable Development

Co-Chairman of the Scientific Assessment Working Group of the Intergovernmental Panel on Climate Change

Chief Executive (previously Director-General) of the Meteorological Office 1983–91

Deputy Director of the Rutherford-Appleton Laboratory, Science and Engineering Research Council 1979–83

Professor of Atmospheric Physics, University of Oxford 1976–83

President, Royal Meteorological Society 1976–78

Vice-President, World Meteorological Organization 1987–91

CHAIRMAN FROM JULY 1998

SIR TOM BLUNDELL FRS*

Sir William Dunn Professor and Head of Department of Biochemistry, University of Cambridge

Director General, Agricultural and Food Research Council 1991–94

Chief Executive, Biotechnology and Biological Sciences Research Council 1994–96

Member, Advisory Council on Science and Technology 1988–90

Honorary Director, Imperial Cancer Research Fund Unit in Structural Biology, Birkbeck College, University of London 1989–96

Professor of Crystallography, Birkbeck College, University of London 1976–90

MEMBERS

SIR GEOFFREY ALLEN PhD FRS FEng FIC FIM FRSC FInstP

Executive Adviser to Kobe Steel Ltd

Chairman of URGENT Steering Committee (Natural Environment Research Council)

Chancellor of the University of East Anglia

Chairman, Science, Technology and Mathematics Council

President of the Institute of Materials 1994–95

THE REVEREND PROFESSOR MICHAEL BANNER MA DPhil

F. D. Maurice Professor of Moral and Social Theology, King's College London

Chairman, Home Office Animal Procedures Committee

Chairman, Government Committee of Inquiry on Ethics of Emerging Technologies in the Breeding of Farm Animals 1993–95

Dean, Fellow and Director of Studies in Philosophy and Theology, Peterhouse College, University of Cambridge 1988–94

Member, Church of England Board for Social Responsibility and its Doctrine Commission

PROFESSOR GEOFFREY S. BOULTON FRS FRSE

Regius Professor of Geology, and Provost and Dean of Science and Engineering, University of Edinburgh
Member of Council, The Royal Society
Member of Council, Scottish Higher Education Funding Council
Member of Council, Scottish Association for Marine Science

PROFESSOR CLAIR E.D. CHILVERS BSc(Econ) DSc Hon MFPHM#

Dean of the Graduate School and Professor of Epidemiology, University of Nottingham
Director, Trent Institute for Health Services Research (Nottingham Unit)
Member, Committee on Carcinogenicity of Chemicals in Food, Consumer Products and the Environment
Non-executive Director, Further Education Development Agency

PROFESSOR ROLAND CLIFT OBE MA PhD FEng FIChemE FRSA

Professor of Environmental Technology and Director of the Centre for Environmental Strategy, University of Surrey
Member, UK Ecolabelling Board
Chairman, Clean Technology Management Committee, Science and Engineering Research Council 1990–94

DR PETER DOYLE CBE FRSE#

Executive Director, Zeneca Group plc responsible for research & development; safety, health and environment; manufacturing; and East and West Europe
Chairman, Biotechnology and Biological Sciences Research Council
Member of Council, Centre for the Exploitation of Science and Technology
Member, Department of Health's Central Research and Development Committee and its Standing Group on Health Technology Assessment
Non-executive Director, Oxford Molecular Group plc

JOHN FLEMMING MA FBA

Warden, Wadham College, University of Oxford
Chief Economist, European Bank for Reconstruction and Development 1991–93
Chief Economist, Bank of England 1980–91
Member, Advisory Board on Research Councils 1977–90
Chairman, National Academies Policy Advisory Group Working Party on Energy and the Environment 1993–95
Chairman, Hansard Society/Economic Policy Forum Commission on the Deregulation of Privatised Utilities 1995–97
Treasurer, British Academy

SIR MARTIN HOLDGATE CB PhD FIBiol

President, Zoological Society of London
Chairman, Energy Advisory Panel 1993–96
Director General, International Union for Conservation of Nature and Natural Resources 1988–94
Chief Scientist, and Deputy Secretary, Department of the Environment 1976–88
Chairman, International Institute for Environment and Development

PROFESSOR RICHARD MACRORY Barrister MA

Professor of Environmental Law, Imperial College of Science, Technology and Medicine
Specialist Adviser, House of Commons Select Committee on the Environment
First Chairman of UK Environmental Law Association 1986–88
Editor-in-Chief, *Journal of Environmental Law*
Honorary Chairman, Merchant Ivory Productions Ltd
Honorary Fellow, Linacre College, Oxford
Honorary Vice-President, National Society for Clean Air and Environmental Protection

PROFESSOR MICHAEL G. MARMOT FRCP PhD FFPHM

Professor of Epidemiology and Public Health, University College London, and Director, International Centre for Health and Society
Medical Research Council Research Professor
Member, Committee on Medical Aspects of Food Policy and Chair of the Cardiovascular Review Group
Member, World Health Organization Advisory Committee for Cardiovascular Disease and Chair of Scientific Group on New Risk Factors
Member, Chief Medical Officer's Working Group on Health of the Nation

PROFESSOR J. GARETH MORRIS CBE DPhil FRS FIBiol

Professor of Microbiology, University of Wales, Aberystwyth
Chairman, Biological Sciences Committee of the Science and Engineering Research Council 1978–81
Chairman, Biological Sciences Committee of the University Grants Committee 1981–86

DR PENELOPE A. ROWLATT

Director, Europe Economics Research Limited
Treasurer, Royal Economic Society
Member, Department of Health Group on the Economic Effects of Air Pollution
Member, *The Guardian* Economics Advisory Panel

THE EARL OF SELBORNE KBE FRS#

Managing Director, The Blackmoor Estate Ltd
Chairman, Agricultural and Food Research Council 1983–89
Chancellor of the University of Southampton
President, Royal Geographical Society (with the Institute of British Geographers)

* Sir Tom Blundell was appointed a Member of the Commission on 25 March 1998 and took over as Chairman on 1 July 1998

\# left the Commission on completion of the Standards Study

ACRONYMS

the 1990 Act	Environmental Protection Act 1990
the 1995 Act	Environment Act 1995
ACTS	Advisory Committee on Toxic Substances
ADI	acceptable daily intake
ALARA	as low as reasonably achievable
ALARP	as low as reasonably practicable
BAT	best available techniques
BATNEEC	best available techniques not entailing excessive cost
BPEO	best practicable environmental option
BPM	best practicable means
BREFs	BAT Reference Documents
BS	British Standard
BSE	bovine spongiform encephalopathy
CEN	Comité Européen de Normalisation (European Committee for Standardisation)
CEST	Centre for Exploitation of Science and Technology
CFCs	chlorofluorocarbons
CITES	Convention on International Trade in Endangered Species of Wild Flora and Fauna
COMEAP	Committee on the Medical Effects of Air Pollutants
DETR	Department of the Environment, Transport and the Regions
DH	Department of Health
DOE	Department of the Environment; since 16 June 1997, the Department of the Environment, Transport and the Regions
EC	European Community
$EC(D)_{50}$	median effective concentration (dose)
EHD	estimated human dose
EIP	examination in public
EMAS	the EU's Eco-Management and Audit Scheme
EPAQS	Expert Panel on Air Quality Standards
EU	European Union
FAO	Food and Agriculture Organization
FGD	flue gas desulphurisation
FSC	Forest Stewardship Council
GATT	General Agreement on Tariffs and Trade
GESAMP	Group of Experts on Scientific Aspects of Marine Pollution
GMOs	genetically modified organisms
HMIP	Her Majesty's Inspectorate of Pollution; since 1 April 1996 part of the Environment Agency
HSC	Health and Safety Commission
HSE	Health and Safety Executive
ICRCL	Interdepartmental Committee on Redevelopment of Contaminated Land
ICRP	International Commission on Radiological Protection
IEEP	Institute for European Environmental Policy
IMO	International Maritime Organization
IPC	integrated pollution control
IPCC	Intergovernmental Panel on Climate Change
IPCS	International Programme on Chemical Safety

IPPC	Integrated Pollution Prevention and Control (EC Directive)
ISO	International Organization for Standardization
LCA	life-cycle assessment
LC(D)$_{50}$	median lethal concentration (dose)
LEAPs	Local Environment Agency Plans
LO(A)EL	lowest observed (adverse) effect level
LRTAP	Long-Range Transboundary Air Pollution (UNECE Convention)
MAFF	Ministry of Agriculture, Fisheries and Food
MCDM	multi-criteria decision making
MEAs	multilateral environmental agreements
MORI	Market and Opinion Research International
MRLs	maximum residue levels
NEPP	(the Netherlands) National Environmental Policy Plan
NGOs	non-governmental organisations
NIMBY	not in my backyard
NO(A)EL	no observed (adverse) effect level
NOEC	no observed effect concentration
NRA	National Rivers Authority; since 1 April 1996 part of the Environment Agency
NRPB	National Radiological Protection Board
OECD	Organisation for Economic Co-operation and Development
Ofwat	Office of Water Services
OPRA	Operator and Pollution Risk Appraisal (Environment Agency scheme)
OST	Office of Science and Technology
PCBs	polychlorinated biphenyls
PEC	predicted environmental concentration
PGNs	(Secretary of State's) Process Guidance Notes
PM$_{10}$	airborne particulate material with a diameter less than 10 μm
PNEC	predicted no effect concentration
QMV	qualified majority voting
QSARs	quantitative structure activity relationships
SEPA	Scottish Environment Protection Agency
SETAC	Society of Environmental Toxicology and Chemistry
SWQOs	statutory water quality objectives
TDI	tolerable daily intake
TEQ/Nm^3	toxic equivalent of dioxins per cubic metre of gas measured under standard (normal) conditions
UNECE	United Nations Economic Commission for Europe
UNEP	United Nations Environment Programme
WHO	World Health Organization
WMO	World Meteorological Organization
WTO	World Trade Organization
ZEV	zero emission vehicle

Index

Terms defined in the text of the report appear in the index in ***bold italics***, with the number of the paragraph or box containing the definition also in ***bold italics***.

Printed in the UK for The Stationery Office on behalf of the
Controller of Her Majesty's Stationery Office
Dd 5068302 9/98 373421 19585 55810